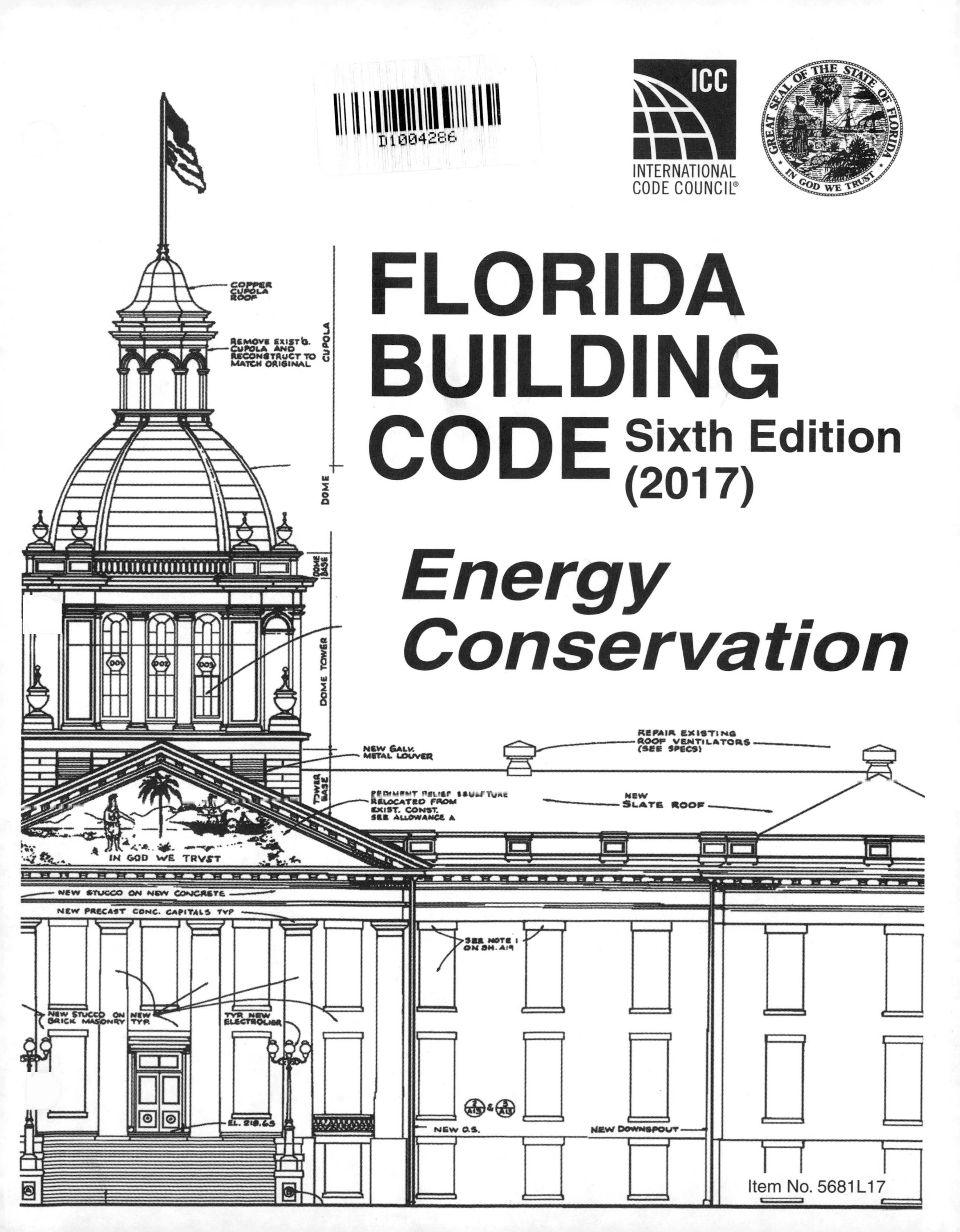

D1004286
ICC
INTERNATIONAL CODE COUNCIL®
GREAT SEAL OF THE STATE OF FLORIDA
IN GOD WE TRUST
FLORIDA BUILDING CODE
Sixth Edition (2017)
Energy Conservation
COPPER CUPOLA ROOF
REMOVE EXIST'G. CUPOLA AND RECONSTRUCT TO MATCH ORIGINAL
CUPOLA
DOME
DOME BASE
DOME TOWER
TOWER BASE
NEW GALV. METAL LOUVER
REPAIR EXISTING ROOF VENTILATORS (SEE SPECS)
NEW SLATE ROOF
IN GOD WE TRVST
NEW STUCCO ON NEW CONCRETE
NEW PRECAST CONC. CAPITALS TYP
NEW STUCCO ON BRICK MASONRY
TYP. NEW ELECTROLIER
EL. 218.65
NEW D.S.
NEW DOWNSPOUT
Item No. 5681L17

Florida Building Code, Energy Conservation, 6th Edition (2017)

First Printing: July 2017

ISBN: 978-1-60983-695-5

T024710

PRINTED IN THE USA

PREFACE

History

The State of Florida first mandated statewide building codes during the 1970s at the beginning of the modern construction boom. The first law required all municipalities and counties to adopt and enforce one of the four state-recognized model codes known as the "state minimum building codes." During the early 1990s a series of natural disasters, together with the increasing complexity of building construction regulation in vastly changed markets, led to a comprehensive review of the state building code system. The study revealed that building code adoption and enforcement was inconsistent throughout the state and those local codes thought to be the strongest proved inadequate when tested by major hurricane events. The consequences of the building codes system failure were devastation to lives and economies and a statewide property insurance crisis. The response was a reform of the state building construction regulatory system that placed emphasis on uniformity and accountability.

The 1998 Florida Legislature amended Chapter 553, *Florida Statutes* (FS), Building Construction Standards, to create a single state building code that is enforced by local governments. As of March 1, 2002, the *Florida Building Code*, which is developed and maintained by the Florida Building Commission, supersedes all local building codes. The *Florida Building Code* is updated every three years and may be amended annually to incorporate interpretations and clarifications.

Scope

The *Florida Building Code* is based on national model building codes and national consensus standards, which are amended where necessary for Florida's specific needs. The code incorporates all building construction-related regulations for public and private buildings in the State of Florida other than those specifically exempted by Section 553.73, *Florida Statutes*. It has been harmonized with the *Florida Fire Prevention Code*, which is developed and maintained by the Department of Financial Services, Office of the State Fire Marshal, to establish unified and consistent standards.

The base codes for the *Florida Building Code*, 6th Edition (2017) include: the 2015 editions of the *International Building Code*®; the *International Plumbing Code*®; the *International Mechanical Code*®; the *International Fuel Gas Code*®; the *International Residential Code*®; the *International Existing Building Code*®; the *International Energy Conservation Code*®; the *National Electrical Code*, 2014 edition; or substantive criteria from ASHRAE Standard 90.1-2013. State and local codes adopted and incorporated into the code include the *Florida Building Code, Accessibility*, and special hurricane protection standards for the High-Velocity Hurricane Zone.

The code is composed of nine main volumes: the *Florida Building Code, Building*, which also includes state regulations for licensed facilities; the *Florida Building Code, Plumbing*; the *Florida Building Code, Mechanical;* the *Florida Building Code, Fuel Gas*; the *Florida Building Code, Existing Building*; the *Florida Building Code, Residential;* the *Florida Building Code, Energy Conservation*; the *Florida Building Code, Accessibility* and the *Florida Building Code, Test Protocols for High-Velocity Hurricane Zones*. Chapter 27 of the *Florida Building Code, Building*, adopts the *National Electrical Code*, NFPA 70, by reference.

Under certain strictly defined conditions, local governments may amend requirements to be more stringent than the code. All local amendments to the *Florida Building Code* must be adopted by local ordinance and reported to the Florida Building Commission then posted on www.floridabuildind.org in Legislative format for a month before being enforced. Local amendments to the *Florida Building Code* and the *Florida Fire Prevention Code* may be obtained from the Florida Building Commission web site, or from the Florida Department of Business and Professional Regulation or the Florida Department of Financial Services, Office of the State Fire Marshal, respectively.

Adoption and Maintenance

The *Florida Building Code* is adopted and updated with new editions triennially by the Florida Building Commission. It is amended annually to incorporate interpretations, clarifications and to update standards. Minimum requirements for permitting, plans review and inspections are established by the code, and local jurisdictions may adopt additional administrative requirements that are more stringent. Local technical amendments are subject to strict criteria established by Section 553.73, FS. They are subject to Commission review and adoption into the code or repeal when the code is updated triennially and are subject to appeal to the Commission according to the procedures established by Section 553.73, FS.

Eleven Technical Advisory Committees (TACs), which are constituted consistent with American National Standards Institute (ANSI) Guidelines, review proposed code changes and clarifications of the code and make recommendations to the Commission. These TACs whose membership is constituted consistent with American National Standards Institute (ANSI) Guidelines include: Accessibility; Joint Building Fire (a joint committee of the Commission and the State Fire Marshal); Building Structural; Code Administration/ Enforcement; Electrical; Energy; Mechanical; Plumbing and Fuel Gas; Roofing; Swimming Pool; and Special Occupancy (state agency construction and facility licensing regulations).

The Commission may only issue official code clarifications using procedures of Chapter 120, *Florida Statutes*. To obtain such a clarification, a request for a Declaratory Statement (DEC) must be made to the Florida Building Commission in a manner that establishes a clear set of facts and circumstances and identifies the section of the code in question. Requests are analyzed by staff, reviewed by the appropriate Technical Advisory Committee, and sent to the Florida Building Commission for action. These interpretations establish precedents for situations having similar facts and circumstances and are typically incorporated into the code in the next code amendment cycle. Non-binding opinions are available from the Building Officials Association of Florida's web site (www.BOAF.net) and a Binding Opinion process is available online at www.floridabuilding.org.

Code Development Committee Responsibilities (Letter Designations in Front of Section Numbers)

In each code development cycle, proposed changes to the code are considered at the Committee Action Hearings by the applicable International Code Development Committee. The IECC—Commercial Provisions (sections designated with a "C" prior to the section number) are primarily maintained by the Commercial Energy Code Development Committee. The IECC—Residential Provisions (sections designated with an "R" prior to the section number) are maintained by the Residential Energy Code Development Committee. This is designated in the chapter headings by a [CE] and [RE], respectively.

Maintenance responsibilities for the IECC are designated as follows:

[CE] = Commercial Energy Code Development Committee

[RE] = Residential Energy Code Development Committee

Marginal Markings

Solid vertical lines in the margins within the body of the code indicate a technical change from the requirements of the 2012 edition. Deletion indicators in the form of an arrow (➡) are provided in the margin where an entire section, paragraph, exception or table has been deleted or an item in a list of items or a table has been deleted.

A single asterisk [*] placed in the margin indicates that text or a table has been relocated within the code. A double asterisk [**] placed in the margin indicates that the text or table immediately following it has been relocated there from elsewhere in the code.

Dotted vertical lines in the margins within the body of the code indicate a change from the requirements of the base codes to the *Florida Building Code, Energy Conservation,* 6th Edition (2017) effective December 31, 2017.

Sections deleted from the base code are designated "Reserved" in order to maintain the structure of the base code.

Italicized Terms

Selected terms set forth in Chapter 2, Definitions, are italicized where they appear in code text. Such terms are not italicized where the definition set forth in Chapter 2 does not impart the intended meaning in the use of the term. The terms selected have definitions that the user should read carefully to facilitate better understanding of the code.

Acknowledgments

The *Florida Building Code* is produced through the efforts and contributions of building designers, contractors, product manufacturers, regulators and other interested parties who participate in the Florida Building Commission's consensus processes, Commission staff and the participants in the national model code development processes.

TABLE OF CONTENTS

COMMERCIAL PROVISIONS

TABLE OF CONTENTS

CHAPTER 1 [CE]

SCOPE AND ADMINISTRATION

PART 1—SCOPE AND APPLICATION

SECTION C101
SCOPE AND GENERAL REQUIREMENTS

C101.1 Title. This code shall be known as the *Florida Building Code, Energy Conservation*, and shall be cited as such. It is referred to herein as "this code."

C101.2 Scope. This code applies to *commercial buildings* and the buildings' sites and associated systems and equipment.

C101.3 Intent. This code shall regulate the design and construction of buildings for the effective use and conservation of energy over the useful life of each building. This code is intended to provide flexibility to permit the use of innovative approaches and techniques to achieve this objective. This code is not intended to abridge safety, health or environmental requirements contained in other applicable codes or ordinances.

*

C101.4 Applicability. Where, in any specific case, different sections of this code specify different materials, methods of construction or other requirements, the most restrictive shall govern. Where there is a conflict between a general requirement and a specific requirement, the specific requirement shall govern.

C101.4.1 Mixed occupancy. Where a building includes both *residential* and *commercial* occupancies, each occupancy shall be separately considered and meet the applicable provisions of *Florida Building Code, Energy Conservation*—Commercial Provisions or *Florida Building Code, Energy Conservation*—Residential Provisions.

C101.4.2 Exempt buildings. Buildings exempt from the provisions of the *Florida Building Code, Energy Conservation*, include existing buildings except those considered renovated buildings, changes of occupancy type or previously unconditioned buildings to which comfort conditioning is added. Exempt buildings include those specified in Sections C101.4.2.1 through C101.4.2.4.

C101.4.2.1 Federal standards. Any building for which federal mandatory standards preempt state energy codes.

C101.4.2.2 Historic buildings. Any building meeting the criteria for historic buildings as defined in Chapter 2 of this Code.

C101.4.2.3 Low-energy buildings as described in Section C402.1.1. Such buildings shall not contain electrical, plumbing or mechanical systems which have been designed to accommodate the future installation of heating or cooling equipment.

C101.4.2.4 Buildings designed for purposes other than general space comfort conditioning. Any building where heating or cooling systems are provided which are designed for purposes other than general space comfort conditioning. Buildings included in this exemption include:

1. Commercial service areas where only ceiling radiant heaters or spot coolers are to be installed which will provide heat or cool only to a single work area and do not provide general heating or cooling for the space.
2. Buildings heated with a system designed to provide sufficient heat only to prevent freezing of products or systems. Such systems shall not provide heating above 50°F (10°C).
3. Premanufactured freezer or refrigerated storage buildings and areas where the temperature is set below 40°F (4°C) and in which no operators work on a regular basis.
4. Electrical equipment switching buildings which provide space conditioning for equipment only and in which no operators work on a regular basis except that the provisions of Section C405 shall apply.
5. Buildings containing a system(s) designed and sold for dehumidification purposes only and controlled only by a humidistat. No thermostat shall be installed on systems thus exempted from this code.

C101.4.3 Limited or special use buildings. Buildings determined by the code official to have a limited energy use potential based on size, configuration or time occupied, or to have a special use requirement shall be considered limited or special use buildings. Code compliance requirements may be adjusted by the code official to handle such cases when nationally recognized energy analysis procedures have been used to demonstrate that the building would use less energy than a code compliant building of the same configuration.

C101.5 Compliance. *Residential buildings* shall meet the provisions of *Florida Building Code, Energy Conservation*—Residential Provisions. *Commercial buildings* shall meet the provisions of *Florida Building Code, Energy Conservation*—Commercial Provisions.

C101.5.1 Compliance materials. The Florida Building Commission shall approve specific computer software. The *code official* shall be permitted to approve worksheets, compliance manuals and other similar materials that meet the intent of this code.

*

C101.5.1.1 Alterations, renovations and building systems. Alterations, renovations and building systems may utilize Form C402. Form C402 can be found in Appendix CA.

SECTION C102 ALTERNATE MATERIALS—METHOD OF CONSTRUCTION, DESIGN OR INSULATING SYSTEMS

C102.1 General. This code is not intended to prevent the use of any material, method of construction, design or insulating system not specifically prescribed herein, provided that such construction, design or insulating system has been *approved* by the *code official* as meeting the intent of this code.

C102.1.1 Above code programs. The *code official* or other authority having jurisdiction shall be permitted to deem a national, state or local energy efficiency program to exceed the energy efficiency required by this code. Buildings *approved* in writing by such an energy efficiency program shall be considered in compliance with this code. The requirements identified as "mandatory" in Chapter 4 shall be met.

PART 2—ADMINISTRATION AND ENFORCEMENT

SECTION C103 CONSTRUCTION DOCUMENTS

C103.1 General. Construction documents and other supporting data shall be submitted in one or more sets with each application for a permit. The construction documents shall be prepared by a registered design professional where required by the statutes of the jurisdiction in which the project is to be constructed. Where special conditions exist, the *code official* is authorized to require necessary construction documents to be prepared by a registered design professional.

Exception: The *code official* is authorized to waive the requirements for construction documents or other supporting data if the *code official* determines they are not necessary to confirm compliance with this code.

C103.1.1 Compliance certification.

C103.1.1.1 Code compliance demonstration.

C103.1.1.1.1 Residential. See *Florida Building Code, Energy Conservation:* Residential Provisions.

C103.1.1.1.2 Commercial and multiple-family residential. Completion of procedures demonstrating compliance with this code for commercial and multiple-family residential buildings shall be in accordance with the provisions of Section 481.229, *Florida Statutes*, or Section 471.003, *Florida Statutes*.

Exception: Where HVAC systems are ≤ 15 tons per system, air conditioning or mechanical contractors licensed in accordance with Chapter 489, *Florida Statutes*, or commercial building energy raters certified in accordance with Section 553.99, *Florida Statutes*, may prepare the code compliance form.

Design professionals responsible under Florida law for the design of lighting, electrical, mechanical, and plumbing systems and the building shell, shall certify compliance of those building systems with the code by signing and providing their professional registration number on the energy code form provided as part of the plans and specifications to the building department.

C103.1.1.2 Code compliance certification. The building's owner, the owner's architect, or other authorized agent legally designated by the owner shall certify that the building is in compliance with the code, as per Section 553.907, *Florida Statutes*, prior to receiving the permit to begin construction or renovation.

C103.2 Information on construction documents. Construction documents shall be drawn to scale upon suitable material. Electronic media documents are permitted to be submitted where *approved* by the *code official*. Construction documents shall be of sufficient clarity to indicate the location, nature and extent of the work proposed, and show in sufficient detail pertinent data and features of the building, systems and equipment as herein governed. Details shall include, but are not limited to, the following as applicable:

1. Insulation materials and their *R*-values.
2. Fenestration *U*-factors and solar heat gain coefficients (SHGCs).
3. Area-weighted *U*-factor and solar heat gain coefficient (SHGC) calculations.
4. Mechanical system design criteria.
5. Mechanical and service water heating system and equipment types, sizes and efficiencies.
6. Economizer description.
7. Equipment and system controls.
8. Fan motor horsepower (hp) and controls.
9. Duct sealing, duct and pipe insulation and location.
10. Lighting fixture schedule with wattage and control narrative.
11. Location of *daylight* zones on floor plans.
12. Air sealing details.

C103.2.1 Building thermal envelope depiction. The *building's thermal envelope* shall be represented on the construction drawings.

C103.3 Examination of documents. The *code official* shall examine or cause to be examined the accompanying construction documents and shall ascertain whether the construction indicated and described is in accordance with the requirements of this code and other pertinent laws or ordinances. The *code official* is authorized to utilize a registered design professional, or other *approved* entity not affiliated with the building design or construction, in conducting the review of the plans and specifications for compliance with the code.

C103.3.1 Approval of construction documents. When the *code official* issues a permit where construction documents are required, the construction documents shall be endorsed in writing and stamped "Reviewed for Code Compliance." Such *approved* construction documents shall not be changed, modified or altered without authorization from the *code official*. Work shall be done in accordance with the *approved* construction documents.

One set of construction documents so reviewed shall be retained by the *code official*. The other set shall be returned to the applicant, kept at the site of work and shall be open to inspection by the *code official* or a duly authorized representative.

C103.3.2 Previous approvals. This code shall not require changes in the construction documents, construction or designated occupancy of a structure for which a lawful permit has been heretofore issued or otherwise lawfully authorized, and the construction of which has been pursued in good faith within 180 days after the effective date of this code and has not been abandoned.

C103.3.3 Phased approval. The *code official* shall have the authority to issue a permit for the construction of part of an energy conservation system before the construction documents for the entire system have been submitted or *approved*, provided adequate information and detailed statements have been filed complying with all pertinent requirements of this code. The holders of such permit shall proceed at their own risk without assurance that the permit for the entire energy conservation system will be granted.

C103.4 Amended construction documents. Changes made during construction that are not in compliance with the *approved* construction documents shall be resubmitted for approval as an amended set of construction documents.

C103.5 Retention of construction documents. One set of *approved* construction documents shall be retained by the *code official* for a period of not less than 180 days from date of completion of the permitted work, or as required by state or local laws.

SECTION C104
INSPECTIONS

C104.1 General. Construction or work for which a permit is required shall be subject to inspection by the *code official* or his or her designated agent, and such construction or work shall remain accessible and exposed for inspection purposes until *approved*. It shall be the duty of the permit applicant to cause the work to remain accessible and exposed for inspection purposes. Neither the *code official* nor the jurisdiction shall be liable for expense entailed in the removal or replacement of any material, product, system or building component required to allow inspection to validate compliance with this code.

C104.2 Required inspections. The *code official* or his or her designated agent, upon notification, shall make the inspections set forth in Sections C104.2.1 through C104.2.6.

C104.2.1 Footing and foundation inspection. Inspections associated with footings and foundations shall verify compliance with the code as to *R*-value, location, thickness, depth of burial and protection of insulation as required by the code and *approved* plans and specifications.

C104.2.2 Framing and rough-in inspection. Inspections at framing and rough-in shall be made before application of interior finish and shall verify compliance with the code as to types of insulation and corresponding *R*-values and their correct location and proper installation; fenestration properties (*U*-factor, SHGC and VT) and proper installation; and air leakage controls as required by the code and approved plans and specifications.

C104.2.3 Plumbing rough-in inspection. Inspections at plumbing rough-in shall verify compliance as required by the code and *approved* plans and specifications as to types of insulation and corresponding *R*-values and protection; required controls; and required heat traps.

C104.2.4 Mechanical rough-in inspection. Inspections at mechanical rough-in shall verify compliance as required by the code and *approved* plans and specifications as to installed HVAC equipment type and size; required controls, system insulation and corresponding *R*-value; system and damper air leakage; and required energy recovery and economizers.

C104.2.5 Electrical rough-in inspection. Inspections at electrical rough-in shall verify compliance as required by the code and *approved* plans and specifications as to installed lighting systems, components and controls; and installation of an electric meter for each dwelling unit.

C104.2.6 Final inspection. The building shall have a final inspection and shall not be occupied until *approved*. The final inspection shall include verification of the installation and proper operation of all required building controls, and documentation verifying activities associated with required *building commissioning* have been conducted and findings of noncompliance corrected. Buildings, or portions thereof, shall not be considered for a final inspection until the *code official* has received a letter of transmittal from the building owner acknowledging that the building owner has received the Preliminary Commissioning Report as required in Section C408.2.4.

C104.3 Reinspection. A building shall be reinspected when determined necessary by the *code official*.

C104.4 Approved inspection agencies. The *code official* is authorized to accept inspection reports in whole or in part from either individuals as defined in Section 553.993(5) or (7), *Florida Statutes* or third-party inspection agencies not affiliated with the building design or construction, provided such agencies are *approved* as to qualifications and reliability relevant to the building components and systems they are inspecting.

C104.5 Inspection requests. It shall be the duty of the holder of the permit or their duly authorized agent to notify the *code official* when work is ready for inspection. It shall be the duty of the permit holder to provide access to and means for inspections of such work that are required by this code.

C104.6 Reinspection and testing. Where any work or installation does not pass an initial test or inspection, the necessary corrections shall be made to achieve compliance with this code. The work or installation shall then be resubmitted to the *code official* for inspection and testing.

C104.7 Approval. After the prescribed tests and inspections indicate that the work complies in all respects with this code, a notice of approval shall be issued by the *code official*.

C104.7.1 Revocation. The *code official* is authorized to, in writing, suspend or revoke a notice of approval issued under the provisions of this code wherever the certificate is issued in error, or on the basis of incorrect information supplied, or where it is determined that the *building* or structure, premise, or portion thereof is in violation of any ordinance or regulation or any of the provisions of this code.

SECTION C105 VALIDITY

C105.1 General. If a portion of this code is held to be illegal or void, such a decision shall not affect the validity of the remainder of this code.

SECTION C106 REFERENCED STANDARDS

C106.1 Referenced codes and standards. The codes and standards referenced in this code shall be those listed in Chapter 6, and such codes and standards shall be considered as part of the requirements of this code to the prescribed extent of each such reference and as further regulated in Sections C106.1.1 and C106.1.2.

C106.1.1 Conflicts. Where conflicts occur between provisions of this code and referenced codes and standards, the provisions of this code shall apply.

C106.1.2 Provisions in referenced codes and standards. Where the extent of the reference to a referenced code or standard includes subject matter that is within the scope of this code, the provisions of this code, as applicable, shall take precedence over the provisions in the referenced code or standard.

C106.2 Application of references. References to chapter or section numbers, or to provisions not specifically identified by number, shall be construed to refer to such chapter, section or provision of this code.

C106.3 Other laws. The provisions of this code shall not be deemed to nullify any provisions of local, state or federal law.

SECTION C107 FEES RESERVED

SECTION C108 STOP WORK ORDER

C108.1 Authority. Where the *code official* finds any work regulated by this code being performed in a manner either contrary to the provisions of this code or dangerous or unsafe, the *code official* is authorized to issue a stop work order.

C108.2 Issuance. The stop work order shall be in writing and shall be given to the owner of the property involved, the owner's authorized agent, or to the person doing the work. Upon issuance of a stop work order, the cited work shall immediately cease. The stop work order shall state the reason for the order and the conditions under which the cited work will be permitted to resume.

C108.3 Emergencies. Reserved.

C108.4 Failure to comply. Any person who shall continue any work after having been served with a stop work order, except such work as that person is directed to perform to remove a violation or unsafe condition, shall be subject to penalties as prescribed by law.

SECTION C109 BOARD OF APPEALS RESERVED

CHAPTER 2 [CE]
DEFINITIONS

SECTION C201
GENERAL

C201.1 Scope. Unless stated otherwise, the following words and terms in this code shall have the meanings indicated in this chapter.

C201.2 Interchangeability. Words used in the present tense include the future; words in the masculine gender include the feminine and neuter; the singular number includes the plural and the plural includes the singular.

C201.3 Terms defined in other codes. Terms that are not defined in this code but are defined in the *Florida Building Code, Building*; *Florida Fire Prevention Code*; *Florida Building Code, Fuel Gas*; *Florida Building Code, Mechanical*; *Florida Building Code, Plumbing* or the *Florida Building Code, Residential* shall have the meanings ascribed to them in those codes.

C201.4 Terms not defined. Terms not defined by this chapter shall have ordinarily accepted meanings such as the context implies.

SECTION C202
GENERAL DEFINITIONS

ABOVE-GRADE WALL. See "Wall, above-grade."

ACCESSIBLE. Admitting close approach as a result of not being guarded by locked doors, elevation or other effective means (see "Readily *accessible*").

ADDITION. An extension or increase in the *conditioned space* floor area or height of a building or structure.

ADJACENT WALL, CEILING or FLOOR. A wall, ceiling or floor of a structure that separates conditioned space from enclosed but unconditioned space, such as an unconditioned attached garage, storage or utility room.

AEROSOL SEALANT. A closure product for duct and plenum systems, which is delivered internally to leak sites as aerosol particles using a pressurized air stream.

AIR BARRIER. Relating to air distribution systems, a material object(s) that impedes or restricts the free movement of air under specified conditions. For fibrous glass duct, the air barrier is its foil cladding; for flexible nonmetal duct, the air barrier is the nonporous core; and for sheet metal duct and air handling units, the air barrier is the metal in contact with the air stream. For mechanical closets, the air barrier may be a uniform panelized material such as gypsum wallboard that meets ASTM C36, or it may be a membrane that alone acts as an air barrier that is attached to a panel, such as the foil cladding of fibrous glass duct board. Relating to the building envelope, air barriers comprise the planes of primary resistance to airflow between the interior spaces of a building and the outdoors and the planes of primary airflow resistance between adjacent air zones of a building, including planes between adjacent conditioned and unconditioned air spaces of a building. To be classed as an air barrier, a building plane must be substantially leak free; that is, it shall have an air leakage rate not greater than 0.5 cfm/ft^2 when subjected to an air pressure gradient of 25 pascal. In general, air barriers are made of durable, nonporous materials and are sealed to adjoining wall, ceiling or floor surfaces with a suitable long-life mastic. House wraps and taped and sealed drywall may constitute an air barrier, but dropped acoustical tile ceilings (T-bar ceilings) may not. Batt insulation facings and asphalt-impregnated fiberboard and felt paper are not considered air barriers.

AIR CONDITIONING. The treatment of air so as to control simultaneously the temperature, humidity, cleanness and distribution of the air to meet the requirements of a conditioned space.

AIR CURTAIN. A device, installed at the building entrance, that generates and discharges a laminar air stream intended to prevent the infiltration of external, unconditioned air into the conditioned spaces, or the loss of interior, conditioned air to the outside.

AIR DISTRIBUTION SYSTEM. Any system of ducts, plenums and air-handling equipment that circulates air within a space or spaces and includes systems made up of one or more air-handling units.

ALTERATION. Any construction, retrofit or renovation to an existing structure other than repair or addition that requires a permit. Also, a change in a building, electrical, gas, mechanical or plumbing system that involves an extension, addition or change to the arrangement, type or purpose of the original installation that requires a permit.

APPROVED. Approval by the *code official* as a result of investigation and tests conducted by him or her, or by reason of accepted principles or tests by nationally recognized organizations.

APPROVED AGENCY. An established and recognized agency regularly engaged in conducting tests or furnishing inspection services, when such agency has been approved by the *code official*.

ATTIC. An enclosed unconditioned space located immediately below an uninsulated roof and immediately above the ceiling of a building.

AUTOMATIC. Self-acting, operating by its own mechanism when actuated by some impersonal influence, as, for example, a change in current strength, pressure, temperature or mechanical configuration (see "*Manual*").

BELOW-GRADE WALL. See "Wall, below-grade."

BOILER, MODULATING. A boiler that is capable of more than a single firing rate in response to a varying temperature or heating load.

BOILER SYSTEM. One or more boilers, their piping and controls that work together to supply steam or hot water to heat output devices remote from the boiler.

BRITISH THERMAL UNIT (Btu). Abbreviation for British thermal unit, which is the quantity of heat required to raise the temperature of 1 pound (454 g) of water 1°F (0.56°C) (1 Btu = 1055 J).

BUBBLE POINT. The refrigerant liquid saturation temperature at a specified pressure.

BUILDING. Any structure used or intended for supporting or sheltering any use or occupancy. For each purpose of this Code, each portion of a building separated from other portions by a firewall shall be considered as a separate building. The term "building" shall be construed as if followed by the words "or part thereof."

BUILDING COMMISSIONING. A process that verifies and documents that the selected building systems have been designed, installed, and function according to the owner's project requirements and construction documents, and to minimum code requirements.

BUILDING ENTRANCE. Any door, set of doors, doorway, or other form of portal that is used to gain access to the building from the outside by the public.

BUILDING SITE. A continguous area of land that is under the ownership or control of one entity.

BUILDING THERMAL ENVELOPE. The basement walls, exterior walls, floor, roof and any other building elements that enclose *conditioned space.* This boundary also includes the boundary between *conditioned space* and any exempt or unconditioned space. See "*Adjacent wall, ceiling or floor*."

***C*-FACTOR (THERMAL CONDUCTANCE).** The coefficient of heat transmission (surface to surface) through a building component or assembly, equal to the time rate of heat flow per unit area and the unit temperature difference between the warm side and cold side surfaces (Btu/h · ft^2 · °F) [W/(m^2 · K)].

CIRCULATING HOT WATER SYSTEM. A specifically designed water distribution system where one or more pumps are operated in the service hot water piping to circulate heated water from the water-heating equipment to the fixture supply and back to the water-heating equipment.

CLIMATE ZONE. A geographical region based on climatic criteria as specified in this code.

CODE OFFICIAL. The officer or other designated authority charged with the administration and enforcement of this code, or a duly authorized representative.

COEFFICENT OF PERFORMANCE (COP) – COOLING. The ratio of the rate of heat input, in consistent units, for a complete refrigerating system or some specific portion of that system under designated operating conditions.

COEFFICIENT OF PERFORMANCE (COP) – HEATING. The ratio of the rate of heat delivered to the rate of energy input, in consistent units, for a complete heat pump system, including the compressor and, if applicable, auxiliary heat, under designated operating conditions.

COMMERCIAL BUILDING. For this code, all buildings that are not included in the definition of "Residential building."

COMPUTER ROOM. A room whose primary function is to house equipment for the processing and storage of electronic data and that has a design electronic data equipment power density exceeding 20 watts per square foot of conditioned floor area.

CONDENSING UNIT. A factory-made assembly of refrigeration components designed to compress and liquefy a specific refrigerant. The unit consists of one or more refrigerant compressors, refrigerant condensers (air-cooled, evaporatively cooled, or water-cooled), condenser fans and motors (where used) and factory-supplied accessories.

CONDITIONED FLOOR AREA. The horizontal projection of that portion of space that is conditioned directly or indirectly by an energy-using system.

CONDITIONED SPACE. An area, room or space that is enclosed within the building thermal envelope and is directly or indirectly heated or cooled. Spaces are indirectly heated or cooled where they communicate through openings with conditioned spaces; where they are separated from conditioned spaces by uninsulated walls, floors or ceilings; or where they contain uninsulated ducts, piping or other sources of heating or cooling. See "*Space*."

CONTINUOUS AIR BARRIER. A combination of materials and assemblies that restrict or prevent the passage of air through the building thermal envelope.

CONTINUOUS INSULATION (ci). Insulating material that is continuous across all structural members without thermal bridges other than fasteners and service openings. It is installed on the interior or exterior or is integral to any opaque surface of the building envelope.

CONTROL. To regulate the operation of equipment.

CONTROL DEVICE. A specialized device used to regulate the operation of equipment.

CRAWL SPACE WALL. The opaque portion of a wall that encloses a crawl space and is partially or totally below grade.

CURTAIN WALL. Fenestration products used to create an external nonload-bearing wall that is designed to separate the exterior and interior environments.

DAYLIGHT RESPONSIVE CONTROL. A device or system that provides automatic control of electric light levels based on the amount of daylight in a space.

DAYLIGHT ZONE. That portion of a building's interior floor area that is illuminated by natural light.

DEMAND CONTROL VENTILATION (DCV). A ventilation system capability that provides for the automatic reduction of outdoor air intake below design rates when the actual occupancy of spaces served by the system is less than design occupancy.

DEMAND RECIRCULATION WATER SYSTEM. A water distribution system where pumps prime the service hot water piping with heated water upon demand for hot water.

DUCT. A tube or conduit utilized for conveying air. The air passages of self-contained systems are not to be construed as air ducts.

DUCT SYSTEM. A continuous passageway for the transmission of air that, in addition to ducts, includes duct fittings, dampers, plenums, fans and accessory air-handling equipment and appliances.

DWELLING UNIT. A single unit providing complete independent living facilities for one or more persons, including permanent provisions for living, sleeping, eating, cooking and sanitation.

DYNAMIC GLAZING. Any fenestration product that has the fully reversible ability to change its performance properties, including *U*-factor, solar heat gain coefficient (SHGC), or visible transmittance (VT).

ECONOMIZER, AIR. A duct and damper arrangement and automatic control system that allows a cooling system to supply outside air to reduce or eliminate the need for mechanical cooling during mild or cold weather.

ECONOMIZER, WATER. A system where the supply air of a cooling system is cooled indirectly with water that is itself cooled by heat or mass transfer to the environment without the use of mechanical cooling.

EFFICIENCY. Performance at specified rating conditions.

ENCLOSED SPACE. A volume surrounded by solid surfaces such as walls, floors, roofs, and openable devices such as doors and operable windows.

ENERGY. The capacity for doing work. It takes a number of forms that may be transformed from one into another such as thermal (heat), mechanical (work), electrical and chemical. Customary measurement units are British thermal units (Btu).

ENERGY ANALYSIS. A method for estimating the annual energy use of the *proposed design* and *standard reference design* based on estimates of energy use.

ENERGY COST. The total estimated annual cost for purchased energy for the building functions regulated by this code, including applicable demand charges.

ENERGY RECOVERY VENTILATION SYSTEM. Systems that employ air-to-air heat exchangers to recover energy from exhaust air for the purpose of preheating, precooling, humidifying or dehumidifying outdoor ventilation air prior to supplying the air to a space, either directly or as part of an HVAC system.

ENERGY SIMULATION TOOL. An *approved* software program or calculation-based methodology that projects the annual energy use of a building.

ENTRANCE DOOR. Fenestration products used for ingress, egress and access in nonresidential buildings, including, but not limited to, exterior entrances that utilize latching hardware and automatic closers and contain over 50-percent glass specifically designed to withstand heavy use and possibly abuse.

EQUIPMENT. Devices for comfort conditioning, electric power, lighting, transportation or service water heating including, but not limited to, furnaces, boilers, air conditioners, heat pumps, chillers, water heaters, lamps, luminaires, ballasts, elevators, escalators or other devices or installations.

EQUIPMENT ROOM. A space that contains either electrical equipment, mechanical equipment, machinery, water pumps or hydraulic pumps that are a function of the building's services.

EXTERIOR WALL. Walls including both above-grade walls and basement walls that form a boundary between a conditioned and an outdoor space.

FAN BRAKE HORSEPOWER (BHP). The horsepower delivered to the fan's shaft. Brake horsepower does not include the mechanical drive losses (belts, gears, etc.).

FAN EFFICIENCY GRADE (FEG). A numerical rating identifying the fan's aerodynamic ability to convert shaft power, or impeller power in the case of a direct-driven fan, to air power.

FAN SYSTEM BHP. The sum of the fan brake horsepower of all fans that are required to operate at fan system design conditions to supply air from the heating or cooling source to the *conditioned spaces* and return it to the source or exhaust it to the outdoors.

FAN SYSTEM DESIGN CONDITIONS. Operating conditions that can be expected to occur during normal system operation that result in the highest supply fan airflow rate to conditioned spaces served by the system.

FAN SYSTEM MOTOR NAMEPLATE HP. The sum of the motor nameplate horsepower of all fans that are required to operate at design conditions to supply air from the heating or cooling source to the *conditioned spaces* and return it to the source or exhaust it to the outdoors.

FENESTRATION. Products classified as either vertical fenestration or skylights.

Skylight. Glass or other transparent or translucent glazing material installed at a slope of less than 60 degrees (1.05 rad) from horizontal. Glazing materials in skylights, including unit skylights, tubular daylighting devices, solariums, sunrooms, roofs and sloped walls are included in this definition.

Vertical fenestration. Windows (fixed or moveable), opaque doors, glazed doors, glazed block and combination opaque/glazed doors composed of glass or other transparent or translucent glazing materials and installed at a slope of at least 60 degrees (1.05 rad) from horizontal.

FENESTRATION AREA. Total area of the fenestration measured using the rough opening and including the glazing, sash and frame. For doors where the glazed vision area is less than 50% of the door area, the fenestration area is the glazed vision area. For all other doors, the fenestration area is the door area.

FENESTRATION PRODUCT, FIELD-FABRICATED. A fenestration product whose frame is made at the construction site of standard dimensional lumber or other materials that were not previously cut, or otherwise formed with the specific intention of being used to fabricate a fenestration product or exterior door. Field fabricated does not include site-built fenestration.

FENESTRATION PRODUCT, SITE-BUILT. A fenestration designed to be made up of field-glazed or field-assembled units using specific factory cut or otherwise factory-formed framing and glazing units. Examples of site-built fenestration include storefront systems, curtain walls and atrium roof systems.

***F*-FACTOR.** The perimeter heat loss factor for slab-on-grade floors (Btu/h • ft • °F) [W/(m • K)].

FLOOR AREA, NET. The actual occupied area not including unoccupied accessory areas such as corridors, stairways, toilet rooms, mechanical rooms and closets.

GASKETING. A compressible, resilient elastic packing, made of foam rubber or of a synthetic foam polymer. A gasket is distinct from the components being joined and must be capable of closing all air leakage pathways between the air barriers of the joint and of creating an air-tight seal.

GENERAL LIGHTING. Lighting that provides a substantially uniform level of illumination throughout an area. General lighting shall not include decorative lighting or lighting that provides a dissimilar level of illumination to serve a specialized application or feature within such area.

GENERAL PURPOSE ELECTRIC MOTOR (SUBTYPE I). A motor that is designed in standard ratings with either of the following:

1. Standard operating characteristics and standard mechanical construction for use under usual service conditions, such as those specified in NEMA MG 1, paragraph 14.02, "Usual Service Conditions," and without restriction to a particular application or type of application.
2. Standard operating characteristics or standard mechanical construction for use under unusual service conditions, such as those specified in NEMA MG 1, paragraph 14.03, "Unusual Service Conditions," or for a particular type of application, and that can be used in most general purpose applications.

General purpose electric motors (Subtype I) are constructed in NEMA T-frame sizes or IEC metric equivalent, starting at 143T.

GENERAL PURPOSE ELECTRIC MOTOR (SUBTYPE II). A motor incorporating the design elements of a general purpose electric motor (Subtype I) that is configured as one of the following:

1. A U-frame motor.
2. A Design C motor.
3. A close-coupled pump motor.
4. A footless motor.
5. A vertical, solid-shaft, normal-thrust motor (as tested in a horizontal configuration).
6. An 8-pole motor (900 rpm).
7. A polyphase motor with voltage of not more than 600 volts (other than 230 or 460 volts).

GREENHOUSE. A structure or a thermally isolated area of a building that maintains a specialized sunlit environment exclusively used for, and essential to, the cultivation, protection or maintenance of plants.

HEAT. The form of energy that is transferred by virtue of a temperature difference or a change in the state of a material.

HEAT TRAP. An arrangement of piping and fittings, such as elbows, or a commercially available heat trap that prevents thermosyphoning of hot water during standby periods.

HEATED SLAB. Slab-on-grade construction in which the heating elements, hydronic tubing, or hot air distribution system is in contact with, or placed within or under, the slab.

HIGH-SPEED DOOR. A nonswinging door used primarily to facilitate vehicular access or material transportation, with a minimum opening rate of 32 inches (813 mm) per second, a minimum closing rate of 24 inches (610 mm) per second and that includes an automatic-closing device.

HISTORIC BUILDING. Any building or structure that is one or more of the following:

1. Listed, or certified as eligible for listing by the State Historic Preservation Officer or the Keeper of the National Register of Historic Places, in the National Register of Historic Places.
2. Designated as historic under an applicable state or local law.
3. Certified as a contributing resource within a National Register-listed, state-designated or locally designated historic district.

HORSEPOWER (hp). Unit of power; work done at a rate equal to 745.7 watts, 550 foot lb. per second, or 33,000 foot lb. per minute.

HUMIDISTAT. A regulatory device, actuated by changes in humidity, used for automatic control of relative humidity.

HVAC. Heating, ventilating and air conditioning.

HVAC SYSTEM. The equipment, distribution systems, and terminals that provide, either collectively or individually, the processes of heating, ventilating or air conditioning to a building or portion of a building.

INDIRECTLY CONDITIONED SPACE. See "Space."

INDOOR. Within the conditioned building envelope.

INFILTRATION. The uncontrolled inward air leakage through cracks and crevices in any building element and around windows and doors of a building caused by pressure differences across these elements due to factors such as wind, inside and outside temperature differences (stack effect), and imbalance between supply and exhaust air systems.

INSULATION. Material mainly used to retard the flow of heat.

INTEGRATED PART LOAD VALUE (IPLV). A single-number figure of merit based on part-load EER, COP or kW/ton expressing part-load efficiency for air-conditioning and heat pump equipment on the basis of weighted operation at various load capacities for equipment.

KILOWATT (kW). The basic unit of electric power, equal to KILOWATT (kW). The basic unit of electric power, equal to 1,000 watts.

LABELED. Equipment, materials or products to which have been affixed a label, seal, symbol or other identifying mark of a nationally recognized testing laboratory, inspection agency or other organization concerned with product evaluation that maintains periodic inspection of the production of the above-labeled items and whose labeling indicates either that the equipment, material or product meets identified standards or has been tested and found suitable for a specified purpose.

LIGHTING SYSTEM. A group of luminaires circuited or controlled to perform a specific function.

LINER SYSTEM (Ls). A system that includes the following:

1. A continuous vapor barrier liner membrane that is installed below the purlins and that is uninterrupted by framing members.
2. An uncompressed, unfaced insulation resting on top of the liner membrane and located between the purlins.

For multilayer installations, the last rated *R-value* of insulation is for unfaced insulation draped over purlins and then compressed when the metal roof panels are attached.

LISTED. Equipment, materials, products or services included in a list published by an organization acceptable to the *code official* and concerned with evaluation of products or services that maintains periodic inspection of production of *listed* equipment or materials or periodic evaluation of services and whose listing states either that the equipment, material, product or service meets identified standards or has been tested and found suitable for a specified purpose.

LOW-SLOPED ROOF. A roof having a slope less than 2 units vertical in 12 units horizontal.

LOW-VOLTAGE DRY-TYPE DISTRIBUTION TRANSFORMER. A transformer that is air-cooled, does not use oil as a coolant, has an input voltage less than or equal to 600 volts and is rated for operation at a frequency of 60 hertz.

LOW-VOLTAGE LIGHTING. Lighting equipment powered through a transformer such as a cable conductor, a rail conductor and track lighting.

MANUAL. Capable of being operated by personal intervention (see "*Automatic*").

MANUFACTURER. The company engaged in the original production and assembly of products or equipment or a company that purchases such products and equipment manufactured in accordance with company specifications.

MECHANICAL CLOSET. For the purposes of this code, a closet used as an air plenum that contains the blower unit or air handler of a central air-conditioning or heating unit.

NAMEPLATE HORSEPOWER. The nominal motor horsepower rating stamped on the motor nameplate.

NONSTANDARD PART LOAD VALUE (NPLV). A single-number part-load efficiency figure of merit calculated and referenced to conditions other than IPLV conditions, for units that are not designed to operate at AHRI standard rating conditions.

OCCUPANCY. The purpose for which a building, or part thereof, is used or intended to be used. For the purposes of determining changes of occupancy for this Code, the occupancy shall be considered the major occupancy group designations established by Chapter 3 of the *Florida Building Code, Building*.

OCCUPANT SENSOR CONTROL. An automatic control device or system that detects the presence or absence of people within an area and causes lighting, equipment or appliances to be regulated accordingly.

ON-SITE RENEWABLE ENERGY. Energy derived from solar radiation, wind, waves, tides, landfill gas, biomass or the internal heat of the earth. The energy system providing on-site renewable energy shall be located on the project site.

OPAQUE DOOR. A door that is not less than 50-percent opaque in surface area.

OUTDOOR. The environment exterior to the building structure.

OUTDOOR (OUTSIDE) AIR. Air that is outside the building envelope or is taken from outside the building that has not been previously circulated through the building.

OUTSIDE. The environment exterior to the conditioned space of the building and may include attics, garages, crawlspaces, etc., but not return air plenums.

PLENUM. A compartment or chamber to which one or more ducts are connected, that forms a part of the air distribution system, and that is not used for occupancy or storage. A plenum often is formed in part or in total by portions of the building.

POSITIVE INDOOR PRESSURE. A positive pressure condition within a conditioned space caused by bringing in more outside air than the amount of air that is exhausted and/or lost through air leakage.

POWERED ROOF/WALL VENTILATORS. A fan consisting of a centrifugal or axial impeller with an integral driver in a weather-resistant housing and with a base designed to fit, usually by means of a curb, over a wall or roof opening.

PRESSURE ENVELOPE. The primary air barrier of a building; that part of the envelope that provides the greatest resistance to airflow to or from the building.

PRESSURE-SENSITIVE TAPE. Tape used for sealing duct system components and air barriers, which adheres when pressure is applied and is not heat activated.

PROPOSED DESIGN. A description or computer representation of the proposed building used to estimate annual energy use for determining compliance based on total building performance or design energy cost.

RADIANT HEATING SYSTEM. A heating system that transfers heat to objects and surfaces within a conditioned space, primarily by infrared radiation.

READILY ACCESSIBLE. Capable of being reached quickly for operation, renewal or inspection without requiring those to whom ready access is requisite to climb over or remove obstacles or to resort to portable ladders or access equipment (see "*Accessible*"). In public facilities, accessibility may be limited to certified personnel through locking covers or by placing equipment in locked rooms.

REFRIGERANT DEW POINT. The refrigerant vapor saturation temperature at a specified pressure.

REFRIGERATED WAREHOUSE COOLER. An enclosed storage space capable of being refrigerated to temperatures above 32°F (0°C), that can be walked into and has a total chilled storage area of not less than 3,000 square feet (279 m^2).

REFRIGERATED WAREHOUSE FREEZER. An enclosed storage space capable of being refrigerated to temperatures at or below 32°F (0°C), that can be walked into and has a total chilled storage area of not less than 3,000 square feet (279 m^2).

REFRIGERATION SYSTEM, LOW TEMPERATURE. Systems for maintaining food product in a frozen state in refrigeration applications.

REFRIGERATION SYSTEM, MEDIUM TEMPERATURE. Systems for maintaining food product above freezing in refrigeration applications.

REGISTERED DESIGN PROFESSIONAL. An individual who is registered or licensed to practice their respective design profession as defined by the statutory requirements of the professional registration laws of the state or jurisdiction in which the project is to be constructed. This includes any registered design professional so long as they are practicing within the scope of their license, which includes those licensed under Chapters 471 and 481, *Florida Statutes*.

RENOVATED BUILDING. A residential or nonresidential building undergoing alteration that varies or changes insulation, HVAC systems, water heating systems or exterior envelope conditions, provided the estimated cost of renovation exceeds 30 percent of the assessed value of the structure.

REPAIR. The reconstruction or renewal of any part of an existing building for the purpose of its maintenance or to correct damage.

REPLACEMENT. The installation of part or all of an existing mechanical or electrical system in an existing building.

REROOFING. The process of recovering or replacing an existing roof covering. See "*Roof recover*" and "*Roof replacement*."

RESIDENTIAL BUILDING. For the purpose of this code, includes R-3 buildings, as well as R-2 and R-4 buildings three stories or less in height above grade plane.

RETROFIT. Modification of existing equipment or systems to incorporate improved performance of operation.

ROOF. The upper portion of the building envelope, including opaque areas and fenestration, that is horizontal or tilted at an angle of less than 60° from horizontal. For the purposes of determining building envelope requirements, the classifications are defined as follows:

1. Attic and other roofs: all other roofs, including roofs with insulation entirely below (inside of) the roof structure (i.e., attics, cathedral ceilings, and single-rafter ceilings), roofs with insulation both above and below the roof structure, and roofs without insulation but excluding metal building roofs.
2. Metal building roof: a roof that is constructed with (a) a metal, structural, weathering surface, (b) has no ventilated cavity, and (c) has the insulation entirely below deck (i.e., does not include composite concrete and metal deck construction nor a roof framing system that is separated from the superstructure by a wood substrate) and whose structure consists of one or more of the following configurations: (1) metal roofing in direct contact with the steel framing members or (2) insulation between the metal roofing and the steel framing members or (3) insulated metal roofing panels installed as described in (1) or (2).
3. Roof with insulation entirely above deck: a roof with all insulation (1) installed above (outside of) the roof structure and (2) continuous (i.e., uninterrupted by framing members).
4. Single-rafter roof: a subcategory of attic roofs where the roof above and the ceiling below are both attached to the same wood rafter and where insulation is located in the space between these wood rafters.

ROOF ASSEMBLY. A system designed to provide weather protection and resistance to design loads. The system consists of a roof covering and roof deck or a single component serving as both the roof covering and the roof deck. A roof assembly includes the roof covering, underlayment, roof deck, insulation, vapor retarder and interior finish.

ROOF RECOVER. The process of installing an additional roof covering over an existing roof covering without removing the existing roof covering.

ROOF REPAIR. Reconstruction or renewal of any part of an existing roof for the purpose of its maintenance.

ROOF REPLACMENT. The process of removing the existing roof covering, repairing any damaged substrate and installing a new roof covering.

ROOFTOP MONITOR. A raised section of a roof containing vertical fenestration along one or more sides.

***R*-VALUE (THERMAL RESISTANCE).** The inverse of the time rate of heat flow through a body from one of its bounding surfaces to the other surface for a unit temperature difference between the two surfaces, under steady state conditions, per unit area ($h \cdot ft^2 \cdot °F/Btu$) [($m^2 \cdot K$)/W].

SATURATED CONDENSING TEMPERATURE. The saturation temperature corresponding to the measured refrigerant pressure at the condenser inlet for single component and azeotropic refrigerants, and the arithmetic average of the dew point and *bubble point* temperatures corresponding to the refrigerant pressure at the condenser entrance for zeotropic refrigerants.

SCREW LAMP HOLDERS. A lamp base that requires a screw-in-type lamp, such as a compact-fluorescent, incandescent or tungsten-halogen bulb.

SERVICE WATER HEATING. Supply of hot water for purposes other than comfort heating.

SLEEPING UNIT. A room or space in which people sleep, which can also include permanent provisions for living, eating, and either sanitation or kitchen facilities but not both. Such rooms and spaces that are also part of a dwelling unit are not *sleeping units*.

SMALL DUCT, HIGH-VELOCITY SYSTEM. A heating and cooling product that contains a blower and indoor coil combination that meets the following:

1) is designed for, and produces, at least 1.2 inches of external static pressure when operated at the certified air volume rate of 220–350 cfm per rated ton of cooling; and

2) when applied in the field, uses high-velocity room outlets generally greater than 1,000 fpm that have less than 6.0 square inches of free area.

SMALL ELECTRIC MOTOR. A general purpose, alternating current, single speed induction motor.

SOLAR HEAT GAIN COEFFICIENT (SHGC). The ratio of the solar heat gain entering the space through the fenestration assembly to the incident solar radiation. Solar heat gain includes directly transmitted solar heat and absorbed solar radiation which is then reradiated, conducted or convected into the space. (See "*Fenestration area.*")

SPACE. An enclosed space within a building. The classifications of spaces are as follows for the purpose of determining building envelope requirements.

1. Conditioned space: a cooled space, heated space or indirectly conditioned space or unvented attic assembly defined as follows:

   a. Cooled space: an enclosed space within a building that is cooled by a cooling system whose sensible output capacity exceeds 5 Btu/h · ft^2 of floor area.

   b. Heated space: an enclosed space within a building that is heated by a heating system whose output capacity relative to the floor area is greater than or equal to 5 Btu/h · ft^2.

   c. Indirectly conditioned space: an enclosed space within a building that is not a heated space or a cooled space, which is heated or cooled indirectly by being connected to adjacent space(s) provided (a) the product of the *U*-factor(s) and surface area(s) of the space adjacent to connected space(s) exceeds the combined sum of the product of the *U*-factor(s) and surface area(s) of the space adjoining the outdoors, unconditioned spaces, and to or from semiheated spaces (e.g., corridors) or (b) that air from heated or cooled spaces is intentionally transferred (naturally or mechanically) into the space at a rate exceeding 3 air changes per hour (ACH) (e.g., atria).

   d. Unvented attic assembly: as defined in Section R806.5 of the *Florida Building Code, Residential.* These spaces shall not require supply or return outlets.

2. Semiheated space: an enclosed space within a building that is heated by a heating system whose output capacity is greater than or equal to 3.4 Btu/h · ft^2 of floor area but is not a conditioned space.

3. Unconditioned space: an enclosed space within a building that is not a conditioned space or a semiheated space. Crawl spaces, attics and parking garages with natural or mechanical ventilation are not considered enclosed spaces.

STANDARD REFERENCE DESIGN. A version of the *proposed design* that meets the minimum requirements of this code and is used to determine the maximum annual energy use requirement for compliance based on total building performance.

STOREFRONT. A nonresidential system of doors and windows mulled as a composite fenestration structure that has been designed to resist heavy use. *Storefront* systems include, but are not limited to, exterior fenestration systems that span from the floor level or above to the ceiling of the same story on commercial buildings.

STRUCTURE. That which is built or constructed.

SUNROOM. For the purposes of this code, the term "sunroom" as used herein shall be as follows and shall include conservatories, sunspaces, solariums and porch or patio covers or enclosures.

1. A room with roof panels that includes sloped glazing that is a one-story structure added to an existing dwelling with an open or glazed area in excess of 40 percent of the gross area of the sunroom structure's exterior walls and roof.

2. A one-story structure added to a dwelling with structural roof panels without sloped glazing. The sunroom walls may have any configuration, provided the open area of the longer wall and one additional wall is equal to at least 65 percent of the area below 6 feet 8 inches of each wall, measured from the floor.

SYSTEM. A combination of equipment and auxiliary devices (e.g., controls, accessories, interconnecting means and terminal elements) by which energy is transformed so it performs a specific function such as HVAC, service water heating or lighting.

TERMINAL. A device by which energy from a system is finally delivered, e.g., registers, diffusers, lighting fixtures, faucets, etc.

THERMAL ENVELOPE. The primary insulation layer of a building; that part of the envelope that provides the greatest resistance to heat flow to or from the building.

THERMOSTAT. An automatic control device used to maintain temperature at a fixed or adjustable set point.

TIME SWITCH CONTROL. An automatic control device or system that controls lighting or other loads, including switching off, based on time schedules.

***U*-FACTOR (THERMAL TRANSMITTANCE).** The coefficient of heat transmission (air to air) through a building component or assembly, equal to the time rate of heat flow per unit area and unit temperature difference between the warm side and cold side air films (Btu/h · ft^2 · °F) [W/(m^2 · K)].

UNCONDITIONED SPACE. See "*Space.*"

VARIABLE REFRIGERANT FLOW MULTI-SPLIT AIR CONDITIONER. A Unit of commercial package air-conditioning and heating equipment that is configured as a split system air conditioner incorporating a single refrigerant circuit, with one or more outdoor units, at least one variable-speed compressor or an alternate compressor combination for varying the capacity of the system by three or more steps, and multiple indoor fan coil units, each of which is individually metered and individually controlled by an integral control device and common communications network and which can operate independently in response to multiple indoor thermostats. Variable refrigerant flow implies three or more steps of capacity control on common, interconnecting piping.

VARIABLE REFRIGERANT FLOW SYSTEM. An engineered direct-expansion (DX) refrigerant system that incorporates a common condensing unit, at least one variable-capacity compressor, a distributed refrigerant piping network to multiple indoor fan heating and cooling units each capable of individual zone temperature control, through integral zone temperature control devices and a common communications network. Variable refrigerant flow utilizes three or more steps of control on common interconnecting piping.

VENTILATION. The natural or mechanical process of supplying conditioned or unconditioned air to, or removing such air from, any space.

VENTILATION AIR. That portion of supply air that comes from outside (outdoors) plus any recirculated air that has been treated to maintain the desired quality of air within a designated space.

VISIBLE TRANSMITTANCE [VT]. The ratio of visible light entering the space through the fenestration product assembly to the incident visible light. Visible transmittance includes the effects of glazing material and frame and is expressed as a number between 0 and 1.

WALK-IN COOLER. An enclosed storage space capable of being refrigerated to temperatures above 32°F (0°C) and less than 55°F (12.8°C) that can be walked into, has a ceiling height of not less than 7 feet (2134 mm) and has a total chilled storage area of less than 3,000 square feet (279 m^2).

WALK-IN FREEZER. An enclosed storage space capable of being refrigerated to temperatures at or below 32°F (0°C) that can be walked into, has a ceiling height of not less than 7 feet (2134 mm) and has a total chilled storage area of less than 3,000 square feet (279 m^2).

WALL, ABOVE-GRADE. A wall associated with the *building thermal envelope* that is more than 15 percent above grade and is on the exterior of the building or any wall that is associated with the *building thermal envelope* that is not on the exterior of the building.

WALL, BELOW-GRADE. A wall associated with the basement or first story of the building that is part of the *building thermal envelope*, is not less than 85 percent below grade and is on the exterior of the building.

WATER HEATER. Any heating appliance or equipment that heats potable water and supplies such water to the potable hot water distribution system.

ZONE. A space or group of spaces within a building with heating or cooling requirements that are sufficiently similar so that desired conditions can be maintained throughout using a single controlling device.

CHAPTER 3 [CE]

GENERAL REQUIREMENTS

SECTION C301 CLIMATE ZONES

C301.1 General. Table C301.1 shall be used in determining the applicable requirements from Chapter 4. Locations are assigned a *climate zone* based on Section C301.3.

Figure C301.1 Climate Zone. Reserved.

C301.2 Warm humid counties. Warm humid counties are identified in Table C301.1 by an asterisk.

C301.3 International climate zones. The *climate zone* for any location outside the United States shall be determined by applying Table C301.3(1) and then Table C301.3(2).

C301.4 Tropical climate zone. The tropical *climate zone* shall be defined as:

1. Hawaii, Puerto Rico, Guam, American Samoa, U.S. Virgin Islands, Commonwealth of Northern Mariana Islands; and
2. Islands in the area between the Tropic of Cancer and the Tropic of Capricorn.

SECTION C302 DESIGN CONDITIONS

C302.1 Interior design conditions. The interior design temperatures used for heating and cooling load calculations shall be a maximum of 72°F (22°C) for heating and minimum of 75°F (24°C) for cooling.

SECTION C303 MATERIALS, SYSTEMS AND EQUIPMENT

C303.1 Identification. Materials, systems and equipment shall be identified in a manner that will allow a determination of compliance with the applicable provisions of this code.

C303.1.1 Building thermal envelope insulation. An *R*-value identification mark shall be applied by the manufacturer to each piece of *building thermal envelope* insulation 12 inches (305 mm) or greater in width. Alternately, the insulation installers shall provide a certification listing the type, manufacturer and *R*-value of insulation installed in each element of the *building thermal envelope*. For blown or sprayed insulation (fiberglass and cellulose), the initial installed thickness, settled thickness, settled *R*-value, installed density, coverage area and number of bags installed shall be *listed* on the certification. For sprayed polyurethane foam (SPF) insulation, the installed thickness of the areas covered and *R*-value of installed thickness shall be *listed* on the certification. For insulated siding, the *R*-value shall be labeled on the product's package and shall be *listed* on the certification. The insulation installer shall sign, date and post the certification in a conspicuous location on the job site.

C303.1.1.1 Blown or sprayed roof/ceiling insulation. The thickness of blown-in or sprayed roof/ceiling insulation (fiberglass or cellulose) shall be written in inches (mm) on markers that are installed at least one for every 300 square feet (28 m^2) throughout the attic space. The markers shall be affixed to the trusses or joists and marked with the minimum initial installed thickness with numbers not less than 1 inch (25 mm) in height. Each marker shall face the attic access opening. Spray polyurethane foam thickness and installed *R*-value shall be *listed* on certification provided by the insulation installer.

C303.1.2 Insulation mark installation. Insulating materials shall be installed such that the manufacturer's *R*-value mark is readily observable upon inspection.

TABLE C301.1
CLIMATE ZONES, MOISTURE REGIMES, AND WARM-HUMID DESIGNATIONS BY COUNTY

Key: A – Moist
Asterisk (*) indicates a warm-humid location.

FLORIDA

2A Alachua*
2A Baker*
2A Bay*
2A Bradford*
2A Brevard*
1A Broward*
2A Calhoun*
2A Charlotte*
2A Citrus*
2A Clay*
1A Collier*
2A Columbia*
2A DeSoto*
2A Dixie*
2A Duval*
2A Escambia*
2A Flagler*
2A Franklin*
2A Gadsden*
2A Gilchrist*
2A Glades*
2A Gulf*
2A Hamilton*
2A Hardee*
1A Hendry*
2A Hernando*
2A Highlands*
2A Hillsborough*
2A Holmes*
2A Indian River*
2A Jackson*
2A Jefferson*
2A Lafayette*
2A Lake*
1A Lee*
2A Leon*
2A Levy*
2A Liberty*
2A Madison*
2A Manatee*
2A Marion*
2A Martin*
1A Miami-Dade*
1A Monroe*
2A Nassau*
2A Okaloosa*
2A Okeechobee*
2A Orange*
2A Osceola*
1A Palm Beach*
2A Pasco*
2A Pinellas*
2A Polk*
2A Putnam*
2A Santa Rosa*
2A Sarasota*
2A Seminole*
2A St. Johns*
2A St. Lucie*
2A Sumter*
2A Suwannee*
2A Taylor*
2A Union*
2A Volusia*
2A Wakulla*
2A Walton*
2A Washington*

TABLE C301.3(1)
INTERNATIONAL CLIMATE ZONE DEFINITIONS

MAJOR CLIMATE TYPE DEFINITIONS

Marine (C) Definition—Locations meeting all four criteria:

1. Mean temperature of coldest month between -3°C (27°F) and 18°C (65°F).
2. Warmest month mean < 22°C (72°F).
3. At least four months with mean temperatures over 10°C (50°F).
4. Dry season in summer. The month with the heaviest precipitation in the cold season has at least three times as much precipitation as the month with the least precipitation in the rest of the year. The cold season is October through March in the Northern Hemisphere and April through September in the Southern Hemisphere.

Dry (B) Definition—Locations meeting the following criteria:

Not marine and $P_{in} < 0.44 \times (TF - 19.5)$ [$P_{cm} < 2.0 \times (TC + 7)$ in SI units]

where:

P_{in} = Annual precipitation in inches (cm)

T = Annual mean temperature in °F (°C)

Moist (A) Definition—Locations that are not marine and not dry.

Warm-humid Definition—Moist (A) locations where either of the following wet-bulb temperature conditions shall occur during the warmest six consecutive months of the year:

1. 67°F (19.4°C) or higher for 3,000 or more hours; or
2. 73°F (22.8°C) or higher for 1,500 or more hours.

For SI: °C = [(°F) - 32]/1.8, 1 inch = 2.54 cm.

TABLE C301.3(2)
INTERNATIONAL CLIMATE ZONE DEFINITIONS

ZONE NUMBER	THERMAL CRITERIA	
	IP Units	SI Units
1	9000 < CDD50°F	5000 < CDD10°C
2	6300 < CDD50°F ≤ 9000	3500 < CDD10°C ≤ 5000
3A and 3B	4500 < CDD50°F ≤ 6300 AND HDD65°F ≤ 5400	2500 < CDD10°C ≤ 3500 AND HDD18°C ≤ 3000
4A and 4B	CDD50°F ≤ 4500 AND HDD65°F ≤ 5400	CDD10°C ≤ 2500 AND HDD18°C ≤ 3000
3C	HDD65°F ≤ 3600	HDD18°C ≤ 2000
4C	3600 < HDD65°F ≤ 5400	2000 < HDD18°C ≤ 3000
5	5400 < HDD65°F ≤ 7200	3000 < HDD18°C ≤ 4000
6	7200 < HDD65°F ≤ 9000	4000 < HDD18°C ≤ 5000
7	9000 < HDD65°F ≤ 12600	5000 < HDD18°C ≤ 7000
8	12600 < HDD65°F	7000 < HDD18°C

For SI: °C = [(°F) - 32]/1.8.

C303.1.3 Fenestration product rating. *U*-factors of fenestration products (windows, doors and skylights) shall be determined in accordance with NFRC 100.

Exception: Where required, garage door *U*-factors shall be determined in accordance with either NFRC 100 or ANSI/DASMA 105.

U-factors shall be determined by an accredited, independent laboratory, and *labeled* and certified by the manufacturer.

Products lacking such a *labeled* *U*-factor shall be assigned a default *U*-factor from Table C303.1.3(1) or C303.1.3(2). The solar heat gain coefficient (SHGC) and *visible transmittance* (VT) of glazed fenestration products (windows, glazed doors and skylights) shall be determined in accordance with NFRC 200 by an accredited, independent laboratory, and *labeled* and certified by the manufacturer. Products lacking such a *labeled* SHGC or VT shall be assigned a default SHGC or VT from Table C303.1.3(3).

C303.1.4 Insulation product rating. The thermal resistance (*R*-value) of insulation shall be determined in accordance with the U.S. Federal Trade Commission *R*-value rule (CFR Title 16, Part 460) in units of $h \cdot ft^2 \cdot °F/Btu$ at a mean temperature of 75°F (24°C).

C303.1.4.1 Insulated siding. The thermal resistance (*R*-value) of insulated siding shall be determined in accordance with ASTM C1363. Installation for testing shall be in accordance with the manufacturer's instructions.

C303.2 Installation. Materials, systems and equipment shall be installed in accordance with the manufacturer's instructions and the *Florida Building Code, Building*.

C303.2.1 Protection of exposed foundation insulation. Insulation applied to the exterior of basement walls, crawlspace walls and the perimeter of slab-on-grade floors shall have a rigid, opaque and weather-resistant protective covering to prevent the degradation of the insulation's thermal performance. The protective covering shall cover the exposed exterior insulation and extend not less than 6 inches (153 mm) below grade.

C303.3 Maintenance information. Maintenance instructions shall be furnished for equipment and systems that require preventive maintenance. Required regular maintenance actions shall be clearly stated and incorporated on a readily accessible label. The label shall include the title or publication number for the operation and maintenance manual for that particular model and type of product.

SECTION C304
MATERIALS TESTING AND THERMAL PROPERTIES

C304.1 Building material thermal properties, general.

C304.1.1 Commercial and residential high rise. *R*-values for *building materials* used to demonstrate code compliance with Chapter C4 shall be taken from ASHRAE 90.1 Normative Appendix A, from manufacturer's product literature or from other nationally recognized engineering sources. Assembly *U*-factor calculations shall follow the procedure(s) detailed in Section C304.3 or be tested in accordance with procedure(s) described in Section C304.2.

Concrete block *R*-values shall be calculated using the isothermal planes method or a two-dimensional calculation program, thermal conductivities from ASHRAE 90.1 Normative Appendix A and dimensions from ASTM C90. The parallel path calculation method is not acceptable.

Exception: *R*-values for *building materials* or thermal conductivities determined from testing in accordance with Section C304.2.

TABLE C303.1.3(1)
DEFAULT GLAZED FENESTRATION *U*-FACTORS

FRAME TYPE	SINGLE PANE	DOUBLE PANE	SKYLIGHT	
			Single	Double
Metal	1.20	0.80	2.00	1.30
Metal with Thermal Break	1.10	0.65	1.90	1.10
Nonmetal or Metal Clad	0.95	0.55	1.75	1.05
Glazed Block	0.60			

TABLE C303.1.3(2)
DEFAULT DOOR *U*-FACTORS

DOOR TYPE	*U*-FACTOR
Uninsulated Metal	1.20
Insulated Metal	0.60
Wood	0.50
Insulated, nonmetal edge, max 45% glazing, any glazing double pane	0.35

TABLE C303.1.3(3)
DEFAULT GLAZED FENESTRATION SHGC AND VT

	SINGLE GLAZED		DOUBLE GLAZED		GLAZED BLOCK
	Clear	Tinted	Clear	Tinted	
SHGC	0.8	0.7	0.7	0.6	0.6
VT	0.6	0.3	0.6	0.3	0.6

C304.2 Testing of building materials thermal properties.

C304.2.1 Single materials. If *building material R*-values or thermal conductivities are determined by testing, one of the following test procedures shall be used:

a. ASTM C177

b. ASTM C236

c. ASTM C518

For concrete, the oven-dried conductivity shall be multiplied by 1.2 to reflect the moisture content as typically installed.

C304.2.2 Assembly *U*-factors. If assembly *U*-factors are determined by testing, ASTM C1363 shall be used. Product samples tested shall be production line material or representative of material as purchased by the consumer or contractor. If the assembly is too large to be tested at one time in its entirety, then either a representative portion shall be tested or different portions shall be tested separately and a weighted average determined. To be representative, the portion tested shall include edges of panels, joints with other panels, typical framing percentages and thermal bridges.

C304.3 Calculation procedures and assumptions. The following procedures and assumptions shall be used for all Chapter 4 code calculations. *R*-values for air films, insulation and *building materials* shall be taken from Section C304.3.1 or C304.3.2, respectively. In addition, the appropriate assumptions listed, including framing factors, shall be used.

C304.3.1 Air Films. Prescribed *R*-values for air films shall be as follows:

R-Value	Condition
0.17	All exterior surfaces
0.46	All semi-exterior surfaces
0.61	Interior horizontal surfaces, heat flow up
0.92	Interior horizontal surfaces, heat flow down
0.68	Interior vertical surfaces

C304.3.1.1 Exterior surfaces are areas exposed to the wind.

C304.3.1.2 Semi-exterior surfaces are protected surfaces that face attics, crawl spaces and parking garages with natural or mechanical ventilation.

C304.3.1.3 Interior surfaces are surfaces within enclosed spaces.

C304.3.1.4 The *R*-value for cavity airspaces shall be taken from ASHRAE 90.1 Normative Appendix A. No credit shall be given for airspaces in cavities that contain any insulation or less than 0.5 inch (12.7 mm). The values for 3.5 inch-cavities (84 mm) shall be used for cavities of that width and greater.

C304.3.2 Assembly *U*-Factor, *C*-Factor and *F*-Factor Calculation.

C304.3.2.1 Pre-calculated assembly *U*-factors, *C*-factors, *F*-factors or heat capacities. The *U-factors, C-factors, F-factors,* and *heat capacities* for typical construction assemblies from ASHRAE 90.1 Normative Appendix A shall be used for all calculations unless otherwise allowed by applicant-determined assembly *U*-factors, *C*-factors, *F*-factors or heat capacities. Interpolation between values for *rated R-values of insulation,* including insulated, sheathing is allowed; extrapolation beyond values in the ASHRAE 90.1 Normative Appendix A tables is not.

C304.3.2.2 Applicant-determined assembly *U*-factors, *C*-factors, *F*-factors or heat capacities. If the *building official* determines that the proposed construction assembly is not adequately represented in the appropriate table of ASHRAE 90.1 Normative Appendix A, the applicant shall determine appropriate values for the assembly using the assumptions in ASHRAE 90.1 Normative Appendix A. An assembly is deemed to be adequately represented if:

a. the interior structure, hereafter referred to as the base assembly, for the *class of construction* is the same as described in Normative Appendix A *and*

b. changes in exterior or interior surface *building materials* added to the base assembly do not increase or decrease the *R*-value by more than 2 from that indicated in the descriptions in ASHRAE 90.1 Normative Appendix A.

Insulation, including insulated sheathing, is not considered a *building material.*

CHAPTER 4 [CE]

COMMERCIAL ENERGY EFFICIENCY

SECTION C401 GENERAL

C401.1 Scope. The provisions in this chapter are applicable to commercial *buildings* and their *building sites.*

C401.2 Application. Commercial buildings shall comply with one of the following:

1. The requirements of ANSI/ASHRAE/IESNA 90.1, excluding section 9.4.1.1(g) of the standard.
2. The requirements of Sections C402 through C405. In addition, commercial buildings shall comply with Section C406 and tenant spaces shall comply with Section C406.1.1.
3. The requirements of Sections C402.5, C403.2, C404, C405.2, C405.3, C405.5, C405.6 and C407. The building energy cost shall be equal to or less than 85 percent of the standard reference design building.

C401.2.1 Application to replacement fenestration products. Where some or all of an existing *fenestration* unit is replaced with a new *fenestration* product, including sash and glazing, the replacement *fenestration* unit shall meet the applicable requirements for *U*-factor and *SHGC* in Table C402.4.

Exception: An area-weighted average of the *U*-factor of replacement fenestration products being installed in the building for each fenestration product category listed in Table C402.4 shall be permitted to satisfy the *U*-factor requirements for each fenestration product category listed in Table C402.4. Individual fenestration products from different product categories listed in Table C402.4 shall not be combined in calculating the area-weighted average *U*-factor.

SECTION C402 BUILDING ENVELOPE REQUIREMENTS

C402.1 General (Prescriptive). Building thermal envelope assemblies for buildings that are intended to comply with the code on a prescriptive basis, in accordance with the compliance path described in Item 2 of Section C401.2, shall comply with the following:

1. The opaque portions of the building thermal envelope shall comply with the specific insulation requirements of Section C402.2 and the thermal requirements of either the *R*-value-based method of Section C402.1.3; the *U*-, *C*- and *F*-factor-based method of Section C402.1.4; or the component performance alternative of Section C402.1.5.
2. Roof solar reflectance and thermal emittance shall comply with Section C402.3.
3. Fenestration in building envelope assemblies shall comply with Section C402.4.
4. Air leakage of building envelope assemblies shall comply with Section C402.5.

Alternatively, where buildings have a vertical fenestration area or skylight area exceeding that allowed in Section C402.4, the building and building thermal envelope shall comply with Section C401.2, Item 1 or Section C401.2, Item 3.

Walk-in coolers, walk-in freezers, refrigerated warehouse coolers and refrigerated warehouse freezers shall comply with Section C403.2.15 or C403.2.16.

**

C402.1.1 Low-energy buildings. The following low-energy buildings, or portions thereof separated from the remainder of the building by *building thermal envelope* assemblies complying with this section, shall be exempt from the *building thermal envelope* provisions of Section C402.

1. Those with a peak design rate of energy usage less than 3.4 Btu/h · ft^2 (10.7 W/m^2) or 1.0 watt per square foot (10.7 W/m^2) of floor area for space conditioning purposes.
2. Those that do not contain *conditioned space.*
3. Greenhouses.

C402.1.2 Equipment buildings. Buildings that comply with the following shall be exempt from the *building thermal envelope* provisions of this code:

1. Are separate buildings with floor area not more than 500 square feet (50 m^2).
2. Are intended to house electronic equipment with installed equipment power totaling not less than 7 watts per square foot (75 W/m^2) and not intended for human occupancy.
3. Have a heating system capacity not greater than (17,000 Btu/hr) (5 kW) and a heating thermostat set point that is restricted to not more than 50°F (10°C).
4. Have an average wall and roof *U* factor less than 0.200 in *Climate Zones* 1 through 5 and less than 0.120 in *Climate Zones* 6 through 8.
5. Comply with the roof solar reflectance and thermal emittance provisions for *Climate Zone* 1.

C402.1.3 Insulation component *R*-value-based method. *Building thermal envelope* opaque assemblies shall meet the requirements of Sections C402.2 and C402.4 based on the *climate zone* specified in Chapter 3. For opaque portions of the *building thermal envelope* intended to comply on an insulation component *R-value* basis, the *R*-values for insulation in framing cavities, where required, and for continuous insulation, where required, shall be not less than that specified in Table C402.1.3, based on the *climate zone* specified in Chapter 3. Commercial buildings or portions of commercial buildings enclosing Group R occupancies shall use the *R*-values from the "Group R" column of Table C402.1.3. Commercial buildings or portions of commercial buildings enclosing occupancies other than Group R shall use the R-values from the "All other" column of Table C402.1.3. The thermal resistance or *R*-value of the insulating material installed continuously within or on the below-grade exterior walls of the building envelope required in accordance with Table C402.1.3 shall extend to a depth of not less than 10 feet (3048 mm) below the outside finished ground level, or to the level of the lowest floor of the conditioned space enclosed by the below grade wall, whichever is less. Opaque swinging doors shall comply with Table C402.1.4 and opaque nonswinging doors shall comply with Table C402.1.3.

C402.1.4 Assembly *U*-factor, *C*-factor or *F*-factor-based method. Building thermal envelope opaque assemblies intended to comply on an assembly *U*-, *C*- or *F*-factor basis shall have a *U*-, *C*- or *F*-factor not greater than that specified in Table C402.1.4. Commercial buildings or portions of commercial buildings enclosing Group R occupancies shall use the *U*-, *C*- or *F*-factor from the "Group R" column of Table C402.1.4. Commercial buildings or portions of commercial buildings enclosing occupancies other than Group R shall use the *U*-, *C*- or *F*-factor from the "All other" column of Table C402.1.4. The *C*-factor for the below-grade exterior walls of the building envelope, as required in accordance with Table C402.1.4, shall extend to a depth of 10 feet (3048 mm) below the outside finished ground level, or to the level of the lowest floor, whichever is less. Opaque swinging doors shall comply with Table C402.1.4 and opaque nonswinging doors shall comply with Table C402.1.3.

C402.1.4.1 Thermal resistance of cold-formed steel walls. *U*-factors of walls with cold-formed steel studs shall be permitted to be determined in accordance with Equation 4-1:

$$U = 1/[R_s + (ER)] \qquad \text{(Equation 4-1)}$$

where:

R_s = The cumulative *R*-value of the wall components along the path of heat transfer, excluding the cavity insulation and steel studs.

ER= The effective *R*-value of the cavity insulation with steel studs.

TABLE C402.1.4.1
EFFECTIVE R-VALUES FOR STEEL STUD WALL ASSEMBLIES

NOMINAL STUD DEPTH (inches)	SPACING OF FRAMING (inches)	CAVITY R-VALUE (insulation)	CORRECTION FACTOR (F_c)	EFFECTIVE R-VALUE (ER) (Cavity R-Value ´ F_c)
31/2	16	13	0.46	5.98
		15	0.43	6.45
31/2	24	13	0.55	7.15
		15	0.52	7.80
6	16	19	0.37	7.03
		21	0.35	7.35
6	24	19	0.45	8.55
		21	0.43	9.03
8	16	25	0.31	7.75
	24	25	0.38	9.50

C402.1.5 Component performance alternative. Building envelope values and fenestration areas determined in accordance with Equation 4-2 shall be permitted in lieu of compliance with the *U*-, *F*- and *C*-factors in Tables C402.1.4 and C402.4 and the maximum allowable fenestration areas in Section C402.4.1.

$$A + B + C + D + E \leq \text{Zero} \qquad \text{(Equation 4-2)}$$

where:

A = Sum of the (UA Dif) values for each distinct assembly type of the building thermal envelope, other than slabs on grade and below-grade walls.

UA Dif = UA Proposed - UA Table.

UA Proposed = Proposed *U*-value · Area.

UA Table = (*U*-factor from Table C402.1.4 or Table C402.4) · Area.

B = Sum of the (FL Dif) values for each distinct slab-on-grade perimeter condition of the building thermal envelope.

FL Dif = FL Proposed - FL Table.

FL Proposed = Proposed *F*-value · Perimeter length.

FL Table = (*F*-factor specified in Table C402.1.4) · Perimeter length.

C = Sum of the (CA Dif) values for each distinct below-grade wall assembly type of the building thermal envelope.

CA Dif = CA Proposed - CA Table.

CA Proposed = Proposed *C*-value · Area.

CA Table = (Maximum allowable *C*-factor specified in Table C402.1.4) · Area.

Where the proposed vertical glazing area is less than or equal to the maximum vertical glazing area allowed by Section C402.4.1, the value of D (Excess Vertical Glazing Value) shall be zero. Otherwise:

D = (DA · UV) - (DA · U Wall), but not less than zero.

DA = (Proposed Vertical Glazing Area) - (Vertical Glazing Area allowed by Section C402.4.1).

UA Wall = Sum of the (UA Proposed) values for each opaque assembly of the exterior wall.

U Wall = Area-weighted average *U*-value of all above-grade wall assemblies.

UAV = Sum of the (UA Proposed) values for each vertical glazing assembly.

UV = UAV/total vertical glazing area.

Where the proposed skylight area is less than or equal to the skylight area allowed by Section C402.4.1, the value of E (Excess Skylight Value) shall be zero. Otherwise:

E = (EA · US) - (EA · U Roof), but not less than zero.

EA = (Proposed Skylight Area) - (Allowable Skylight Area as specified in Section C402.4.1).

U Roof = Area-weighted average *U*-value of all roof assemblies.

UAS = Sum of the (UA Proposed) values for each skylight assembly.

US = UAS/total skylight area.

TABLE C402.1.3
OPAQUE THERMAL ENVELOPE INSULATION COMPONENT MINIMUM REQUIREMENTS, R-VALUE METHOD[a]

CLIMATE ZONE	1		2		3		4 EXCEPT MARINE		5 AND MARINE 4		6		7		8	
	All other	Group R	All other	Group R	All other	Group R	All other	Group R	All other	Group R	All other	Group R	All other	Group R	All other	Group R
Roofs																
Insulation entirely above roof deck	R-20ci	R-25ci	R-25ci	R-25ci	R-25ci	R-25ci	R-30ci	R-30ci	R-30ci	R-30ci	R-30ci	R-30ci	R-35ci	R-35ci	R-35ci	R-35ci
Metal building[a, b]	R-19 + R-11 LS	R-19 + R-11 LS	R-19 + R11 LS	R-19 + R-11 LS	R-19 + R-11 LS	R-19 + R-11 LS	R-19 + R-11 LS	R-19 + R-11 LS	R-19 + R-11 LS	R-19 + R-11 LS	R-25 + R-11 LS	R-25 + R-11 LS	R-30 + R-11 LS	R-30 + R-11 LS	R-30 + R-11 LS	R-30 + R-11 LS
Attic and other	R-38	R-38	R-38	R-38	R-38	R-38	R-38	R-38	R-38	R-49	R-49	R-49	R-49	R-49	R-49	R-49
Walls, above grade																
Mass	R-5.7ci[c]	R-5.7ci[c]	R-5.7ci[c]	R-7.6ci	R-7.6ci	R-9.5ci	R-9.5ci	R-11.4ci	R-11.4ci	R-13.3ci	R-13.3ci	R-15.2ci	R-15.2ci	R-15.2ci	R-25ci	R-25ci
Metal building	R-13+ R-6.5ci	R-13 + R-6.5ci	R13 + R-6.5ci	R-13 + R-13ci	R-13 + R-6.5ci	R-13 + R-13ci	R-13 + R-13ci	R-13 + R-13ci	R-13 + R-13ci	R-13 + R-13ci	R-13 + R-13ci	R-13 + R-13ci	R-13 + R-13ci	R-13+ R-19.5ci	R-13 + R-13ci	R-13+ R-19.5ci
Metal framed	R-13 + R-5ci	R-13 + R-5ci	R-13 + R-5ci	R-13 + R-7.5ci	R-13 + R-7.5ci	R-13 + R-7.5ci	R-13 + R-7.5ci	R-13 + R-7.5ci	R-13 + R-7.5ci	R-13 + R-7.5ci	R-13 + R-7.5ci	R-13 + R-7.5ci	R-13 + R-7.5ci	R-13 + R-15.6ci	R-13 + R-7.5ci	R-13+ R17.5ci
Wood framed and other	R-13 + R-3.8ci or R-20	R-13 + R-3.8ci or R-20	R-13 + R-3.8ci or R-20	R-13 + R-3.8ci or R-20	R-13 + R-3.8ci or R-20	R-13 + R-3.8ci or R-20	R-13 + R-3.8ci or R-20	R-13 + R-3.8ci or R-20	R-13 + R-3.8ci or R-20	R-13 + R-7.5ci or R-20 + R-3.8ci	R-13 + R-7.5ci or R-20 + R-3.8ci	R-13 + R-7.5ci or R-20 + R-3.8ci	R-13 + R-7.5ci or R-20 + R-3.8ci	R-13 + R-7.5ci or R-20 + R-3.8ci	R13 + R-15.6ci or R-20 + R-10ci	R13 + R-15.6ci or R-20 + R-10ci
Walls, below grade																
Below-grade wall[d]	NR	NR	NR	NR	NR	NR	R-7.5ci	R-7.5ci	R-7.5ci	R-7.5ci	R-7.5ci	R-7.5ci	R-10ci	R-10ci	R-10ci	R-12.5ci
Floors																
Mass[e]	NR	NR	R-6.3ci	R-8.3ci	R-10ci	R-10ci	R-10ci	R-10.4ci	R-10ci	R-12.5ci	R-12.5ci	R-12.5ci	R-15ci	R-16.7ci	R-15ci	R-16.7ci
Joist/framing	NR	NR	R-30	R-30	R-30	R-30	R-30	R-30	R-30	R-30	R-30	R-30[f]	R-30[f]	R-30[f]	R-30[f]	R-30[f]
Slab-on-grade floors																
Unheated slabs	NR	NR	NR	NR	NR	NR	R-10 for 24″ below	R-10 for 24″ below	R-10 for 24″ below	R-10 for 24″ below	R-10 for 24″ below	R-15 for 24″ below	R-15 for 24″ below	R-15 for 24″ below	R-15 for 24″ below	R-20 for 24″ below
Heated slabs[f]	R-7.5 for 12″ below	R-7.5 for 12″ below	R-7.5 for 12″ below	R-7.5 for 12″ below	R-10 for 24″ below	R-10 for 24″ below	R-15 for 24″ below	R-15 for 24″ below	R-15 for 36″ below	R-15 for 36″ below	R-15 for 36″ below	R-20 for 48″ below	R-20 for 24″ below	R-20 for 48″ below	R-20 for 48″ below	R-20 for 48″ below
Opaque doors																
Nonswinging	R-4.75	R-4.75	R-4.75	R-4.75	R-4.75	R-4.75	R-4.75	R-4.75	R-4.75	R-4.75	R-4.75	R-4.75	R-4.75	R-4.75	R-4.75	R-4.75

For SI: 1 inch = 25.4 mm, 1 pound per square foot = 4.88 kg/m^2, 1 pound per cubic foot = 16 kg/m^3.

ci = Continuous insulation, NR = No requirement, LS = Liner system.

a. Assembly descriptions can be found in ANSI/ASHRAE/IESNA Appendix A.

b. Where using *R*-value compliance method, a thermal spacer block shall be provided, otherwise use the *U*-factor compliance method in Table C402.1.4.

c. R-5.7ci is allowed to be substituted with concrete block walls complying with ASTM C90, ungrouted or partially grouted at 32 inches or less on center vertically and 48 inches or less on center horizontally, with ungrouted cores filled with materials having a maximum thermal conductivity of 0.44 Btu-in/h·f^2 °F.

d. Where heated slabs are below grade, below-grade walls shall comply with the exterior insulation requirements for heated slabs.

e. "Mass floors" shall include floors weighing not less than:

1. 35 pounds per square foot of floor surface area; or
2. 25 pounds per square foot of floor surface area where the material weight is not more than 120 pounds per cubic foot.

f. Steel floor joist systems shall be insulated to R-38.

TABLE C402.1.4
OPAQUE THERMAL ENVELOPE ASSEMBLY MAXIMUM REQUIREMENTS, U-FACTOR METHOD[a, b]

CLIMATE ZONE	1		2		3		4 EXCEPT MARINE		5 AND MARINE 4		6		7		8	
	All other	Group R	All other	Group R	All other	Group R	All other	Group R	All other	Group R	All other	Group R	All other	Group R	All other	Group R
Roofs																
Insulation entirely above roof deck	U-0.048	U-0.039	U-0.039	U-0.039	U-0.039	U-0.039	U-0.032	U-0.032	U-0.032	U-0.032	U-0.032	U-0.032	U-0.028	U-0.028	U-0.028	U-0.028
Metal buildings	U-0.044	U-0.035	U-0.035	U-0.035	U-0.035	U-0.035	U-0.035	U-0.035	U-0.035	U-0.035	U-0.031	U-0.031	U-0.029	U-0.029	U-0.029	U-0.029
Attic and other	U-0.027	U-0.027	U-0.027	U-0.027	U-0.027	U-0.027	U-0.027	U-0.027	U-0.027	U-0.021	U-0.021	U-0.021	U-0.021	U-0.021	U-0.021	U-0.021
Walls, above grade																
Mass	U-0.151	U-0.151	U-0.151	U-0.123	U-0.123	U-0.104	U-0.104	U-0.090	U-0.090	U-0.080	U-0.080	U-0.071	U-0.071	U-0.061	U-0.061	U-0.061
Metal building	U-0.079	U-0.079	U-0.079	U-0.079	U-0.079	U-0.052	U-0.052	U-0.052	U-0.052	U-0.052	U-0.052	U-0.052	U-0.052	U-0.039	U-0.052	U-0.039
Metal framed	U-0.077	U-0.077	U-0.077	U-0.064	U-0.064	U-0.064	U-0.064	U-0.064	U-0.064	U-0.064	U-0.064	U-0.057	U-0.064	U-0.052	U-0.045	U-0.045
Wood framed and other[c]	U-0.064	U-0.064	U-0.064	U-0.064	U-0.064	U-0.064	U-0.064	U-0.064	U-0.064	U-0.064	U-0.051	U-0.051	U-0.051	U-0.051	U-0.036	U-0.036
Walls, below grade																
Below-grade wall[c]	C-1.140[e]	C-1.140[e]	C-1.140[e]	C-1.140[e]	C-1.140[e]	C-1.140[e]	C-0.119	C-0.119	C-0.119	C-0.119	C-0.119	C-0.119	C-0.092	C-0.092	C-0.092	C-0.092
Floors																
Mass[d]	U-0.322[e]	U-0.322[e]	U-0.107	U-0.087	U-0.076	U-0.076	U-0.076	U-0.074	U-0.074	U-0.064	U-0.064	U-0.057	U-0.055	U-0.051	U-0.055	U-0.051
Joist/framing	U-0.066[e]	U-0.066[e]	U-0.033	U-0.033	U-0.033	U-0.033	U-0.033	U-0.033	U-0.033	U-0.033	U-0.033	U-0.033	U-0.033	U-0.033	U-0.033	U-0.033
Slab-on-grade floors																
Unheated slabs	F-0.73[e]	F-0.73[e]	F-0.73[e]	F-0.73[e]	F-0.73[e]	F-0.73[e]	F-0.54	F-0.54	F-0.54	F-0.54	F-0.54	F-0.52	F-0.40	F-0.40	F-0.40	F-0.40
Heated slabs[f]	F-0.70	F-0.70	F-0.70	F-0.70	F-0.70	F-0.70	F-0.65	F-0.65	F-0.65	F-0.65	F-0.58	F-0.58	F-0.55	F-0.55	F-0.55	F-0.55
Opaque doors																
Swinging	U-0.61	U-0.61	U-0.61	U-0.61	U-0.61	U-0.61	U-0.61	U-0.61	U-0.37	U-0.37	U-0.37	U-0.37	U-0.37	U-0.37	U-0.37	U-0.37

For SI: 1 pound per square foot = 4.88 kg/m^2, 1 pound per cubic foot = 16 kg/m^3.

ci = Continuous insulation, NR = No requirement, LS = Liner system.

a. Use of Opaque assembly *U*-factors, *C*-factors, and *F*-factors from ANSI/ASHRAE/IESNA 90.1 Appendix A shall be permitted, provided the construction, excluding the cladding system on walls, complies with the appropriate construction details from ANSI/ASHRAE/ISNEA 90.1 Appendix A.

b. Opaque assembly *U*-factors based on designs tested in accordance with ASTM C1363 shall be permitted. The *R*-value of continuous insulation shall be permitted to be added to or subtracted from the original tested design.

c. Where heated slabs are below grade, below-grade walls shall comply with the *F*-factor requirements for heated slabs.

d. "Mass floors" shall include floors weighing not less than:
   1. 35 pounds per square foot of floor surface area; or
   2. 25 pounds per square foot of floor surface area where the material weight is not more than 120 pounds per cubic foot.

e. These *C*-, *F*- and *U*-factors are based on assemblies that are not required to contain insulation.

f. Evidence of compliance with the *F*-factors indicated in the table for heated slabs shall be demonstrated by the application of the unheated slab *F*-factors and *R-values* derived from ASHRAE 90.1 Appendix A.

C402.2 Specific building thermal envelope insulation requirements (Prescriptive). Insulation in building thermal envelope opaque assemblies shall comply with Sections C402.2.1 through C402.2.6 and Table C402.1.3.

*

C402.2.1 Multiple layers of continuous insulation board. Where two or more layers of continuous insulation board are used in a construction assembly, the continuous insulation boards shall be installed in accordance with Section C303.2. Where the continuous insulation board manufacturer's instructions do not address installation of two or more layers, the edge joints between each layer of continuous insulation boards shall be staggered.

C402.2.2 Roof assembly. The minimum thermal resistance (*R*-value) of the insulating material installed either between the roof framing or continuously on the roof assembly shall be as specified in Table C402.1.3, based on construction materials used in the roof assembly. Skylight curbs shall be insulated to the level of roofs with insulation entirely above deck or R-5, whichever is less.

Exceptions:

1. Continuously insulated roof assemblies where the thickness of insulation varies 1 inch (25 mm) or less and where the area-weighted *U*-factor is equivalent to the same assembly with the *R*-value specified in Table C402.1.3.
2. Where tapered insulation is used with insulation entirely above deck, the *R*-value where the insulation thickness varies 1 inch (25 mm) or less from the minimum thickness of tapered insulation shall comply with the *R*-value specified in Table C402.1.3.
3. Unit skylight curbs included as a component of a skylight listed and labeled in accordance with NFRC 100 shall not be required to be insulated.

Insulation installed on a suspended ceiling with removable ceiling tiles shall not be considered part of the minimum thermal resistance of the roof insulation.

C402.2.3 Thermal resistance of above-grade walls. The minimum thermal resistance (*R*-value) of materials installed in the wall cavity between framing members and continuously on the walls shall be as specified in Table C402.1.3, based on framing type and construction materials used in the wall assembly. The *R*-value of integral insulation installed in concrete masonry units shall not be used in determining compliance with Table C402.1.3.

"Mass walls" shall include walls:

1. Weighing not less than 35 psf (170 kg/m^2) of wall surface area.
2. Weighing not less than 25 psf (120 kg/m^2) of wall surface area where the material weight is not more than 120 pcf (1900 kg/m^3).
3. Having a heat capacity exceeding 7 Btu/ft^2 · °F (144 kJ/m^2 · K).
4. Having a heat capacity exceeding 5 Btu/ft^2 · °F (103 kJ/m^2 · K), where the material weight is not more than 120 pcf (1900 kg/m^3).

C402.2.4 Floors. The thermal properties (component *R*-values or assembly *U*-, *C*- or *F*-factors) of floor assemblies over outdoor air or unconditioned space shall be as specified in Table C402.1.3 or C402.1.4 based on the construction materials used in the floor assembly. Floor framing cavity insulation or structural slab insulation shall be installed to maintain permanent contact with the underside of the subfloor decking or structural slabs.

Exceptions:

1. The floor framing cavity insulation or structural slab insulation shall be permitted to be in contact with the top side of sheathing or continuous insulation installed on the bottom side of floor assemblies where combined with insulation that meets or exceeds the minimum *R*-value in Table C402.1.3 for "Metal framed" or "Wood framed and other" values for "Walls, Above Grade" and extends from the bottom to the top of all perimeter floor framing or floor assembly members.
2. Insulation applied to the underside of concrete floor slabs shall be permitted an airspace of not more than 1 inch (25 mm) where it turns up and is in contact with the underside of the floor under walls associated with the *building thermal envelope*.

C402.2.5 Slabs-on-grade perimeter insulation. Where the slab on grade is in contact with the ground, the minimum thermal resistance (*R*-value) of the insulation around the perimeter of unheated or heated slab-on-grade floors designed in accordance with the *R*-value method of Section C402.1.3 shall be as specified in Table C402.1.3. The insulation shall be placed on the outside of the foundation or on the inside of the foundation wall. The insulation shall extend downward from the top of the slab for a minimum distance as shown in the table or to the top of the footing, whichever is less, or downward to at least the bottom of the slab and then horizontally to the interior or exterior for the total distance shown in the table. Insulation extending away from the building shall be protected by pavement or by not less than of 10 inches (254 mm) of soil.

Exception: Where the slab-on-grade floor is greater than 24 inches (61 mm) below the finished exterior grade, perimeter insulation is not required.

C402.2.6 Insulation of radiant heating systems. *Radiant heating system* panels, and their associated components that are installed in interior or exterior assemblies shall be insulated with a minimum of R-3.5 (0.62 m^2/K · W) on all surfaces not facing the space being heated. *Radiant heating system* panels that are installed in the *building thermal envelope* shall be separated from the exterior of the building or unconditioned or exempt spaces by not less than the *R*-value of insulation installed in the opaque assembly in which they are installed or the assembly shall comply with Section C402.1.4.

Exception: Heated slabs on grade insulated in accordance with Section C402.2.5.

C402.3 Roof solar reflectance and thermal emittance. Low-sloped roofs directly above cooled conditioned spaces in *Climate Zones* 1, 2 and 3 shall comply with one or more of the options in Table C402.3.

Exceptions: The following roofs and portions of roofs are exempt from the requirements of Table C402.3:

1. Portions of the roof that include or are covered by the following:
   1.1. Photovoltaic systems or components.
   1.2. Solar air or water-heating systems or components.
   1.3. Roof gardens or landscaped roofs.
   1.4. Above-roof decks or walkways.
   1.5. Skylights.
   1.6. HVAC systems and components, and other opaque objects mounted above the roof.
2. Portions of the roof shaded during the peak sun angle on the summer solstice by permanent features of the building or by permanent features of adjacent buildings.
3. Portions of roofs that are ballasted with a minimum stone ballast of 17 pounds per square foot [74 kg/m^2] or 23 psf [117 kg/m^2] pavers.
4. Roofs where not less than 75 percent of the roof area complies with one or more of the exceptions to this section.

C402.3.1 Aged roof solar reflectance. Where an aged solar reflectance required by Section C402.3 is not available, it shall be determined in accordance with Equation 4-3.

$$R_{aged} = [0.2 + 0.7(R_{initial} - 0.2)] \quad \text{(Equation 4-3)}$$

where:

R_{aged} = The aged solar reflectance.

$R_{initial}$ = The initial solar reflectance determined in accordance with CRRC-1 Standard.

C402.4 Fenestration (Prescriptive). Fenestration shall comply with Sections C402.4 through C402.4.4 and Table C402.4. Daylight responsive controls shall comply with this section and Section C405.2.3.1.

C402.4.1 Maximum area. The vertical fenestration area (not including opaque doors and opaque spandrel panels) shall not be greater than 30 percent of the gross above-grade wall area. The skylight area shall not be greater than 3 percent of the gross roof area.

TABLE C402.3
MINIMUM ROOF REFLECTANCE AND EMITTANCE OPTIONS[a]

Options
Three-year aged solar reflectance[b] of 0.55 and 3-year aged thermal emittance[c] of 0.75
Three-year-aged solar reflectance index[d] of 64

a. The use of area-weighted averages to comply with these requirements shall be permitted. Materials lacking 3-year-aged tested values for either solar reflectance or thermal emittance shall be assigned both a 3-year-aged solar reflectance in accordance with Section C402.3.1 and a 3-year-aged thermal emittance of 0.90.

b. Aged solar reflectance tested in accordance with ASTM C1549, ASTM E903 or ASTM E1918 or CRRC-1 Standard.

c. Aged thermal emittance tested in accordance with ASTM C1371 or ASTM E408 or CRRC-1 Standard.

d. Solar reflectance index (SRI) shall be determined in accordance with ASTM E1980 using a convection coefficient of 2.1 Btu/h · ft^2 ·°F (12W/m^2 · K). Calculation of aged SRI shall be based on aged tested values of solar reflectance and thermal emittance.

TABLE C402.4
BUILDING ENVELOPE FENESTRATION MAXIMUM *U*-FACTOR AND SHGC REQUIREMENTS

CLIMATE ZONE	1		2		3		4 EXCEPT MARINE		5 AND MARINE 4		6		7		8	
Vertical fenestration																
***U*-factor**																
Fixed fenestration	0.50		0.50		0.46		0.38		0.38		0.36		0.29		0.29	
Operable fenestration	0.65		0.65		0.60		0.45		0.45		0.43		0.37		0.37	
Entrance doors	1.10		0.83		0.77		0.77		0.77		0.77		0.77		0.77	
SHGC																
Orientation[a]	SEW	N	SEW	N	SEW	N	SEW	N	SEW	N	SEW	N	SEW	N	SEW	N
PF < 0.2	0.25	0.33	0.25	0.33	0.25	0.33	0.40	0.53	0.40	0.53	0.40	0.53	0.45	NR	0.45	NR
0.2 ≤ PF < 0.5	0.30	0.37	0.30	0.37	0.30	0.37	0.48	0.58	0.48	0.58	0.48	0.58	NR	NR	NR	NR
PF ≥ 0.5	0.40	0.40	0.40	0.40	0.40	0.40	0.64	0.64	0.64	0.64	0.64	0.64	NR	NR	NR	NR
Skylights																
U-factor	0.75		0.65		0.55		0.50		0.50		0.50		0.50		0.50	
SHGC	0.35		0.35		0.35		0.40		0.40		0.40		NR		NR	

NR = No requirement, PF = Projection factor.

a. "N" indicates vertical fenestration oriented within 45 degrees of true north. "SEW" indicates orientations other than "N." For buildings in the southern hemisphere, reverse south and north. Buildings located at less than 23.5 degrees latitude shall use SEW for all orientations.

C402.4.1.1 Increased vertical fenestration area with daylight responsive controls. In Climate Zones 1 through 6, not more than 40 percent of the gross above-grade wall area shall be permitted to be vertical fenestration, provided all of the following requirements are met:

1. In buildings not greater than two stories above grade, not less than 50 percent of the net floor area is within a *daylight zone.*
2. In buildings three or more stories above grade, not less than 25 percent of the net floor area is within a *daylight zone.*
3. *Daylight responsive controls* complying with Section C405.2.3.1 are installed in *daylight zones.*
4. Visible transmittance (VT) of vertical fenestration is not less than 1.1 times solar heat gain coefficient (SHGC).

   Exception: Fenestration that is outside the scope of NFRC 200 is not required to comply with Item 4.

C402.4.1.2 Increased skylight area with daylight responsive controls. The skylight area shall be permitted to be not more than 5 percent of the roof area provided *daylight responsive controls* complying with Section C405.2.3.1 are installed in *daylight zones* under skylights.

C402.4.2 Minimum skylight fenestration area. In an enclosed space greater than 2,500 square feet (232 m^2) in floor area, directly under a roof with not less than 75 percent of the ceiling area with a ceiling height greater than 15 feet (4572 mm), and used as an office, lobby, atrium, concourse, corridor, storage space, gymnasium/exercise center, convention center, automotive service area, space where manufacturing occurs, nonrefrigerated warehouse, retail store, distribution/sorting area, transportation depot or workshop, the total *daylight zone* under skylights shall be not less than half the floor area and shall provide one of the following:

1. A minimum skylight area to *daylight zone* under skylights of not less than 3 percent where all skylights have a VT of at least 0.40 as determined in accordance with Section C303.1.3.
2. A minimum skylight effective aperture of at least 1 percent, determined in accordance with Equation 4-4.

$$\text{Skylight Effective Aperture} = \frac{0.85 \cdot \text{Skylight Area} \cdot \text{Skylight VT} \cdot \text{WF}}{\text{Daylight zone under skylight}}$$

(Equation 4-4)

where:

Skylight area = Total fenestration area of skylights.

Skylight VT = Area weighted average visible transmittance of skylights.

WF = Area weighted average well factor, where well factor is 0.9 if light well depth is less than 2 feet (610 mm), or 0.7 if light well depth is 2 feet (610 mm) or greater.

Light well depth = Measure vertically from the underside of the lowest point of the skylight glazing to the ceiling plane under the skylight.

Exception: Skylights above *daylight zones* of enclosed spaces are not required in:

1. Buildings in *Climate Zones* 6 through 8.
2. Spaces where the designed *general lighting* power densities are less than 0.5 W/ft^2 (5.4 W/m^2).
3. Areas where it is documented that existing structures or natural objects block direct beam sunlight on at least half of the roof over the enclosed area for more than 1,500 daytime hours per year between 8 a.m. and 4 p.m.
4. Spaces where the *daylight zone* under rooftop monitors is greater than 50 percent of the enclosed space floor area.
5. Spaces where the total area minus the area of *daylight zones* adjacent to vertical fenestration is less than 2,500 square feet (232 m^2), and where the lighting is controlled according to Section C405.2.3.

C402.4.2.1 Lighting controls in daylight zones under skylights. *Daylight responsive controls* complying with Section C405.2.3.1 shall be provided to control all electric lights within *daylight zones* under skylights.

C402.4.2.2 Haze factor. Skylights in office, storage, automotive service, manufacturing, nonrefrigerated warehouse, retail store and distribution/sorting area spaces shall have a glazing material or diffuser with a haze factor greater than 90 percent when tested in accordance with ASTM D1003.

Exception: Skylights designed and installed to exclude direct sunlight entering the occupied space by the use of fixed or automated baffles or the geometry of skylight and light well.

C402.4.3 Maximum *U*-factor and SHGC. The maximum *U*-factor and solar heat gain coefficient (SHGC) for fenestration shall be as specified in Table C402.4.

The window projection factor shall be determined in accordance with Equation 4-5.

$$PF = A/B$$ **(Equation 4-5)**

where:

PF = Projection factor (decimal).

A = Distance measured horizontally from the farthest continuous extremity of any overhang, eave or permanently attached shading device to the vertical surface of the glazing.

B = Distance measured vertically from the bottom of the glazing to the underside of the overhang, eave or permanently attached shading device.

Where different windows or glass doors have different *PF* values, they shall each be evaluated separately.

C402.4.3.1 Increased skylight SHGC. In *Climate Zones* 1 through 6, skylights shall be permitted a maximum SHGC of 0.60 where located above *daylight zones* provided with *daylight responsive controls*.

C402.4.3.2 Increased skylight *U*-factor. Where skylights are installed above *daylight zones* provided with *daylight responsive controls*, a maximum *U*-factor of 0.9 shall be permitted in *Climate Zones* 1 through 3 and a maximum *U*-factor of 0.75 shall be permitted in *Climate Zones* 4 through 8.

C402.4.3.3 Dynamic glazing. Where *dynamic glazing* is intended to satisfy the SHGC and VT requirements of Table C402.4, the ratio of the higher to lower labeled SHGC shall be greater than or equal to 2.4, and the *dynamic glazing* shall be automatically controlled to modulate the amount of solar gain into the space in multiple steps. Dynamic glazing shall be considered separately from other fenestration, and area-weighted averaging with other fenestration that is not dynamic glazing shall not be permitted.

Exception: Dynamic glazing is not required to comply with this section where both the lower and higher labeled SHGC already comply with the requirements of Table C402.4.

C402.4.3.4 Area-weighted *U*-factor. An area-weighted average shall be permitted to satisfy the *U*-factor requirements for each fenestration product category listed in Table C402.4. Individual fenestration products from different fenestration product categories listed in Table C402.4 shall not be combined in calculating area-weighted average *U*-factor.

C402.4.4 Doors. *Opaque doors* shall comply with the applicable requirements for doors as specified in Tables C402.1.3 and C402.1.4 and be considered part of the gross area of above-grade walls that are part of the building *thermal envelope*. Other doors shall comply with the provisions of Section C402.4.3 for vertical fenestration.

C402.5 Air leakage—thermal envelope (Mandatory). The *thermal envelope* of buildings shall comply with Sections C402.5.1 through C402.5.8, or the building *thermal envelope* shall be tested in accordance with ASTM E779 at a pressure differential of 0.3 inch water gauge (75 Pa) or an equivalent method approved by the code official and deemed to comply with the provisions of this section when the tested air leakage rate of the building thermal envelope is not greater than 0.40 cfm/ft^2 (2.0 L/s · m^2). Where compliance is based on such testing, the building shall also comply with Sections C402.5.5, C402.5.6 and C402.5.7.

C402.5.1 Air barriers. A continuous air barrier shall be provided throughout the building thermal envelope. The air barriers shall be permitted to be located on the inside or outside of the building envelope, located within the assemblies composing the envelope, or any combination thereof. The air barrier shall comply with Sections C402.5.1.1 and C402.5.1.2.

Exception: Air barriers are not required in buildings located in *Climate Zone* 2B.

C402.5.1.1 Air barrier construction. The *continuous air barrier* shall be constructed to comply with the following:

1. The air barrier shall be continuous for all assemblies that are the thermal envelope of the building and across the joints and assemblies.
2. Air barrier joints and seams shall be sealed, including sealing transitions in places and changes in materials. The joints and seals shall be securely installed in or on the joint for its entire length so as not to dislodge, loosen or otherwise impair its ability to resist positive and negative pressure from wind, stack effect and mechanical ventilation.
3. Penetrations of the air barrier shall be caulked, gasketed or otherwise sealed in a manner compatible with the construction materials and location. Joints and seals associated with penetrations shall be sealed in the same manner or taped or covered with moisture vapor-permeable wrapping material. Sealing materials shall be appropriate to the construction materials being sealed and shall be securely installed around the penetration so as not to dislodge, loosen or otherwise impair the penetrations' ability to resist positive and negative pressure from wind, stack effect and mechanical ventilation. Sealing of concealed fire sprinklers, where required, shall be in a manner that is recommended by the manufacturer. Caulking or other adhesive sealants shall not be used to fill voids between fire sprinkler cover plates and walls or ceilings.
4. Recessed lighting fixtures shall comply with Section C402.5.8. Where similar objects are installed that penetrate the air barrier, provisions shall be made to maintain the integrity of the air barrier.

C402.5.1.2 Air barrier compliance options. A continuous air barrier for the opaque building envelope shall comply with Section C402.5.1.2.1 or C402.5.1.2.2.

C402.5.1.2.1 Materials. Materials with an air permeability not greater than 0.004 cfm/ft^2 (0.02 L/s · m^2) under a pressure differential of 0.3 inch water gauge (75 Pa) when tested in accordance with ASTM E2178 shall comply with this section. Materials in Items 1 through 16 shall be deemed to comply with this section, provided joints are sealed and materials are installed as air barriers in accordance with the manufacturer's instructions.

1. Plywood with a thickness of not less than $^3/_8$ inch (10 mm).
2. Oriented strand board having a thickness of not less than $^3/_8$ inch (10 mm).
3. Extruded polystyrene insulation board having a thickness of not less than $^1/_2$ inch (12.7 mm).
4. Foil-back polyisocyanurate insulation board having a thickness of not less than $^1/_2$ inch (12.7 mm).

5. Closed-cell spray foam a minimum density of 1.5 pcf (2.4 kg/m^3) having a thickness of not less than 1$^1/_2$ inches (38 mm).
6. Open-cell spray foam with a density between 0.4 and 1.5 pcf (0.6 and 2.4 kg/m^3) and having a thickness of not less than 4.5 inches (113 mm).
7. Exterior or interior gypsum board having a thickness of not less than $^1/_2$ inch (12.7 mm).
8. Cement board having a thickness of not less than $^1/_2$ inch (12.7 mm).
9. Built-up roofing membrane.
10. Modified bituminous roof membrane.
11. Fully adhered single-ply roof membrane.
12. A Portland cement/sand parge, or gypsum plaster having a thickness of not less than $^5/_8$ inch (15.9 mm).
13. Cast-in-place and precast concrete.
14. Fully grouted concrete block masonry.
15. Sheet steel or aluminum.
16. Solid or hollow masonry constructed of clay or shale masonry units.

C402.5.1.2.2 Assemblies. Assemblies of materials and components with an average air leakage not greater than 0.04 cfm/ft^2 (0.2 L/s · m^2) under a pressure differential of 0.3 inch of water gauge (w.g.)(75 Pa) when tested in accordance with ASTM E2357, ASTM E1677 or ASTM E283 shall comply with this section. Assemblies listed in Items 1 through 3 shall be deemed to comply, provided joints are sealed and the requirements of Section C402.5.1.1 are met.

1. Concrete masonry walls coated with either one application of block filler or two applications of a paint or sealer coating.
2. Masonry walls constructed of clay or shale masonry units with a nominal width of 4 inches (102 mm) or more.
3. A Portland cement/sand parge, stucco or plaster not less than $^1/_2$ inch (12.7 mm) in thickness.

** **C402.5.2 Air leakage of fenestration.** The air leakage of fenestration assemblies shall meet the provisions of Table C402.5.2. Testing shall be in accordance with the applicable reference test standard in Table C402.5.2 by an accredited, independent testing laboratory and *labeled* by the manufacturer.

Exceptions:

1. Field-fabricated fenestration assemblies that are sealed in accordance with Section C402.5.1.
2. Fenestration in buildings that comply with the testing alternative of Section C402.5 are not required to meet the air leakage requirements in Table C402.5.2.

C402.5.3 Rooms containing fuel-burning appliances. In *Climate Zones* 3 through 8, where open combustion air ducts provide combustion air to open combustion space conditioning fuel-burning appliances, the appliances and combustion air openings shall be located outside of the *building thermal envelope* or enclosed in a room isolated from inside the thermal envelope. Such rooms shall be sealed and insulated in accordance with the envelope requirements of Table C402.1.3 or C402.1.4, where the walls, floors and ceilings shall meet the minimum of the below-grade wall *R*-value requirement. The door into the room shall be fully gasketed, and any water lines and ducts in the room insulated in accordance with Section C403. The combustion air duct shall be insulated, where it passes through conditioned space, to a minimum of R-8.

Exceptions:

1. Direct vent appliances with both intake and exhaust pipes installed continuous to the outside.
2. Fireplaces and stoves complying with Sections 901 through 905 of the *Florida Building Code, Mechanical,* and Section 2111.13 of the *Florida Building Code, Building.*

TABLE C402.5.2
MAXIMUM AIR LEAKAGE RATE FOR FENESTRATION ASSEMBLIES

FENESTRATION ASSEMBLY	MAXIMUM RATE (CFM/FT^2)	TEST PROCEDURE
Windows	0.20 [a]	AAMA/WDMA/ CSA101/I.S.2/A440 or NFRC 400
Sliding doors	0.20 [a]	
Swinging doors	0.20 [a]	
Skylights – with condensation weepage openings	0.30	
Skylights – all other	0.20 [a]	
Curtain walls	0.06	NFRC 400 or ASTM E283 at1.57 psf (75 Pa)
Storefront glazing	0.06	
Commercial glazed swinging entrance doors	1.00	
Revolving doors	1.00	
Garage doors	0.40	ANSI/DASMA 105, NFRC 400, or ASTM E283 at 1.57 psf (75 Pa)
Rolling doors	1.00	
High-speed doors	1.30	

For SI: 1 cubic foot per minute = 0.47 L/s, 1 square foot = 0.093 m^2.

a. The maximum rate for windows, sliding and swinging doors, and skylights is permitted to be 0.3 cfm per square foot of fenestration or door area when tested in accordance with AAMA/WDMA/CSA101/I.S.2/A440 at 6.24 psf (300 Pa).

C402.5.4 Doors and access openings to shafts, chutes, stairways and elevator lobbies. Doors and access openings from conditioned space to shafts, chutes stairways and elevator lobbies not within the scope of the fenestration assemblies covered by Section C402.5.2 shall be gasketed, weatherstripped or sealed.

Exceptions:

1. Door openings required to comply with Section 716 or 716.5 of the *Florida Building Code, Building.*
2. Doors and door openings required to comply with UL 1784 by the *Florida Building Code, Building.*

C402.5.5 Air intakes, exhaust openings, stairways and shafts. Stairway enclosures, elevator shaft vents and other outdoor air intakes and exhaust openings integral to the building envelope shall be provided with dampers in accordance with Section C403.2.4.3.

C402.5.6 Loading dock weatherseals. Cargo doors and loading dock doors shall be equipped with weatherseals to restrict infiltration when vehicles are parked in the doorway.

C402.5.7 Vestibules. Building entrances shall be protected with an enclosed vestibule, with all doors opening into and out of the vestibule equipped with self-closing devices. Vestibules shall be designed so that in passing through the vestibule it is not necessary for the interior and exterior doors to open at the same time. The installation of one or more revolving doors in the building entrance shall not eliminate the requirement that a vestibule be provided on any doors adjacent to revolving doors.

Exceptions: Vestibules are not required for the following:

1. Buildings in *Climate Zones* 1 and 2.
2. Doors not intended to be used by the public, such as doors to mechanical or electrical equipment rooms, or intended solely for employee use.
3. Doors opening directly from a *sleeping unit* or dwelling unit.
4. Doors that open directly from a space less than 3,000 square feet (298 m^2) in area.
5. Revolving doors.
6. Doors used primarily to facilitate vehicular movement or material handling and adjacent personnel doors.
7. Doors that have an air curtain with a velocity of not less than 6.56 feet per second (2 m/s) at the floor that have been tested in accordance with ANSI/AMCA 220 and installed in accordance with the manufacturer's instructions. Manual or automatic controls shall be provided that will operate the air curtain with the opening and closing of the door. Air curtains and their controls shall comply with Section C408.2.3.

C402.5.8 Recessed lighting. Recessed luminaires installed in the *building thermal envelope* shall be all of the following:

1. IC-rated.
2. Labeled as having an air leakage rate of not more 2.0 cfm (0.944 L/s) when tested in accordance with ASTM E283 at a 1.57 psf (75 Pa) pressure differential.
3. Sealed with a gasket or caulk between the housing and interior wall or ceiling covering.

C402.5.9 Building cavities.

C402.5.9.1 Vented dropped ceiling cavities. Where vented dropped ceiling cavities occur over conditioned spaces, the ceiling shall be considered to be both the upper thermal envelope and pressure envelope of the building and shall contain a continuous air barrier between the conditioned space and the vented unconditioned space that is also sealed to the air barrier of the walls. See the definition of air barrier in Section C202.

C402.5.9.2 Unvented dropped ceiling cavities. Where unvented dropped ceiling cavities occur over conditioned spaces that do not have an air barrier between the conditioned and unconditioned space (such as T-bar ceilings), they shall be completely sealed from the exterior environment (at the roof plane) and adjacent spaces by a continuous air barrier that is also sealed to the air barrier of the walls. In that case, the roof assembly shall constitute both the upper thermal envelope and pressure envelope of the building.

C402.5.9.3 Separate tenancies. Unconditioned spaces above separate tenancies shall contain dividing partitions between the tenancies to form a continuous air barrier that is sealed at the ceiling and roof to prevent airflow between them.

C402.5.9.4 Air distribution system components. Building cavities designed to be air distribution system components shall be sealed according to the criteria for air ducts, plenums, etc., in Section C403.2.9.

SECTION C403
BUILDING MECHANICAL SYSTEMS

C403.1 General. Mechanical systems and equipment serving the building heating, cooling or ventilating needs shall comply with Section C403.2 and shall comply with Sections C403.3 and C403.4 based on the equipment and systems provided.

Walk-in coolers, walk-in freezers, refrigerated warehouse coolers and refrigerated warehouse freezers shall comply with Section C403.2.15 or C403.2.16.

C403.2 Provisions applicable to all mechanical systems (Mandatory). Mechanical systems and equipment serving the building heating, cooling or ventilating needs shall comply with Sections C403.2.1 through C403.2.16.

C403.2.1 Calculation of heating and cooling loads. Design loads associated with heating, ventilating and air conditioning of the building shall be determined in accordance with ANSI/ASHRAE/ACCA Standard 183 or ACCA Manual N or by an *approved* equivalent computational procedure using the design parameters specified in Chapter 3. Heating and cooling loads shall be adjusted to account for load reductions that are achieved where energy recovery systems are utilized in the HVAC system in accordance with the ASHRAE *HVAC Systems and Equipment Handbook* by an approved equivalent computational procedure. Design loads shall be attached to the code compliance form submitted to the building department when the building is permitted or, in the event the mechanical permit is obtained at a later time, the sizing calculation shall be submitted with the application for the mechanical permit.

Exception: Where mechanical systems are designed by a registered engineer, the engineer has the option of submitting a signed and sealed summary sheet to the building department in lieu of the complete sizing calculation(s). Such summary sheet shall include the following (by zone):

1. Project name/owner
2. Project address
3. Area in square feet
4. Sizing method used
5. Outdoor dry bulb use
6. Indoor dry bulb
7. Outdoor wet bulb used
8. Grains water (difference)
9. Total sensible gain
10. Total latent gain
11. Relative humidity
12. Total cooling required with outside air
13. Total heating required with outside air

C403.2.2 Equipment sizing. The output capacity of heating and cooling equipment shall be not greater than the loads calculated in accordance with Section C403.2.1. A single piece of equipment providing both heating and cooling shall satisfy this provision for one function with the capacity for the other function as small as possible, within available equipment options.

Exceptions:

1. Required standby equipment and systems provided with controls and devices that allow such systems or equipment to operate automatically only when the primary equipment is not operating.
2. Multiple units of the same equipment type with combined capacities exceeding the design load and provided with controls that have the capability to sequence the operation of each unit based on load.

TABLE C403.2.3(1)
MINIMUM EFFICIENCY REQUIREMENTS:
ELECTRICALLY OPERATED UNITARY AIR CONDITIONERS AND CONDENSING UNITS

EQUIPMENT TYPE	SIZE CATEGORY	HEATING SECTION TYPE	SUBCATEGORY OR RATING CONDITION	MINIMUM EFFICIENCY		TEST PROCEDURE[a]
				Before 1/1/2016	As of 1/1/2016	
Air conditioners, air cooled	< 65,000 Btu/h[b]	All	Split System	13.0 SEER	13.0 SEER	AHRI 210/240
			Single Package	13.0 SEER	14.0 SEER[c]	
Through-the-wall (air cooled)	≤ 30,000 Btu/h[b]	All	Split system	12.0 SEER	12.0 SEER	
			Single Package	12.0 SEER	12.0 SEER	
Small-duct high-velocity (air cooled)	< 65,000 Btu/h[b]	All	Split System	11.0 SEER	11.0 SEER	
Air conditioners, air cooled	≥ 65,000 Btu/h and < 135,000 Btu/h	Electric Resistance (or None)	Split System and Single Package	11.2 EER 11.4 IEER	11.2 EER 12.8 IEER	AHRI 340/360
		All other	Split System and Single Package	11.0 EER 11.2 IEER	11.0 EER 12.6 IEER	
	≥ 135,000 Btu/h and < 240,000 Btu/h	Electric Resistance (or None)	Split System and Single Package	11.0 EER 11.2 IEER	11.0 EER 12.4 IEER	
		All other	Split System and Single Package	10.8 EER 11.0 IEER	10.8 EER 12.2 IEER	
	≥ 240,000 Btu/h and < 760,000 Btu/h	Electric Resistance (or None)	Split System and Single Package	10.0 EER 10.1 IEER	10.0 EER 11.6 IEER	
		All other	Split System and Single Package	9.8 EER 9.9 IEER	9.8 EER 11.4 IEER	
	≥ 760,000 Btu/h	Electric Resistance (or None)	Split System and Single Package	9.7 EER 9.8 IEER	9.7 EER 11.2 IEER	
		All other	Split System and Single Package	9.5 EER 9.6 IEER	9.5 EER 11.0 IEER	

(continued)

TABLE C403.2.3(1)—continued
MINIMUM EFFICIENCY REQUIREMENTS:
ELECTRICALLY OPERATED UNITARY AIR CONDITIONERS AND CONDENSING UNITS

EQUIPMENT TYPE	SIZE CATEGORY	HEATING SECTION TYPE	SUB-CATEGORY OR RATING CONDITION	MINIMUM EFFICIENCY		TEST PROCEDURE[a]
				Before 1/1/2016	As of 1/1/2016	
Air conditioners, water cooled	< 65,000 Btu/h[b]	All	Split System and Single Package	12.1 EER 12.3 IEER	12.1 EER 12.3 IEER	AHRI 210/240
	≥ 65,000 Btu/h and < 135,000 Btu/h	Electric Resistance (or None)	Split System and Single Package	12.1 EER 12.3 IEER	12.1 EER 13.9 IEER	AHRI 340/360
		All other	Split System and Single Package	11.9 EER 12.1 IEER	11.9 EER 13.7 IEER	
	≥ 135,000 Btu/h and < 240,000 Btu/h	Electric Resistance (or None)	Split System and Single Package	12.5 EER 12.5 IEER	12.5 EER 13.9 IEER	
		All other	Split System and Single Package	12.3 EER 12.5 IEER	12.3 EER 13.7 IEER	
	≥ 240,000 Btu/h and < 760,000 Btu/h	Electric Resistance (or None)	Split System and Single Package	12.4 EER 12.6 IEER	12.4 EER 13.6 IEER	
		All other	Split System and Single Package	12.2 EER 12.4 IEER	12.2 EER 13.4 IEER	
	≥ 760,000 Btu/h	Electric Resistance (or None)	Split System and Single Package	12.2 EER 12.4 IEER	12.2 EER 13.5 IEER	
		All other	Split System and Single Package	12.0 EER 12.2 IEER	12.0 EER 13.3 IEER	
Air conditioners, evaporatively cooled	< 65,000 Btu/h[b]	All	Split System and Single Package	12.1 EER 12.3 IEER	12.1 EER 12.3 IEER	AHRI 210/240
	≥ 65,000 Btu/h and < 135,000 Btu/h	Electric Resistance (or None)	Split System and Single Package	12.1 EER 12.3 IEER	12.1 EER 12.3 IEER	AHRI 340/360
		All other	Split System and Single Package	11.9 EER 12.1 IEER	11.9 EER 12.1 IEER	
	≥ 135,000 Btu/h and < 240,000 Btu/h	Electric Resistance (or None)	Split System and Single Package	12.0 EER 12.2 IEER	12.0 EER 12.2 IEER	
		All other	Split System and Single Package	11.8 EER 12.0 IEER	11.8 EER 12.0 IEER	
	≥ 240,000 Btu/h and < 760,000 Btu/h	Electric Resistance (or None)	Split System and Single Package	11.9 EER 12.1 IEER	11.9 EER 12.1 IEER	
		All other	Split System and Single Package	11.7 EER 11.9 IEER	11.7 EER 11.9 IEER	
	≥ 760,000 Btu/h	Electric Resistance (or None)	Split System and Single Package	11.7 EER 11.9 IEER	11.7 EER 11.9 IEER	
		All other	Split System and Single Package	11.5 EER 11.7 IEER	11.5 EER 11.7 IEER	
Condensing units, air cooled	≥ 135,000 Btu/h			10.5 EER 11.8 IEER	10.5 EER 11.8 IEER	AHRI 365
Condensing units, water cooled	≥ 135,000 Btu/h			13.5 EER 14.0 IEER	13.5 EER 14.0 IEER	
Condensing units, evaporatively cooled	≥ 135,000 Btu/h			13.5 EER 14.0 IEER	13.5 EER 14.0 IEER	

For SI: 1 British thermal unit per hour = 0.2931 W.

a. Chapter 6 contains a complete specification of the referenced test procedure, including the reference year version of the test procedure.

b. Single-phase, air-cooled air conditioners less than 65,000 Btu/h are regulated by NAECA. SEER values are those set by NAECA.

c. Minimum efficiency as of January 1, 2015.

TABLE C403.2.3(2)
MINIMUM EFFICIENCY REQUIREMENTS:
ELECTRICALLY OPERATED UNITARY AND APPLIED HEAT PUMPS

EQUIPMENT TYPE	SIZE CATEGORY	HEATING SECTION TYPE	SUBCATEGORY OR RATING CONDITION	MINIMUM EFFICIENCY		TEST PROCEDURE[a]
				Before 1/1/2016	As of 1/1/2016	
Air cooled (cooling mode)	< 65,000 Btu/h[b]	All	Split System	13.0 SEER[c]	14.0 SEER[c]	AHRI 210/240
			Single Package	13.0 SEER[c]	14.0 SEER[c]	
Through-the-wall, air cooled	≤ 30,000 Btu/h[b]	All	Split System	12.0 SEER	12.0 SEER	
			Single Package	12.0 SEER	12.0 SEER	
Single-duct high-velocity air cooled	< 65,000 Btu/h[b]	All	Split System	11.0 SEER	11.0 SEER	
Air cooled (cooling mode)	≥ 65,000 Btu/h and < 135,000 Btu/h	Electric Resistance (or None)	Split System and Single Package	11.0 EER 11.2 IEER	11.0 EER 12.0 IEER	AHRI 340/360
		All other	Split System and Single Package	10.8 EER 11.0 IEER	10.8 EER 11.8 IEER	
	≥ 135,000 Btu/h and < 240,000 Btu/h	Electric Resistance (or None)	Split System and Single Package	10.6 EER 10.7 IEER	10.6 EER 11.6 IEER	
		All other	Split System and Single Package	10.4 EER 10.5 IEER	10.4 EER 11.4 IEER	
	≥ 240,000 Btu/h	Electric Resistance (or None)	Split System and Single Package	9.5 EER 9.6 IEER	9.5 EER 10.6 IEER	
		All other	Split System and Single Package	9.3 EER 9.4 IEER	9.3 EER 9.4 IEER	
Water to Air: Water Loop (cooling mode)	< 17,000 Btu/h	All	86°F entering water	12.2 EER	12.2 EER	ISO 13256-1
	≥ 17,000 Btu/h and < 65,000 Btu/h	All	86°F entering water	13.0 EER	13.0 EER	
	≥ 65,000 Btu/h and < 135,000 Btu/h	All	86°F entering water	13.0 EER	13.0 EER	
Water to Air: Ground Water (cooling mode)	< 135,000 Btu/h	All	59°F entering water	18.0 EER	18.0 EER	ISO 13256-1
Brine to Air: Ground Loop (cooling mode)	< 135,000 Btu/h	All	77°F entering water	14.1 EER	14.1 EER	ISO 13256-1
Water to Water: Water Loop (cooling mode)	< 135,000 Btu/h	All	86°F entering water	10.6 EER	10.6 EER	ISO 13256-2
Water to Water: Ground Water (cooling mode)	< 135,000 Btu/h	All	59°F entering water	16.3 EER	16.3 EER	
Brine to Water: Ground Loop (cooling mode)	< 135,000 Btu/h	All	77°F entering fluid	12.1 EER	12.1 EER	

(continued)

TABLE C403.2.3(2)—continued
MINIMUM EFFICIENCY REQUIREMENTS:
ELECTRICALLY OPERATED UNITARY AND APPLIED HEAT PUMPS

EQUIPMENT TYPE	SIZE CATEGORY	HEATING SECTION TYPE	SUBCATEGORY OR RATING CONDITION	MINIMUM EFFICIENCY		TEST PROCEDURE[a]
				Before 1/1/2016	As of 1/1/2016	
Air cooled (heating mode)	< 65,000 Btu/h[b]	—	Split System	7.7 HSPF[c]	8.2 HSPF[c]	AHRI 210/240
		—	Single Package	7.7 HSPF[c]	8.0 HSPF[c]	
Through-the-wall, (air cooled, heating mode)	≤ 30,000 Btu/h[b] (cooling capacity)	—	Split System	7.4 HSPF	7.4 HSPF	
		—	Single Package	7.4 HSPF	7.4 HSPF	
Small-duct high velocity (air cooled, heating mode)	< 65,000 Btu/h[b]	—	Split System	6.8 HSPF	6.8 HSPF	
Air cooled (heating mode)	≥ 65,000 Btu/h and < 135,000 Btu/h (cooling capacity)	—	47°F db/43°F wb outdoor air	3.3 COP	3.3 COP	AHRI 340/360
			17°F db/15°F wb outdoor air	2.25 COP	2.25 COP	
	≥ 135,000 Btu/h (cooling capacity)	—	47°F db/43°F wb outdoor air	3.2 COP	3.2 COP	
			17°F db/15°F wb outdoor air	2.05 COP	2.05 COP	
Water to Air: Water Loop (heating mode)	< 135,000 Btu/h (cooling capacity)	—	68°F entering water	4.3 COP	4.3 COP	ISO 13256-1
Water to Air: Ground Water (heating mode)	< 135,000 Btu/h (cooling capacity)	—	50°F entering water	3.7 COP	3.7 COP	
Brine to Air: Ground Loop (heating mode)	< 135,000 Btu/h (cooling capacity)	—	32°F entering fluid	3.2 COP	3.2 COP	
Water to Water: Water Loop (heating mode)	< 135,000 Btu/h (cooling capacity)	—	68°F entering water	3.7 COP	3.7 COP	ISO 13256-2
Water to Water: Ground Water (heating mode)	< 135,000 Btu/h (cooling capacity)	—	50°F entering water	3.1 COP	3.1 COP	
Brine to Water: Ground Loop (heating mode)	< 135,000 Btu/h (cooling capacity)	—	32°F entering fluid	2.5 COP	2.5 COP	

For SI: 1 British thermal unit per hour = 0.2931 W, °C = [(°F) - 32]/1.8.

a. Chapter 6 contains a complete specification of the referenced test procedure, including the reference year version of the test procedure.

b. Single-phase, air-cooled air conditioners less than 65,000 Btu/h are regulated by NAECA. SEER values are those set by NAECA.

c. Minimum efficiency as of January 1, 2015.

TABLE C403.2.3(3)
MINIMUM EFFICIENCY REQUIREMENTS:
ELECTRICALLY OPERATED PACKAGED TERMINAL AIR CONDITIONERS, PACKAGED TERMINAL HEAT PUMPS, SINGLE-PACKAGE VERTICAL AIR CONDITIONERS, SINGLE VERTICAL HEAT PUMPS, ROOM AIR CONDITIONERS AND ROOM AIR-CONDITIONER HEAT PUMPS

EQUIPMENT TYPE	SIZE CATEGORY (INPUT)	SUBCATEGORY OR RATING CONDITION	MINIMUM EFFICIENCY	TEST PROCEDURE[a]
PTAC (cooling mode) new construction	All Capacities	95°F db outdoor air	14.0 – (0.300 × Cap/1000) EER[c]	AHRI 310/380
PTAC (cooling mode) replacements[b]	All Capacities	95°F db outdoor air	10.9 - (0.213 × Cap/1000) EER	
PTHP (cooling mode) new construction	All Capacities	95°F db outdoor air	14.0 - (0.300 × Cap/1000) EER	
PTHP (cooling mode) replacements[b]	All Capacities	95°F db outdoor air	10.8 - (0.213 × Cap/1000) EER	
PTHP (heating mode) new construction	All Capacities	—	3.2 - (0.026 × Cap/1000) COP	
PTHP (heating mode) replacements[b]	All Capacities	—	2.9 - (0.026 × Cap/1000) COP	
SPVAC (cooling mode)	< 65,000 Btu/h	95°F db/ 75°F wb outdoor air	9.0 EER	AHRI 390
	≥ 65,000 Btu/h and < 135,000 Btu/h	95°F db/ 75°F wb outdoor air	8.9 EER	
	≥ 135,000 Btu/h and < 240,000 Btu/h	95°F db/ 75°F wb outdoor air	8.6 EER	
SPVHP (cooling mode)	< 65,000 Btu/h	95°F db/ 75°F wb outdoor air	9.0 EER	
	≥ 65,000 Btu/h and < 135,000 Btu/h	95°F db/ 75°F wb outdoor air	8.9 EER	
	≥ 135,000 Btu/h and < 240,000 Btu/h	95°F db/ 75°F wb outdoor air	8.6 EER	
SPVHP (heating mode)	< 65,000 Btu/h	47°F db/ 43°F wb outdoor air	3.0 COP	AHRI 390
	≥ 65,000 Btu/h and < 135,000 Btu/h	47°F db/ 43°F wb outdoor air	3.0 COP	
	≥ 135,000 Btu/h and < 240,000 Btu/h	47°F db/ 75°F wb outdoor air	2.9 COP	
Room air conditioners, with louvered sides	< 6,000 Btu/h	—	9.7 SEER	ANSI/ AHAM RAC-1
	≥ 6,000 Btu/h and < 8,000 Btu/h	—	9.7 EER	
	≥ 8,000 Btu/h and < 14,000 Btu/h	—	9.8 EER	
	≥ 14,000 Btu/h and < 20,000 Btu/h	—	9.7 SEER	
	≥ 20,000 Btu/h	—	8.5 EER	
Room air conditioners, without louvered sides	< 8,000 Btu/h	—	9.0 EER	
	≥ 8,000 Btu/h and < 20,000 Btu/h	—	8.5 EER	
	≥ 20,000 Btu/h	—	8.5 EER	
Room air-conditioner heat pumps with louvered sides	< 20,000 Btu/h	—	9.0 EER	
	≥ 20,000 Btu/h	—	8.5 EER	
Room air-conditioner heat pumps without louvered sides	< 14,000 Btu/h	—	8.5 EER	
	≥ 14,000 Btu/h	—	8.0 EER	

(continued)

TABLE C403.2.3(3)—continued
MINIMUM EFFICIENCY REQUIREMENTS:
ELECTRICALLY OPERATED PACKAGED TERMINAL AIR CONDITIONERS,
PACKAGED TERMINAL HEAT PUMPS, SINGLE-PACKAGE VERTICAL AIR CONDITIONERS,
SINGLE VERTICAL HEAT PUMPS, ROOM AIR CONDITIONERS AND ROOM AIR-CONDITIONER HEAT PUMPS

EQUIPMENT TYPE	SIZE CATEGORY (INPUT)	SUBCATEGORY OR RATING CONDITION	MINIMUM EFFICIENCY	TEST PROCEDURE[a]
Room air conditioner casement only	All capacities	—	8.7 EER	ANSI/ AHAM RAC-1
Room air conditioner casement-slider	All capacities	—	9.5 EER	

For SI: 1 British thermal unit per hour = 0.2931 W, °C = [(°F) - 32]/1.8, wb = wet bulb, db = dry bulb.

"Cap" = The rated cooling capacity of the project in Btu/h. Where the unit's capacity is less than 7000 Btu/h, use 7000 Btu/h in the calculation. Where the unit's capacity is greater than 15,000 Btu/h, use 15,000 Btu/h in the calculations.

a. Chapter 6 contains a complete specification of the referenced test procedure, including the referenced year version of the test procedure.

b. Replacement unit shall be factory labeled as follows: "MANUFACTURED FOR REPLACEMENT APPLICATIONS ONLY: NOT TO BE INSTALLED IN NEW CONSTRUCTION PROJECTS." Replacement efficiencies apply only to units with existing sleeves less than 16 inches (406 mm) in height and less than 42 inches (1067 mm) in width.

c. Before January 1, 2015, the minimum efficiency shall be 13.8 - (0.300 x Cap/1000) EER.

TABLE 403.2.3(4)
WARM AIR FURNACES AND COMBINATION WARM AIR FURNACES/AIR-CONDITIONING UNITS,
WARM-AIR DUCT FURNACES AND UNIT HEATERS, MINIMUM EFFICIENCY REQUIREMENTS

EQUIPMENT TYPE	SIZE CATEGORY (INPUT)	SUBCATEGORY OR RATING CONDITION	MINIMUM EFFICIENCY[d, e]	TEST PROCEDURE[a]
Warm air furnaces, gas-fired	< 225,000 Btu/h	—	80% AFUE or $80\%E_t$[c]	DOE 10 CFR, Part 430 or Section 2.39, Thermal Efficiency of ANSI Z 21.47
Non-weatherized			81% AFUE	
Weatherized gas furnace	≥ 225,000 Btu/h	Maximum capacity[c]	$80\%E_t$[f]	Section 2.39, Thermal Efficiency of ANSI Z21.47
Warm air furnaces, oil-fired	< 225,000 Btu/h	—	83% AFUE or $80\%E_t$[c]	DOE 10 CFR, Part 430 or Section 42, Combustion, of UL 727
Non-weatherized			78% AFUE	
Weatherized oil-fired furnace	≥ 225,000 Btu/h	Maximum capacity[b]	$81\%E_t$[g]	Section 42, Combustion, of UL 727
Warm air duct furnaces, gas-fired	All capacities	Maximum capacity[b]	$80\%E_c$	Section 2.10, Efficiency of ANSI Z83.8
Warm air unit heaters, gas-fired	All capacities	Maximum capacity[b]	$80\%E_c$	Section 2.10, Efficiency of ANSI Z83.8
Warm air unit heaters, oil-fired	All capacities	Maximum capacity[b]	$80\%E_c$	Section 40, Combustion, of UL 731
Mobile home furnace, gas-fired	< 225,000 Btu/h	—	80% AFUE	DOE 10 CFR, Part 430
Mobile home furnace, oil-fired	< 225,000 Btu/h	—	75% AFUE	DOE 10 CFR, Part 430

For SI: 1 British thermal unit per hour = 0.2931 W.

a. Chapter 6, Referenced Standards, contains a complete specification of the referenced test procedure, including the referenced year version of the test procedure.

b. Minimum and maximum ratings as provided for and allowed by the unit's controls.

c. Combination units not covered by the National Appliance Energy Conservation Act of 1987 (NAECA) (3-phase power or cooling capacity greater than or equal to 65,000 Btu/h [19 kW]) shall comply with either rating.

d. E_t = Thermal efficiency. See test procedure for detailed discussion.

e. E_c = Combustion efficiency (100% less flue losses). See test procedure for detailed discussion.

f. E_c = Combustion efficiency. Units shall also include an IID, have jackets not exceeding 0.75 percent of the input rating, and have either power venting or a flue damper. A vent damper is an acceptable alternative to a flue damper for those furnaces where combustion air is drawn from the conditioned space.

g. E_t = Thermal efficiency. Units shall also include an IID, have jacket losses not exceeding 0.75 percent of the input rating, and have either power venting or a flue damper. A vent damper is an acceptable alternative to a flue damper for those furnaces where combustion air is drawn from the conditioned space.

TABLE C403.2.3(5)
MINIMUM EFFICIENCY REQUIREMENTS: GAS- AND OIL-FIRED BOILERS

EQUIPMENT TYPE[a]	SUBCATEGORY OR RATING CONDITION	SIZE CATEGORY (INPUT)	MINIMUM EFFICIENCY[d, e]	TEST PROCEDURE
Boilers, hot water	Gas-fired	< 300,000 Btu/h	80% AFUE	10 CFR Part 430
		≥ 300,000 Btu/h and ≤ 2,500,000 Btu/h[b]	80% E_t	10 CFR Part 431
		> 2,500,000 Btu/h[a]	82% E_c	
	Oil-fired[c]	< 300,000 Btu/h	80% AFUE	10 CFR Part 430
		≥ 300,000 Btu/h and ≤ 2,500,000 Btu/h[b]	82% E_t	10 CFR Part 431
		> 2,500,000 Btu/h[a]	84% E_c	
Boilers, steam	Gas-fired	< 300,000 Btu/h	75% AFUE	10 CFR Part 430
	Gas-fired- all, except natural draft	≥ 300,000 Btu/h and ≤ 2,500,000 Btu/h[b]	79% E_t	10 CFR Part 431
		> 2,500,000 Btu/h[a]	79% E_t	
	Gas-fired-natural draft	≥ 300,000 Btu/h and ≤ 2,500,000 Btu/h[b]	77% E_t	
		> 2,500,000 Btu/h[a]	77% E_t	
	Oil-fired[c]	< 300,000 Btu/h	80% AFUE	10 CFR Part 430
		≥ 300,000 Btu/h and ≤ 2,500,000 Btu/h[b]	81% E_t	10 CFR Part 431
		> 2,500,000 Btu/h[a]	81% E_t	

For SI: 1 British thermal unit per hour = 0.2931 W.

a. These requirements apply to boilers with rated input of 8,000,000 Btu/h or less that are not packaged boilers and to all packaged boilers. Minimum efficiency requirements for boilers cover all capacities of packaged boilers.

b. Maximum capacity – minimum and maximum ratings as provided for and allowed by the unit's controls.

c. Includes oil-fired (residual).

d. E_c = Combustion efficiency (100 percent less flue losses).

e. E_t = Thermal efficiency. See referenced standard for detailed information.

TABLE C403.2.3(6)
MINIMUM EFFICIENCY REQUIREMENTS: CONDENSING UNITS, ELECTRICALLY OPERATED

EQUIPMENT TYPE	SIZE CATEGORY	MINIMUM EFFICIENCY[b]	TEST PROCEDURE[a]
Condensing units, air cooled	≥ 135,000 Btu/h	10.1 EER 11.2 IPLV	AHRI 365
Condensing units, water or evaporatively cooled	≥ 135,000 Btu/h	13.1 EER 13.1 IPLV	

For SI: 1 British thermal unit per hour = 0.2931 W.

a. Chapter 6 contains a complete specification of the referenced test procedure, including the referenced year version of the test procedure.

b. IPLVs are only applicable to equipment with capacity modulation.

TABLE C403.2.3(7)
WATER CHILLING PACKAGES – EFFICIENCY REQUIREMENTS[a, b, d]

EQUIPMENT TYPE	SIZE CATEGORY	UNITS	BEFORE 1/1/2015		AS OF 1/1/2015		TEST PROCEDURE[c]
			Path A	Path B	Path A	Path B	
Air-cooled chillers	< 150 tons	EER (Btu/W)	≥ 9.562 FL	NA[c]	≥ 10.100 FL	≥ 9.700 FL	AHRI 550/ 590
			≥ 12.500 IPLV		≥ 13.700 IPLV	≥ 15,800 IPLV	
	≥ 150 tons		≥ 9.562 FL	NA[c]	≥ 10.100 FL	≥ 9.700 FL	
			≥ 12.500 IPLV		≥ 14.000 IPLV	≥ 16.100 IPLV	
Air cooled without condenser, electrically operated	All capacities	EER (Btu/W)	Air-cooled chillers without condenser shall be rated with matching condensers and complying with air-cooled chiller efficiency requirements.				
Water cooled, electrically operated positive displacement	< 75 tons	kW/ton	≤ 0.780 FL	≤ 0.800 FL	≤ 0.750 FL	≤ 0.780 FL	
			≤ 0.630 IPLV	≤ 0.600 IPLV	≤ 0.600 IPLV	≤ 0.500 IPLV	
	≥ 75 tons and < 150 tons		≤ 0.775 FL	≤ 0.790 FL	≤ 0.720 FL	≤ 0.750 FL	
			≤ 0.615 IPLV	≤ 0.586 IPLV	≤ 0.560 IPLV	≤ 0.490 IPLV	
	≥ 150 tons and < 300 tons		≤ 0.680 FL	≤ 0.718 FL	≤ 0.660 FL	≤ 0.680 FL	
			≤ 0.580 IPLV	≤ 0.540 IPLV	≤ 0.540 IPLV	≤ 0.440 IPLV	
	≥ 300 tons and < 600 tons		≤ 0.620 FL	≤ 0.639 FL	≤ 0.610 FL	≤ 0.625 FL	
			≤ 0.540 IPLV	≤ 0.490 IPLV	≤ 0.520 IPLV	≤ 0.410 IPLV	
	≥ 600 tons		≤ 0.620 FL	≤ 0.639 FL	≤ 0.560 FL	≤ 0.585 FL	
			≤ 0.540 IPLV	≤ 0.490 IPLV	≤ 0.500 IPLV	≤ 0.380 IPLV	
Water cooled, electrically operated centrifugal	< 150 tons	kW/ton	≤ 0.634 FL	≤ 0.639 FL	≤ 0.610 FL	≤ 0.695 FL	
			≤ 0.596 IPLV	≤ 0.450 IPLV	≤ 0.550 IPLV	≤ 0.440 IPLV	
	≥ 150 tons and < 300 tons		≤ 0.634 FL	≤ 0.639 FL	≤ 0.610 FL	≤ 0.635 FL	
			≤ 0.596 IPLV	≤ 0.450 IPLV	≤ 0.550 IPLV	≤ 0.400 IPLV	
	≥ 300 tons and < 400 tons		≤ 0.576 FL	≤ 0.600 FL	≤ 0.560 FL	≤ 0.595 FL	
			≤ 0.549 IPLV	≤ 0.400 IPLV	≤ 0.520 IPLV	≤ 0.390 IPLV	
	≥ 400 tons and < 600 tons		≤ 0.576 FL	≤ 0.600 FL	≤ 0.560 FL	≤ 0.585 FL	
			≤ 0.549 IPLV	≤ 0.400 IPLV	≤ 0.500 IPLV	≤ 0.380 IPLV	
	≥ 600 tons		≤ 0.570 FL	≤ 0.590 FL	≤ 0.560 FL	≤ 0.585 FL	
			≤ 0.539 IPLV	≤ 0.400 IPLV	≤ 0.500 IPLV	≤ 0.380 IPLV	
Air cooled, absorption, single effect	All capacities	COP	≥ 0.600 FL	NA[c]	≥ 0.600 FL	NA[c]	AHRI 560
Water cooled absorption, single effect	All capacities	COP	≥ 0.700 FL	NA[c]	≥ 0.700 FL	NA[c]	
Absorption, double effect, indirect fired	All capacities	COP	≥ 1.000 FL	NA[c]	≥ 1.000 FL	NA[c]	
			≥ 1.050 IPLV		≥ 1.050 IPLV		
Absorption double effect direct fired	All capacities	COP	≥ 1.000 FL	NA[c]	≥ 1.000 FL	NA[c]	
			≥ 1.000 IPLV		≥ 1.050 IPLV		

a. The requirements for centrifugal chiller shall be adjusted for nonstandard rating conditions in accordance with Section C403.2.3.1 and are only applicable for the range of conditions listed in Section C403.2.3.1. The requirements for air-cooled, water-cooled positive displacement and absorption chillers are at standard rating conditions defined in the reference test procedure.

b. Both the full-load and IPLV requirements shall be met or exceeded to comply with this standard. Where there is a Path B, compliance can be with either Path A or Path B for any application.

c. NA means the requirements are not applicable for Path B and only Path A can be used for compliance.

d. FL represents the full-load performance requirements and IPLV the part-load performance requirements.

TABLE C403.2.3(8)
MINIMUM EFFICIENCY REQUIREMENTS:
HEAT REJECTION EQUIPMENT

EQUIPMENT TYPE[a]	TOTAL SYSTEM HEAT REJECTION CAPACITY AT RATED CONDITIONS	SUBCATEGORY OR RATING CONDITION[i]	PERFORMANCE REQUIRED[b, c, d, g, h]	TEST PROCEDURE[e, f]
Propeller or axial fan open-circuit cooling towers	All	95°F entering water 85°F leaving water 75°F entering wb	≥ 40.2 gpm/hp	CTI ATC-105 and CTI STD-201
Centrifugal fan open-circuit cooling towers	All	95°F entering water 85°F leaving water 75°F entering wb	≥ 20.0 gpm/hp	CTI ATC-105 and CTI STD-201
Propeller or axial fan closed-circuit cooling towers	All	102°F entering water 90°F leaving water 75°F entering wb	≥ 14.0 gpm/hp	CTI ATC-105S and CTI STD-201
Centrifugal fan closed-circuit cooling towers	All	102°F entering water 90°F leaving water 75°F entering wb	≥ 7.0 gpm/hp	CTI ATC-105S and CTI STD-201
Propeller or axial fan evaporative condensers	All	Ammonia Test Fluid 140°F entering gas temperature 96.3°F condensing temperature 75°F entering wb	≥ 134,000 Btu/h·hp	CTI ATC-106
Centrifugal fan evaporative condensers	All	Ammonia Test Fluid 140°F entering gas temperature 96.3°F condensing temperature 75°F entering wb	≥110,000 Btu/h·hp	CTI ATC-106
Propeller or axial fan evaporative condensers	All	R-507A Test Fluid 165°F entering gas temperature 105°F condensing temperature 75°F entering wb	≥ 157,000 Btu/h·hp	CTI ATC-106
Centrifugal fan evaporative condensers	All	R-507A Test Fluid 165°F entering gas temperature 105°F condensing temperature 75°F entering wb	≥ 135,000 Btu/h·hp	CTI ATC-106
Air-cooled condensers	All	125°F Condensing Temperature 190°F Entering Gas Temperature 15°F subcooling 95°F entering db	≥ 176,000 Btu/h·hp	AHRI 460

For SI: °C = [(°F)-32]/1.8, L/s · kW = (gpm/hp)/(11.83), COP = (Btu/h · hp)/(2550.7),
db = dry bulb temperature, °F, wb = wet bulb temperature, °F.

a. The efficiencies and test procedures for both open- and closed-circuit cooling towers are not applicable to hybrid cooling towers that contain a combination of wet and dry heat exchange sections.

b. For purposes of this table, open circuit cooling tower performance is defined as the water flow rating of the tower at the thermal rating condition listed in Table 403.2.3(8) divided by the fan nameplate-rated motor power.

c. For purposes of this table, closed-circuit cooling tower performance is defined as the water flow rating of the tower at the thermal rating condition listed in Table 403.2.3(8) divided by the sum of the fan nameplate-rated motor power and the spray pump nameplate-rated motor power.

d. For purposes of this table, air-cooled condenser performance is defined as the heat rejected from the refrigerant divided by the fan nameplate-rated motor power.

e. Chapter 6 contains a complete specification of the referenced test procedure, including the referenced year version of the test procedure. The certification requirements do not apply to field-erected cooling towers.

f. Where a certification program exists for a covered product and it includes provisions for verification and challenge of equipment efficiency ratings, then the product shall be listed in the certification program; or, where a certification program exists for a covered product, and it includes provisions for verification and challenge of equipment efficiency ratings, but the product is not listed in the existing certification program, the ratings shall be verified by an independent laboratory test report.

g. Cooling towers shall comply with the minimum efficiency listed in the table for that specific type of tower with the capacity effect of any project-specific accessories and/or options included in the capacity of the cooling tower.

h. For purposes of this table, evaporative condenser performance is defined as the heat rejected at the specified rating condition in the table divided by the sum of the fan motor nameplate power and the integral spray pump nameplate power.

i. Requirements for evaporative condensers are listed with ammonia (R-717) and R-507A as test fluids in the table. Evaporative condensers intended for use with halocarbon refrigerants other than R-507A shall meet the minimum efficiency requirements listed in this table with R-507A as the test fluid.

TABLE C403.2.3(9)
MINIMUM EFFICIENCY AIR CONDITIONERS AND CONDENSING UNITS SERVING COMPUTER ROOMS

EQUIPMENT TYPE	NET SENSIBLE COOLING CAPACITY[a]	MINIMUM SCOP-127[b] EFFICIENCY DOWNFLOW UNITS / UPFLOW UNITS	TEST PROCEDURE
Air conditioners, air cooled	< 65,000 Btu/h	2.20 / 2.09	ANSI/ASHRAE 127
	≥ 65,000 Btu/h and < 240,000 Btu/h	2.10 / 1.99	
	≥ 240,000 Btu/h	1.90 / 1.79	
Air conditioners, water cooled	< 65,000 Btu/h	2.60 / 2.49	
	≥ 65,000 Btu/h and < 240,000 Btu/h	2.50 / 2.39	
	≥ 240,000 Btu/h	2.40 /2.29	
Air conditioners, water cooled with fluid economizer	< 65,000 Btu/h	2.55 /2.44	
	≥ 65,000 Btu/h and < 240,000 Btu/h	2.45 / 2.34	
	≥ 240,000 Btu/h	2.35 / 2.24	
Air conditioners, glycol cooled (rated at 40% propylene glycol)	< 65,000 Btu/h	2.50 / 2.39	
	≥ 65,000 Btu/h and < 240,000 Btu/h	2.15 / 2.04	
	≥ 240,000 Btu/h	2.10 / 1.99	
Air conditioners, glycol cooled (rated at 40% propylene glycol) with fluid economizer	< 65,000 Btu/h	2.45 / 2.34	
	≥ 65,000 Btu/h and < 240,000 Btu/h	2.10 / 1.99	
	≥ 240,000 Btu/h	2.05 / 1.94	

For SI: 1 British thermal unit per hour = 0.2931 W.

a. Net sensible cooling capacity: the total gross cooling capacity less the latent cooling less the energy to the air movement system. (Total Gross – latent – Fan Power).

b. Sensible coefficient of performance (SCOP-127): a ratio calculated by dividing the net sensible cooling capacity in watts by the total power input in watts (excluding reheaters and humidifiers) at conditions defined in ASHRAE Standard 127. The net sensible cooling capacity is the gross sensible capacity minus the energy dissipated into the cooled space by the fan system.

TABLE C403.2.3(10)
HEAT TRANSFER EQUIPMENT

EQUIPMENT TYPE	SUBCATEGORY	MINIMUM EFFICIENCY	TEST PROCEDURE[a]
Liquid-to-liquid heat exchangers	Plate type	NR	AHRI 400

NR = No Requirement.

a. Chapter 6 contains a complete specification of the referenced test procedure, including the referenced year version of the test procedure.

TABLE C403.2.3(11)
MINIMUM EFFICIENCY REQUIREMENTS
VARIABLE REFRIGERANT FLOW MULTI-SPLIT AIR CONDITIONERS AND HEAT PUMPS

EQUIPMENT TYPE	SIZE CATEGORY	HEATING TYPE[a]	MINIMUM EFFICIENCY	TEST PROCEDURE[b]
VRF Multi-split Air Conditioners (Air-cooled)	< 65,000 Btu/h	All	13.0 SEER	AHRI 1230 (omit Sections 5.1.2 and 6.6)
	≥ 65,000 Btu/h and < 135,000 Btu/h	Electric resistance (or none)	11.2 EER	
		All other	11.0 EER	
	≥ 135,000 Btu/h and < 240,000 Btu/h	Electric resistance (or none)	11.0 EER	
		All other	10.8 EER	
	≥ 240,000 Btu/h and < 760,000 Btu/h	Electric resistance (or none)	10.0 EER	
		All other	9.8 EER	
VRF Multi-split Heat Pumps (Air-cooled)	< 65,000 Btu/h	All	13.0 SEER 7.7 HSPF	
	≥ 65,000 Btu/h and < 135,000 Btu/h	Electric resistance (or none)	11.0 EER 3.3 COP	
		All other	10.8 EER 3.3 COP	
	≥ 135,000 Btu/h and < 240,000 Btu/h	Electric resistance (or none)	10.6 EER 3.2 COP	
		All other	10.4 EER 3.2 COP	
	≥ 240,000 Btu/h and < 760,000 Btu/h	Electric resistance (or none)	9.5 EER 3.2 COP	
		All other	9.8 EER	
VRF Multi-split Air Conditioners (Water-source)	< 17,000 Btu/h	Without heat recovery	12.0 EER 4.2 COP	
		With heat recovery	11.8 EER 4.2 COP	
	≥ 17,000 Btu/h and < 65,000 Btu/h	All	12.0 EER 4.2 COP	
	≥ 65,000 Btu/h and < 135,000 Btu/h	All	12.0 EER 4.2 COP	
	≥ 135,000 Btu/h and < 760,000 Btu/h	Without heat recovery	10.0 EER 3.9 COP	
		With heat recovery	9.8 EER 3.9 COP	

For SI: 1 British thermal unit per hour = 0.2931 W, °C = [(°F) – 32]/1.8

a. VRAF Multi-split Heat Pumps (air-cooled) with heat recovery fall under the category of "All Other Types of Heating" unless they also have electric resistance heating, in which case it falls under the category for "No Heating or Electric Resistance Heating."

b. Chapter 6, Referenced Standards, contains a complete specification of the referenced test procedure, including the reference year version of the test procedure.

C403.2.3 HVAC equipment performance requirements. Equipment shall meet the minimum efficiency requirements of Tables C403.2.3(1), C403.2.3(2), C403.2.3(3), C403.2.3(4), C403.2.3(5), C403.2.3(6), C403.2.3(7), C403.2.3(8) and C403.2.3(9) when tested and rated in accordance with the applicable test procedure. Plate-type liquid-to-liquid heat exchangers shall meet the minimum requirements of Table C403.2.3(10).

The efficiency shall be verified through certification under an *approved* certification program or, where a certification program does not exist, the equipment efficiency ratings shall be supported by data furnished by the manufacturer. Where multiple rating conditions or performance requirements are provided, the equipment shall satisfy all stated requirements. Where components, such as indoor or outdoor coils, from different manufacturers are used, calculations and supporting data shall be furnished by the designer that demonstrates that the combined efficiency of the specified components meets the requirements herein.

C403.2.3.1 Water-cooled centrifugal chilling packages. Equipment not designed for operation at AHRI Standard 550/590 test conditions of 44°F (7°C) leaving chilled-water temperature and 2.4 gpm/ton evaporator fluid flow and 85°F (29°C) entering condenser water temperature with 3 gpm/ton (0.054 I/s · kW) condenser water flow shall have maximum full-load kW/ton (FL) and part-load ratings requirements adjusted using Equations 4-6 and 4-7.

$FLadj = FL/Kadj$ **(Equation 4-6)**

$PLV_{adj} = IPLV/K_{adj}$ **(Equation 4-7)**

where:

K_{adj} = $A \times B$

FL = Full-load kW/ton value as specified in Table C403.2.3(7).

FL_{adj} = Maximum full-load kW/ton rating, adjusted for nonstandard conditions.

$IPLV$ = Value as specified in Table C403.2.3(7).

PLV_{adj} = Maximum NPLV rating, adjusted for nonstandard conditions.

A = $0.00000014592 \cdot (LIFT)^4 - 0.0000346496 \cdot (LIFT)^3 + 0.00314196 \cdot (LIFT)^2 - 0.147199 \cdot (LIFT) + 3.9302$

B = $0.0015 \cdot L_{vg}E_{vap} + 0.934$

$LIFT$ = $L_{vg}Cond - L_{vg}E_{vap}$

$L_{vg}Cond$ = Full-load condenser leaving fluid temperature (°F).

$L_{vg}E_{vap}$ = Full-load evaporator leaving temperature (°F).

The FL_{adj} and PLV_{adj} values are only applicable for centrifugal chillers meeting all of the following full-load design ranges:

1. Minimum evaporator leaving temperature: 36°F.
2. Maximum condenser leaving temperature: 115°F.
3. $20°F \leq LIFT \leq 80°F$.

C403.2.3.2 Positive displacement (air- and water-cooled) chilling packages. Equipment with a leaving fluid temperature higher than 32°F (0°C) and water-cooled positive displacement chilling packages with a condenser leaving fluid temperature below 115°F (46°C) shall meet the requirements of Table C403.2.3(7) when tested or certified with water at standard rating conditions, in accordance with the referenced test procedure.

C403.2.4 HVAC system controls. Each heating and cooling system shall be provided with thermostatic controls as specified in Section C403.2.4.1, C403.2.4.1.3, C403.2.4.2, C403.2.4.3, C403.3.1, C403.4, C403.4.1 or C403.4.4.

C403.2.4.1 Thermostatic controls. The supply of heating and cooling energy to each *zone* shall be controlled by individual thermostatic controls capable of responding to temperature within the *zone*. Where humidification or dehumidification or both is provided, at least one humidity control device shall be provided for each humidity control system.

Exception: Independent perimeter systems that are designed to offset only building envelope heat losses, gains or both serving one or more perimeter *zones* also served by an interior system provided:

1. The perimeter system includes at least one thermostatic control *zone* for each building exposure having exterior walls facing only one orientation (within +/-45 degrees) (0.8 rad) for more than 50 contiguous feet (15 240 mm); and
2. The perimeter system heating and cooling supply is controlled by thermostats located within the *zones* served by the system.

C403.2.4.1.1 Heat pump supplementary heat. Heat pumps having supplementary electric resistance heat shall have controls that, except during defrost, prevent supplementary heat operation where the heat pump can provide the heating load.

C403.2.4.1.2 Deadband. Where used to control both heating and cooling, *zone* thermostatic controls shall be capable of providing a temperature range or deadband of at least 5°F (2.8°C) within which the supply of heating and cooling energy to the *zone* is capable of being shut off or reduced to a minimum.

Exceptions:

1. Thermostats requiring manual changeover between heating and cooling modes.
2. Occupancies or applications requiring precision in indoor temperature control as *approved* by the *code official*.

C403.2.4.1.3 Set point overlap restriction. Where a *zone* has a separate heating and a separate cooling thermostatic control located within the *zone*, a limit switch, mechanical stop or direct digital control system with software programming shall be provided with the capability to prevent the heating set point from exceeding the cooling set point and to maintain a deadband in accordance with Section C403.2.4.1.2.

C403.2.4.2 Off-hour controls. Each *zone* shall be provided with thermostatic setback controls that are controlled by either an automatic time clock or programmable control system.

Exceptions:

1. *Zones* that will be operated continuously.
2. *Zones* with a full HVAC load demand not exceeding 6,800 Btu/h (2 kW) and having a readily accessible manual shutoff switch.

C403.2.4.2.1 Thermostatic setback capabilities. Thermostatic setback controls shall have the capability to set back or temporarily operate the system to maintain *zone* temperatures down to 55°F (13°C) or up to 85°F (29°C).

C403.2.4.2.2 Automatic setback and shutdown capabilities. Automatic time clock or programmable controls shall be capable of starting and stopping the system for seven different daily schedules per week and retaining their programming and time setting during a loss of power for at least 10 hours. Additionally, the controls shall have a manual override that allows temporary operation of the system for up to 2 hours; a manually operated timer capable of being adjusted to operate the system for up to 2 hours; or an occupancy sensor.

C403.2.4.2.3 Automatic start capabilities. Automatic start controls shall be provided for each HVAC system. The controls shall be capable of automatically adjusting the daily start time of the HVAC system in order to bring each space to the desired occupied temperature immediately prior to scheduled occupancy.

C403.2.4.2.4 Humidistatic control. Where humidification, dehumidification or both is provided, the following shall be met:

1. At least one humidity control device shall be provided for each humidity control system.
2. Controls shall be provided capable of preventing simultaneous operation of humidification and dehumidification equipment.

Exceptions:

1. Zones served by desiccant systems used with direct evaporative cooling in series.
2. Systems serving zones where specific humidity levels are required, such as computer rooms, museums and hospitals, as approved by the building official.

C403.2.4.3 Shutoff dampers. Outdoor air intake and exhaust openings and stairway and shaft vents shall be provided with Class I motorized dampers. The dampers shall have an air leakage rate not greater than 4 cfm/ft^2 (20.3 L/s · m^2) of damper surface area at 1.0 inch water gauge (249 Pa) and shall be labeled by an approved agency when tested in accordance with AMCA 500D for such purpose.

Outdoor air intake and exhaust dampers shall be installed with automatic controls configured to close when the systems or spaces served are not in use or during unoccupied period warm-up and setback operation, unless the systems served require outdoor or exhaust air in accordance with the *Florida Building Code, Mechanical* or the dampers are opened to provide intentional economizer cooling.

Stairway and shaft vent dampers shall be installed with automatic controls configured to open upon the activation of any fire alarm initiating device of the building's fire alarm system or the interruption of power to the damper.

Exception: Gravity (nonmotorized) dampers shall be permitted to be used as follows:

1. In buildings less than three stories in height above grade plane.
2. In buildings of any height located in *Climate Zones* 1, 2 or 3.
3. Where the design exhaust capacity is not greater than 300 cfm (142 L/s).

Gravity (nonmotorized) dampers shall have an air leakage rate not greater than 20 cfm/ft^2 (101.6 L/s · m^2) where not less than 24 inches (610 mm) in either dimension and 40 cfm/ft^2 (203.2 L/s · m^2) where less than 24 inches (610 mm) in either dimension. The rate of air leakage shall be determined at 1.0 inch water gauge (249 Pa) when tested in accordance with AMCA 500D for such purpose. The dampers shall be labeled by an approved agency.

C403.2.4.4 Zone isolation. HVAC systems serving *zones* that are over 25,000 square feet (2323 m^2) in floor area or that span more than one floor and are designed to operate or be occupied nonsimultaneously shall be divided into isolation areas. Each isolation area shall be equipped with isolation devices and controls configured to automatically shut off the supply of conditioned air and outdoor air to and exhaust air from the isolation area. Each isolation area shall be controlled independently by a device meeting the requirements of Section C403.2.4.2.2. Central systems and plants shall be provided with controls and devices that will allow system and equipment operation for any length of time while serving only the smallest isolation area served by the system or plant.

Exceptions:

1. Exhaust air and outdoor air connections to isolation areas where the fan system to which they connect is not greater than 5,000 cfm (2360 L/s).
2. Exhaust airflow from a single isolation area of less than 10 percent of the design airflow of the exhaust system to which it connects.
3. Isolation areas intended to operate continuously or intended to be inoperative only when all other isolation areas in a *zone* are inoperative.

C403.2.4.5 Snow- and ice-melt system controls. Snow- and ice-melting systems shall include automatic controls capable of shutting off the system when the pavement temperature is above 50°F (10°C) and no precipitation is falling and an automatic or manual control that will allow shutoff when the outdoor temperature is above 40°F (4°C).

C403.2.4.6 Freeze protection system controls. Freeze protection systems, such as heat tracing of outdoor piping and heat exchangers, including self-regulating heat tracing, shall include automatic controls configured to shut off the systems when outdoor air temperatures are above 40°F (4°C) or when the conditions of the protected fluid will prevent freezing.

C403.2.4.7 Economizer fault detection and diagnostics (FDD). Air-cooled unitary direct-expansion units listed in Tables C403.2.3(1) through C403.2.3(3) and variable refrigerant flow (VRF) units that are equipped with an economizer in accordance with Section C403.3

shall include a fault detection and diagnostics (FDD) system complying with the following:

1. The following temperature sensors shall be permanently installed to monitor system operation:
   1.1. Outside air.
   1.2. Supply air.
   1.3. Return air.
2. Temperature sensors shall have an accuracy of ±2°F (1.1°C) over the range of 40°F to 80°F (4°C to 26.7°C).
3. Refrigerant pressure sensors, where used, shall have an accuracy of ±3 percent of full scale.
4. The unit controller shall be capable of providing system status by indicating the following:
   4.1. Free cooling available.
   4.2. Economizer enabled.
   4.3. Compressor enabled.
   4.4. Heating enabled.
   4.5. Mixed air low limit cycle active.
   4.6. The current value of each sensor.
5. The unit controller shall be capable of manually initiating each operating mode so that the operation of compressors, economizers, fans and the heating system can be independently tested and verified.
6. The unit shall be capable of reporting faults to a fault management application accessible by day-to-day operating or service personnel, or annunciated locally on zone thermostats.
7. The FDD system shall be capable of detecting the following faults:
   7.1. Air temperature sensor failure/fault.
   7.2. Not economizing when the unit should be economizing.
   7.3. Economizing when the unit should not be economizing.
   7.4. Damper not modulating.
   7.5. Excess outdoor air.

C403.2.5 Hot water boiler outdoor temperature setback control. Hot water boilers that supply heat to the building through one- or two-pipe heating systems shall have an outdoor setback control that lowers the boiler water temperature based on the outdoor temperature.

C403.2.6 Ventilation. Ventilation, either natural or mechanical, shall be provided in accordance with Chapter 4 of the *Florida Building Code, Mechanical*. Where mechanical ventilation is provided, the system shall provide the capability to reduce the outdoor air supply to the minimum required by Chapter 4 of the *Florida Building Code, Mechanical.*

C403.2.6.1 Demand controlled ventilation. Demand control ventilation (DCV) shall be provided for spaces larger than 500 square feet (46.5 m^2) and with an average occupant load of 25 people per 1,000 square feet (93 m^2) of floor area (as established in Table 403.3.1.1 of the *Florida Building Code, Mechanical*) and served by systems with one or more of the following:

1. An air-side economizer.
2. Automatic modulating control of the outdoor air damper.
3. A design outdoor airflow greater than 3,000 cfm (1416 L/s).

Exception: Demand control ventilation is not required for systems and spaces as follows:

1. Systems with energy recovery complying with Section C403.2.7.
2. Multiple-*zone* systems without direct digital control of individual *zones* communicating with a central control panel.
3. Systems with a design outdoor airflow less than 1,200 cfm (566 L/s).
4. Spaces where the supply airflow rate minus any makeup or outgoing transfer air requirement is less than 1,200 cfm (566 L/s).
5. Ventilation provided for process loads only.

C403.2.6.2 Enclosed parking garage ventilation controls. Enclosed parking garages used for storing or handling automobiles operating under their own power shall employ contamination-sensing devices and automatic controls configured to stage fans or modulate fan average airflow rates to 50 percent or less of design capacity, or intermittently operate fans less than 20 percent of the occupied time or as required to maintain acceptable contaminant levels in accordance with *Florida Building Code, Mechanical* provisions. Failure of contamination sensing devices shall cause the exhaust fans to operate continuously at design airflow.

Exceptions:

1. Garages with a total exhaust capacity less than 22,500 cfm (10 620 L/s) with ventilation systems that do not utilize heating or mechanical cooling.
2. Garages that have a garage area to ventilation system motor nameplate power ratio that exceeds 1125 cfm/hp (710 L/s/kW) and do not utilize heating or mechanical cooling.

C403.2.7 Energy recovery ventilation systems. Where the supply airflow rate of a fan system exceeds the values specified in Tables C403.2.7(1) and C403.2.7(2), the system shall include an energy recovery system. The energy recovery system shall have the capability to provide a change in the enthalpy of the outdoor air supply of not less than 50 percent of the difference between the outdoor air and return air enthalpies, at design conditions. Where an air economizer is required, the energy recovery system shall include a bypass or controls which permit operation of the economizer as required by Section C403.3.

Exception: An energy recovery ventilation system shall not be required in any of the following conditions:

1. Where energy recovery systems are prohibited by the *Florida Building Code, Mechanical.*

2. Laboratory fume hood systems that include at least one of the following features:
   2.1. Variable-air-volume hood exhaust and room supply systems capable of reducing exhaust and makeup air volume to 50 percent or less of design values.
   2.2. Direct makeup (auxiliary) air supply equal to at least 75 percent of the exhaust rate, heated not warmer than 2°F (1.1°C) above room setpoint, cooled to not cooler than 3°F (1.7°C) below room setpoint, no humidification added, and no simultaneous heating and cooling used for dehumidification control.
3. Systems serving spaces that are heated to less than 60°F (15.5°C) and are not cooled.
4. Where more than 60 percent of the outdoor heating energy is provided from site-recovered or site solar energy.
5. Heating energy recovery in *Climate Zones* 1 and 2.
6. Cooling energy recovery in *Climate Zones* 3C, 4C, 5B, 5C, 6B, 7 and 8.
7. Systems requiring dehumidification that employ energy recovery in series with the cooling coil.
8. Where the largest source of air exhausted at a single location at the building exterior is less than 75 percent of the design *outdoor air* flow rate.
9. Systems expected to operate less than 20 hours per week at the *outdoor air* percentage covered by Table C403.2.7(1).
10. Systems exhausting toxic, flammable, paint or corrosive fumes or dust.
11. Commercial kitchen hoods used for collecting and removing grease vapors and smoke.

C403.2.8 Kitchen exhaust systems. Replacement air introduced directly into the exhaust hood cavity shall not be greater than 10 percent of the hood exhaust airflow rate. Conditioned supply air delivered to any space shall not exceed the greater of the following:

1. The ventilation rate required to meet the space heating or cooling load.
2. The hood exhaust flow minus the available transfer air from adjacent space where available transfer air is considered that portion of outdoor ventilation air not required to satisfy other exhaust needs, such as restrooms, and not required to maintain pressurization of adjacent spaces.

Where total kitchen hood exhaust airflow rate is greater than 5,000 cfm (2360 L/s), each hood shall be a factory-built commercial exhaust hood listed by a nationally recognized testing laboratory in compliance with UL 710. Each hood shall have a maximum exhaust rate as specified in Table C403.2.8 and shall comply with one of the following:

1. Not less than 50 percent of all replacement air shall be transfer air that would otherwise be exhausted.

TABLE C403.2.7(1)
ENERGY RECOVERY REQUIREMENT
(Ventilation systems operating less than 8,000 hours per year)

CLIMATE ZONE	PERCENT (%) OUTDOOR AIR AT FULL DESIGN AIRFLOW RATE							
	≥ 10% and < 20%	≥ 20% and < 30%	≥ 30% and < 40%	≥ 40% and < 50%	≥ 50% and < 60%	≥ 60% and < 70%	≥ 70% and < 80%	≥ 80%
	DESIGN SUPPLY FAN AIRFLOW RATE (cfm)							
3B, 3C, 4B, 4C, 5B	NR	NR	NR	NR	NR	NR	NR	NR
1B, 2B, 5C	NR	NR	NR	NR	> 26,000	> 12,000	> 5,000	> 4,000
6B	≥ 28,000	≥ 26,5000	≥ 11,000	≥ 5,500	≥ 4,500	≥ 3,500	≥ 2,500	≥ 1,500
1A, 2A, 3A, 4A, 5A, 6A	≥ 26,000	≥ 16,000	≥ 5,500	≥ 4,500	≥ 3,500	≥ 2,000	≥ 1,000	> 0
7, 8	≥ 4,500	≥ 4,000	≥ 2,500	≥ 1,000	> 0	> 0	> 0	> 0

For SI: 1 cfm = 0.4719 L/s.
NR = Not Required.

TABLE C403.2.7(2)
ENERGY RECOVERY REQUIREMENT
(Ventilation systems operating not less than 8,000 hours per year)

CLIMATE ZONE	PERCENT (%) OUTDOOR AIR AT FULL DESIGN AIRFLOW RATE							
	≥ 10% and < 20%	≥ 20% and < 30%	≥ 30% and < 40%	≥ 40% and < 50%	≥ 50% and < 60%	≥ 60% and < 70%	≥ 70% and < 80%	≥ 80%
	Design Supply Fan Airflow Rate (cfm)							
3C	NR	NR	NR	NR	NR	NR	NR	NR
1B, 2B, 3B, 4C, 5C	NR	≥ 19,500	≥ 9,000	≥ 5,000	≥ 4,000	≥ 3,000	≥ 1,500	> 0
1A, 2A, 3A, 4B, 5B	≥ 2,500	≥ 2,000	≥ 1,000	≥ 500	> 0	> 0	> 0	> 0
4A, 5A, 6A, 6B, 7, 8	> 0	> 0	> 0	> 0	> 0	> 0	> 0	> 0

For SI: 1 cfm = 0.4719 L/s.
NR = Not required

TABLE C403.2.8
MAXIMUM NET EXHAUST FLOW RATE, CFM PER LINEAR FOOT OF HOOD LENGTH

TYPE OF HOOD	LIGHT-DUTY EQUIPMENT	MEDIUM-DUTY EQUIPMENT	HEAVY-DUTY EQUIPMENT	EXTRA-HEAVY-DUTY EQUIPMENT
Wall-mounted canopy	140	210	280	385
Single island	280	350	420	490
Double island (per side)	175	210	280	385
Eyebrow	175	175	NA	NA
Backshelf/Pass-over	210	210	280	NA

For SI: 1 cfm = 0.4719 L/s; 1 foot = 305 mm.
NA = Not Allowed.

2. Demand ventilation systems on not less than 75 percent of the exhaust air that are capable of not less than a 50-percent reduction in exhaust and replacement air system airflow rates, including controls necessary to modulate airflow in response to appliance operation and to maintain full capture and containment of smoke, effluent and combustion products during cooking and idle.
3. Listed energy recovery devices with a sensible heat recovery effectiveness of not less than 40 percent on not less than 50 percent of the total exhaust airflow.

Where a single hood, or hood section, is installed over appliances with different duty ratings, the maximum allowable flow rate for the hood or hood section shall be based on the requirements for the highest appliance duty rating under the hood or hood section.

Exception: Where not less than 75 percent of all the replacement air is transfer air that would otherwise be exhausted

C403.2.9 Duct and plenum insulation, construction and sealing (Mandatory).

C403.2.9.1 Insulation.

C403.2.9.1.1 Insulation required. All supply and return air ducts and plenums shall be insulated to the levels shown in Table C403.2.9.1.

Exceptions:

1. When located within equipment.
2. When the design temperature difference between the interior and exterior of the duct or plenum does not exceed 15°F (8°C).
3. For runouts less than 10 feet (3048 mm) in length to air terminals or air outlets, the rated *R*-value of insulation need not exceed R-5.
4. Backs of air outlets and outlet plenums exposed to unconditioned or indirectly conditioned spaces with face areas exceeding 5 square feet (.46 m^2) need not exceed R-2; those 5 square feet (.46 m^2) or smaller need not be insulated.
5. Return air ducts meeting all the requirements for building cavities that will be used as return air plenums.

TABLE C403.2.9.1
MINIMUM DUCT INSULATION *R*-VALUES, HEATING AND COOLING SUPPLY AND RETURN DUCTS

LOCATION	SUPPLY DUCT	RETURN DUCT
Exterior of building	R-6	R-4.2
Ventilated Attic	R-6	R-4.2
Unvented attic above insulated ceiling	R-6	R-4.2
Unvented attic with roof insulation	R-4.2	None
Unconditioned spaces[1]	R-4.2	R-4.2
Indirectly conditioned spaces[2]	None	None
Conditioned spaces	None	None
Buried	R-4.2	None

1. Includes crawl spaces, both ventilated and nonventilated.
2. Includes return air plenums with or without exposed roofs above.

C403.2.9.1.2 Insulation protection. Insulation shall be protected from damage, including that due to sunlight, moisture, equipment maintenance and wind, but not limited to the following:

1. Insulation exposed to weather shall be suitable for outdoor service, e.g., protected by aluminum, sheet metal, painted canvas or plastic cover. Cellular foam insulation shall be protected as above or painted with a coating that is water retardant and provides shielding from solar radiation that can cause degradation of the material.
2. Insulation covering cooling ducts located outside the conditioned space shall include a vapor retardant located outside the insulation (unless the insulation is inherently vapor retardant), all penetrations and joints of which shall be sealed.

C403.2.9.1.3 Condensation control. Additional insulation with vapor barrier shall be provided where the minimum duct insulation requirements of Section C403.2.9.1.1 are determined to be insufficient to prevent condensation.

C403.2.9.2 Duct construction. All ducts, air handlers, filter boxes, building cavities, mechanical closets and enclosed support platforms that form the primary air containment passageways for air distribution systems shall be considered ducts or plenum chambers and shall be constructed and erected in accordance with Table C403.2.9.2 and with Chapter 6 of the *Florida Building Code, Mechanical*. Ducts shall be constructed, braced, reinforced and installed to provide structural strength and durability. All transverse joints, longitudinal seams and fitting connections shall be securely fastened in accordance with the applicable standards of this section.

C403.2.9.3 Sealing, general (Mandatory). All ducts, air handlers, filter boxes, building cavities, mechanical closets and enclosed support platforms that form the primary air containment passageways for air distribution systems shall be sealed in accordance with the applicable criteria of this section and Table C403.2.9.2.

TABLE C403.2.9.2
DUCT SYSTEM CONSTRUCTION AND SEALING

DUCT TYPE/ CONNECTION	SEALING REQUIREMENTS	MECHANICAL ATTACHMENT	TEST STANDARD
Metal duct, rigid and flexible			
Pressures less than 1-inch water gauge	Closure systems as described in Section C403.2.9.3: 1. Continuous welds. 2. Snaplock seams and grooved, standing, double-corner, single-corner and Pittsburgh-lock seams and all other rolled mechanical seams. 3. Mastic, mastic-plus-embedded fabric or mastic ribbons. 4. Gaskets. 5. Pressure-sensitive tape. 6. Aerosol sealant.	Mechanical attachments approved: 1. Continuous welds. 2. Snaplock seams and grooved, standing, double corner, single-corner and Pittsburgh-lock seams and all other rolled mechanical seams. Crimp joints for round metal ducts shall have a contact lap of at least $1^1/_2$ inches (38 mm). Round metal ducts shall be mechanically fastened by means of at least three sheet-metal screws or rivets equally spaced around the joint.[1]	SMACNA HVAC Air Duct Leakage Test Manual
Pressures 1-inch water gauge or greater	Closure systems as described in Section C403.2.9.3: 1. Continuous welds. 2. Mastic or mastic-plus-embedded fabric systems. 3. Gaskets.	Mechanical attachments approved: Continuous welds. Round metal ducts shall be mechanically fastened by means of at least three sheet-metal screws or rivets equally spaced around the joint. [1]	SMACNA HVAC Air Duct Leakage Test Manual
High-pressure duct systems designed to operate at pressures greater than 3-inch water gauge (4-inch water gauge pressure class)	The tested duct leakage class, at a test pressure equal to the design duct pressure class rating, shall be equal to or less than Leakage Class 6. Leakage testing may be limited to representative sections of the duct system but in no case shall such tested sections include less than 25 percent of the total installed duct area for the designated pressure class.		SMACNA HVAC Air Duct Leakage Test Manual
Plastic duct	See Section 603.8.3 of the *Florida Building Code, Mechanical.*	Joints between plastic ducts and plastic fittings shall be made in accordance with the manufacturer's installation instructions.	ASTM D2412
Fibrous glass duct, rigid	All joints, seams and duct wall penetrations between sections of duct and between duct and other distribution system components shall be sealed with closure systems as described in Section C403.2.9.3: 1. Heat-activated tapes. 2. Pressure-sensitive tapes. 3. Mastics or mastic-plus-embedded fabric systems.	Mechanically fastened per standard to secure the sections independent of the closure system(s). Attachments of ductwork to air-handling equipment shall be by mechanical fasteners. Where access is limited, two fasteners on one side shall be acceptable.	NAIMA Fibrous Glass Duct Construction Standards UL 181 UL 181A
Flexible duct systems, nonmetal	All duct collar fittings shall have a minimum $^5/_8$-inch (16 mm) integral flange for sealing to other components and a minimum 3-inch (76 mm) shaft for insertion into the inner duct core. Flexible ducts having porous inner cores shall not be used. **Exception:** Ducts having a nonporous liner between the porous inner core and the outer jacket. Fastening and sealing requirements shall be applied to such intermediate liners.	Flexible nonmetal ducts shall be joined to all other air distribution system components by either terminal or intermediate fittings. Mechanical fasteners for use with flexible nonmetallic air ducts shall comply with UL 181B and shall be marked 181B-C. See Section 603.10 of the *Florida Building Code, Mechanical,* for duct support requirements.	UL 181 UL 181B ADC FDPIS

(continued)

TABLE C403.2.9.2—continued
DUCT SYSTEM CONSTRUCTION AND SEALING

DUCT TYPE/ CONNECTION	SEALING REQUIREMENTS	MECHANICAL ATTACHMENT	TEST STANDARD
Duct core to duct fitting	The reinforced lining shall be sealed to the duct fitting using one of the following sealing materials, which conforms to the approved closure and mechanical attachment requirements of Section C403.2.9.3: 1. Gasketing. 2. Mastic, mastic-plus-embedded fabric or mastic ribbons. 3. Pressure-sensitive tape. 4. Aerosol sealants, provided that their use is consistent with UL 181.	The reinforced core shall be mechanically attached to the duct fitting by a drawband installed directly over the wire-reinforced core and the duct fitting. The duct fitting shall extend a minimum of 2 inches (51 mm) into each section of duct core. When the flexible duct is larger than 12 inches (303 mm) in diameter or the design pressure exceeds 1-inch water gauge, the drawband shall be secured by a raised bead or indented groove on the fitting.	
Duct outer jacket to duct collar fitting	The outer jacket of a flexible duct section shall be secured at the juncture of the air distribution system component and intermediate or terminal fitting in such a way as to prevent excess condensation. The outer jacket of a flexible duct section shall not be interposed between the flange of the duct fitting and the flexible duct, rigid fibrous glass duct board or sheet metal to which it is mated.		
Duct collar fitting to rigid duct	The duct collar fitting's integral flange shall be sealed to the rigid duct board or sheet metal using one of the following closure systems/ materials, which conforms to the approved closure and mechanical attachment standards of Section C403.2.9.3: 1. Gasketing. 2. Mastic or mastic-plus-embedded fabric systems. 3. Mastic ribbons when used to attach a duct collar to sheet metal. 4. Pressure-sensitive tape. 5. Aerosol sealants, provided that their use is consistent with UL 181.	The duct collar fitting shall be mechanically attached to the rigid duct board or sheet metal by appropriate mechanical fasteners, either screws, spin-in flanges or dovetail flanges.	
Terminal and intermediate fittings. **Fittings and joints between dissimilar duct types** **Terminal fittings and air ducts to building envelope components**	Approved closure systems shall be as designated by air distribution system component material type in Section C403.2.9.3. **Exception:** When the components of a joint are fibrous glass duct board and metal duct, including collar fittings and metal equipment housings, the closure systems approved for fibrous glass duct shall be used. Terminal fittings and air ducts that penetrate the building envelope shall be mechanically attached to the structure and sealed to the envelope component penetrated and shall use one of the following closure systems/materials which conform to the approved closure and mechanical application requirements of Section C403.2.9.3: 1. Mastics or mastic-plus-embedded fabrics. 2. Gaskets used in terminal fitting/grille assemblies that compress the gasket material between the fitting and the wall, ceiling or floor sheathing.		
Air-handling units	Air-handling units located outside the conditioned space shall be sealed using approved closure systems described in Section C403.2.9.3 for metallic ducts.	All air-handling units shall be mechanically attached to other air distribution system components.	
Return plenums	Building cavities that will be used as return air plenums shall be lined with a continuous air barrier made of durable nonporous materials. All penetrations to the air barrier shall be sealed with a suitable long-life mastic material. **Exception:** Surfaces between the plenum and conditioned spaces from which the return/mixed air is drawn. Roof decks above building cavities used as a return air plenum shall be insulated to at least R-19.		

(continued)

TABLE C403.2.9.2—continued
DUCT SYSTEM CONSTRUCTION AND SEALING

DUCT TYPE/ CONNECTION	SEALING REQUIREMENTS	MECHANICAL ATTACHMENT	TEST STANDARD
Mechanical closets	All joints between the air barriers of walls, ceiling, floor and door framing and all penetrations of the air barrier shall be sealed to the air barrier with approved closure systems. Through-wall, through-floor and through-ceiling air passageways into the closet shall be framed and sealed to form an air-tight passageway. **Exception:** Air passageways into the closet from conditioned space that are specifically designed for return airflow. The following air barriers are approved for use in mechanical closets: 1. One-half-inch-thick (12.7 mm) or greater gypsum wallboard, taped and sealed with joint compound over taped joints between gypsum wallboard panels. 2. Other panelized materials having inward facing surfaces with an air porosity no greater than that of a duct product meeting Section 22 of UL 181, which are sealed on all interior surfaces to create a continuous air barrier by one of the following: a. Sealants complying with the product and application standards of this table for fibrous glass ductboard or b. A suitable long-life caulk or mastic for all applications.		
Enclosed support platforms in unconditioned spaces	Enclosed support platforms located between the return air inlet(s) from conditioned space and the inlet of the air-handling unit or furnace, shall contain a duct section constructed entirely of rigid metal, rigid fibrous glass duct board or flexible duct, which is constructed and sealed according to the respective requirements of Section C403.2.9.2 and insulated according to the requirements of Section C403.2.9.1. 1. No portion of the building structure, including adjoining walls, floors and ceilings, shall be in contact with the return air stream or function as a component of this duct section. 2. The duct section shall not be penetrated by a refrigerant line, chase, wiring, pipe or any object other than a component of the air distribution system. 3. Through-wall, through-floor and through-ceiling penetrations into the duct system shall contain a branch duct fabricated of rigid fibrous glass duct board or rigid metal and shall extend to and be sealed by both the duct section and the grille side wall surface.	The branch duct shall be fabricated and attached to the duct insert in accordance with requirements for the duct type used.	

1. Where a duct connection is made that is partially inaccessible, three screws or rivets shall be equally spaced on the exposed portion of the joint so as to prevent a hinge effect.

C403.2.9.3.1 Mechanical fastening. All joints between sections of air ducts and plenums, between intermediate and terminal fittings and other components of air distribution systems, and between subsections of these components shall be mechanically fastened to secure the sections independently of the closure system(s).

C403.2.9.3.2 Sealing. Air distribution system components shall be sealed with approved closure systems.

C403.2.9.3.3 Space provided. Sufficient space shall be provided adjacent to all mechanical components located in or forming a part of the air distribution system to assure adequate access for: (1) construction and sealing in accordance with the requirements of Section C403.2.9, (2) inspection and (3) cleaning and maintenance. A minimum of 4 inches (102 mm) is considered sufficient space around air-handling units.

Exception: Retrofit or replacement units not part of a renovation.

C403.2.9.3.4 Product application. Closure products shall be applied to the air barriers of air distribution system components being joined in order to form a continuous barrier or they may be applied in accordance with the manufacturer's instructions or appropriate industry installation standard where more restrictive.

C403.2.9.3.5 Surface preparation. The surfaces upon which closure products are to be applied shall be clean and dry in accordance with the manufacturer's installation instructions.

C403.2.9.3.6 Approved mechanical attachments. Approved mechanical attachments for air distribution system components include screws, rivets, welds, interlocking joints crimped and rolled, staples, twist in (screw attachment), and compression systems created by bend tabs or screw tabs and flanges or by clinching straps. Mechanical attachments shall be selected from Table C403.2.9.2 to be appropriate to the duct system type.

C403.2.9.3.7 Approved closure systems. The following closure systems and materials are approved for air distribution construction and sealing for the applications and pressure classes shown in Table C403.2.9.2:

1. Metal closures.
   a. Welds applied continuously along metal seams or joints through which air could leak.
   b. Snaplock seams and grooved, standing, double-corner, single-corner and Pittsburgh-lock seams, as defined by SMACNA, as well as all other rolled mechanical seams. All seams shall be rolled or crimped.
2. Gasketing, which achieves a 25/50 flame spread/smoke-density-development rating under ASTM E84 or UL 723, provided that it is used only between mated surfaces that are mechanically fastened with sufficient force to compress the gasket and to fill all voids and cracks through which air leakage would otherwise occur.
3. Mastic closures. Mastics shall be placed over the entire joint between mated surfaces. Mastics shall not be diluted. Approved mastics include the following:
   a. Mastic or mastic-plus-embedded fabric systems applied to fibrous glass ductboard that are listed and labeled in accordance with UL 181A, Part III.
   b. Mastic or mastic-plus-embedded fabric systems applied to nonmetal flexible duct that are listed and labeled in accordance with UL 181B, Part II.
   c. Mastic ribbons, which achieve a 25/50 flame spread/smoke density development rating under ASTM E84 or UL 723, provided that they may be used only in flange-joints and lap-joints, such that the mastic resides between two parallel surfaces of the air barrier and that those surfaces are mechanically fastened.
4. Tapes. Tapes shall be applied such that they extend not less than 1 inch onto each of the mated surfaces and shall totally cover the joint. When used on rectangular ducts, tapes shall be used only on joints between parallel rigid surfaces and on right angle joints. Approved tapes include the following:
   a. Pressure-sensitive tapes.
      i. Pressure-sensitive tapes applied to fibrous glass ductboard that are listed and labeled in accordance with UL 181A, Part I.
      ii. Pressure-sensitive tapes applied to nonmetal flexible duct that are listed and labeled in accordance with UL 181B, Part I.
   b. Heat-activated tapes applied to fibrous glass ductboard that are listed and labeled in accordance with UL 181A, Part II.
5. Aerosol sealant. Such sealants shall be installed by manufacturer-certified installers following manufacturer's instructions and shall achieve 25/50 flame spread/smoke-density-development ratings under ASTM E84 or UL 723.

C403.2.9.4 Cavities of the building structure. Cavities in framed spaces, such as dropped soffits and walls, shall not be used to deliver air from or return air to the conditioning system unless they contain an air duct insert that is insulated in accordance with Section C403.2.9.1 and constructed and sealed in accordance with the requirements of Section C403.2.9.2 appropriate for the duct materials used.

Exception: Return air plenums beneath a roof deck that is insulated to at least R-19.

C403.2.9.5 Air distribution system sizing and design. All air distribution systems shall be sized and designed in accordance with recognized engineering standards such as ACCA Manual D or other standards based on the following:

1. Calculation of the supply air for each room shall be based on the greater of the heating load or sensible cooling load for that room.
2. Duct size shall be determined by the supply air requirements of each room, the available static pressure and the total equivalent length of the various duct runs.
3. Friction loss data shall correspond to the type of material used in duct construction.

C403.2.9.6 Air-handling units. Air-handling units shall not be allowed in attics of commercial buildings.

C403.2.10 Piping insulation. Piping serving as part of a heating or cooling system shall be thermally insulated in accordance with Table C403.2.10.

Exceptions:

1. Factory-installed piping within HVAC equipment tested and rated in accordance with a test procedure referenced by this code.
2. Factory-installed piping within room fan-coils and unit ventilators tested and rated according to AHRI 440 (except that the sampling and variation provisions of Section 6.5 shall not apply) and AHRI 840, respectively.
3. Piping that conveys fluids that have a design operating temperature range between 60°F (15°C) and 105°F (41°C).
4. Piping that conveys fluids that have not been heated or cooled through the use of fossil fuels or electric power.

TABLE C403.2.10
MINIMUM PIPE INSULATION THICKNESS (in inches)[a, c]

FLUID OPERATING TEMPERATURE RANGE AND USAGE (°F)	INSULATION CONDUCTIVITY		NOMINAL PIPE OR TUBE SIZE (inches)				
	Conductivity Btu · in./(h · ft² · °F)[b]	Mean Rating Temperature, °F	< 1	1 to < $1^1/_2$	$1^1/_2$ to < 4	4 to < 8	≥ 8
> 350	0.32 – 0.34	250	4.5	5.0	5.0	5.0	5.0
251 – 350	0.29 – 0.32	200	3.0	4.0	4.5	4.5	4.5
201 – 250	0.27 – 0.30	150	2.5	2.5	2.5	3.0	3.0
141 – 200	0.25 – 0.29	125	1.5	1.5	2.0	2.0	2.0
105 – 140	0.21 – 0.28	100	1.0	1.0	1.5	1.5	1.5
40 – 60	0.21 – 0.27	75	0.5	0.5	1.0	1.0	1.0
< 40	0.20 – 0.26	50	0.5	1.0	1.0	1.0	1.5

For SI: 1 inch = 25.4 mm, °C = [(°F) - 32]/1.8.

a. For piping smaller than $1^1/_2$ inches and located in partitions within conditioned spaces, reduction of these thicknesses by 1 inch shall be permitted (before thickness adjustment required in footnote b) but not to a thickness less than 1 inch.

b. For insulation outside the stated conductivity range, the minimum thickness (T) shall be determined as follows:

$T = r\{(1 + t/r)K/k - 1\}$

where:

T = minimum insulation thickness,
r = actual outside radius of pipe,
t = insulation thickness listed in the table for applicable fluid temperature and pipe size,
K = conductivity of alternate material at mean rating temperature indicated for the applicable fluid temperature Btu · in/(h · ft² · °F) and
k = the upper value of the conductivity range listed in the table for the applicable fluid temperature.

c. For direct-buried heating and hot water system piping, reduction of these thicknesses by $1^1/_2$ inches (38 mm) shall be permitted (before thickness adjustment required in footnote b but not to thicknesses less than 1 inch (25 mm).

5. Strainers, control valves, and balancing valves associated with piping 1 inch (25 mm) or less in diameter.
6. Direct buried piping that conveys fluids at or below 60°F (15°C).

C403.2.10.1 Protection of piping insulation. Piping insulation exposed to the weather shall be protected from damage, including that due to sunlight, moisture, equipment maintenance and wind, and shall provide shielding from solar radiation that can cause degradation of the material. Adhesive tape shall not be permitted.

C403.2.11 Mechanical systems commissioning and completion requirements. Mechanical systems shall be commissioned and completed in accordance with Section C408.2.

C403.2.12 Air system design and control. Each HVAC system having a total fan system motor nameplate horsepower (hp) exceeding 5 hp (3.7 kW) shall comply with the provisions of Sections C403.2.12.1 through C403.2.12.3.

C403.2.12.1 Allowable fan motor horsepower. Each HVAC system at fan system design conditions shall not exceed the allowable *fan system motor nameplate hp* (Option 1) or *fan system bhp* (Option 2) as shown in Table C403.2.12.1(1). This includes supply fans, exhaust fans, return/relief fans, and fan-powered terminal units associated with systems providing heating or cooling capability. Single-*zone* variable air volume systems shall comply with the constant volume fan power limitation.

Exceptions:

1. Hospital, vivarium and laboratory systems that utilize flow control devices on exhaust or return to maintain space pressure relationships necessary for occupant health and safety or environmental control shall be permitted to use variable volume fan power limitation.
2. Individual exhaust fans with motor nameplate horsepower of 1 hp (0.746 kW) or less are exempt from the allowable fan horsepower requirement.

C403.2.12.2 Motor nameplate horsepower. For each fan, the fan brake horsepower shall be indicated on the construction documents and the selected motor shall be not larger than the first available motor size greater than the following:

1. For fans less than 6 bhp (4413 W), 1.5 times the fan brake horsepower.
2. For fans 6 bhp (4413 W) and larger, 1.3 times the fan brake horsepower.
3. Systems complying with Section C403.2.12.1 *fan system motor nameplate hp* (Option 1).

C403.2.12.3 Fan efficiency. Fans shall have a fan efficiency grade (FEG) of not less than 67 when determined in accordance with AMCA 205 by an *approved,* independent testing laboratory. The total efficiency of the fan at the design point of operation shall be within

TABLE C403.2.12.1(1)
FAN POWER LIMITATION

	LIMIT	CONSTANT VOLUME	VARIABLE VOLUME
Option 1: Fan system motor nameplate hp	Allowable nameplate motor hp	$hp \leq CFM_S \cdot 0.0011$	$hp \leq CFM_S \cdot 0.0015$
Option 2: Fan system bhp	Allowable fan system bhp	$bhp \leq CFM_S \cdot 0.00094 + A$	$bhp \leq CFM_S \cdot 0.0013 + A$

For SI: 1 bhp = 735.5 W, 1 hp = 745.5 W, 1 cfm = 0.4719 L/s.
where:

CFM_S = The maximum design supply airflow rate to conditioned spaces served by the system in cubic feet per minute.
hp = The maximum combined motor nameplate horsepower.
Bhp = The maximum combined fan brake horsepower.
A = Sum of $[PD \times CFM_D / 4131]$

where:

PD = Each applicable pressure drop adjustment from Table C403.2.12.1(2) in. w.c.
CFM_D = The design airflow through each applicable device from Table C403.2.12.1(2) in cubic feet per minute.

TABLE C403.2.12.1(2)
FAN POWER LIMITATION PRESSURE DROP ADJUSTMENT

DEVICE	ADJUSTMENT
Credits	
Fully ducted return and/or exhaust air systems	0.5 inch w.c. (2.15 in w.c. for laboratory and vivarium systems)
Return and/or exhaust airflow control devices	0.5 inch w.c.
Exhaust filters, scrubbers or other exhaust treatment	The pressure drop of device calculated at fan system design condition
Particulate filtration credit: MERV 9 thru 12	0.5 inch w.c.
Particulate filtration credit: MERV 13 thru 15	0.9 inch. w.c.
Particulate filtration credit: MERV 16 and greater and electronically enhanced filters	Pressure drop calculated at 2× clean filter pressure drop at fan system design condition
Carbon and other gas-phase air cleaners	Clean filter pressure drop at fan system design condition
Biosafety cabinet	Pressure drop of device at fan system design condition
Energy recovery device, other than coil runaround loop	(2.2 × energy recovery effectiveness) – 0.5 inch w.c. for each airstream
Coil runaround loop	0.6 inch w.c. for each airstream
Evaporative humidifier/cooler in series with another cooling coil	Pressure drop of device at fan system design conditions
Sound attenuation section (fans serving spaces with design background noise goals below NC35)	0.15 inch w.c.
Exhaust system serving fume hoods	0.35 inch w.c.
Laboratory and vivarium exhaust systems in high-rise buildings	0.25 inch w.c./100 feet of vertical duct exceeding 75 feet
Deductions	
Systems without central cooling device	- 0.6 in. w.c.
Systems without central heating device	- 0.3 in. w.c.
Systems with central electric resistance heat	- 0.2 in. w.c.

For SI: 1 inch w.c. = 249 Pa, 1 inch = 25.4 mm.
w.c. = water column, NC = Noise criterion.

15 percentage points of the maximum total efficiency of the fan.

Exception: The following fans are not required to have a fan efficiency grade:

1. Fans of 5 hp (3.7 kW) or less as follows:
   1.1. Single fan with a motor nameplate horsepower of 5 hp (3.7 kW) or less, unless Exception 1.2 applies.
   1.2. Multiple fans in series or parallel that have a combined motor nameplate horsepower of 5 hp (3.7 kW) or less and are operated as the functional equivalent of a single fan.
2. Fans that are part of equipment covered under Section C403.2.3.
3. Fans included in an equipment package certified by an *approved agency* for air or energy performance.
4. Powered wall/roof ventilators.
5. Fans outside the scope of AMCA 205.
6. Fans that are intended to operate only during emergency conditions.

C403.2.13 Heating outside a building. Systems installed to provide heat outside a building shall be radiant systems.

Such heating systems shall be controlled by an occupancy sensing device or a timer switch, so that the system is automatically deenergized when no occupants are present.

C403.2.14 Refrigeration equipment performance. Refrigeration equipment shall have an energy use in kWh/day not greater than the values of Tables C403.2.14(1) and C403.2.14(2) when tested and rated in accordance with AHRI Standard 1200. The energy use shall be verified through certification under an approved certification program or, where a certification program does not exist, the energy use shall be supported by data furnished by the equipment manufacturer.

C403.2.15 Walk-in coolers, walk-in freezers, refrigerated warehouse coolers and refrigerated warehouse freezers. *Refrigerated warehouse coolers* and *refrigerated warehouse freezers* shall comply with this section. *Walk-in coolers* and *walk-in freezers* that are not either site assembled or site constructed shall comply with the following:

1. Be equipped with automatic door-closers that firmly close walk-in doors that have been closed to within 1 inch (25 mm) of full closure.

   Exception: Automatic closers are not required for doors more than 45 inches (1143 mm) in width or more than 7 feet (2134 mm) in height.

2. Doorways shall have strip doors, curtains, spring-hinged doors or other method of minimizing infiltration when doors are open.
3. *Walk-in coolers* and *refrigerated warehouse coolers* shall contain wall, ceiling, and door insulation of not less than R-25 and *walk-in freezers* and *refrigerated warehouse freezers* shall contain wall, ceiling and door insulation of not less than R-32.

   Exception: Glazed portions of doors or structural members need not be insulated.

4. *Walk-in freezers* shall contain floor insulation of not less than R-28.
5. Transparent reach-in doors for *walk-in freezers* and windows in *walk-in freezer* doors shall be of triple-pane glass, either filled with inert gas or with heat-reflective treated glass.
6. Windows and transparent reach-in doors for *walk-in coolers* shall be of double-pane or triple-pane, inert gas-filled, heat-reflective treated glass.
7. Evaporator fan motors that are less than 1 hp (0.746 kW) and less than 460 volts shall use electronically commutated motors, brushless direct-current motors, or 3-phase motors.
8. Condenser fan motors that are less than 1 hp (0.746 kW) shall use electronically commutated motors, permanent split capacitor-type motors or 3-phase motors.
9. Where antisweat heaters without antisweat heater controls are provided, they shall have a total door rail, glass and frame heater power draw of not more than 7.1 W/ft^2 (76 W/m^2) of door opening for *walk-in freezers* and 3.0 W/ft^2 (32 W/m^2) of door opening for *walk-in coolers*.
10. Where antisweat heater controls are provided, they shall reduce the energy use of the antisweat heater as a function of the relative humidity in the air outside the door or to the condensation on the inner glass pane.
11. Lights in *walk-in coolers*, *walk-in freezers*, *refrigerated warehouse coolers* and *refrigerated warehouse freezers* shall either use light sources with an efficacy of not less than 40 lumens per watt, including ballast losses, or shall use light sources with an efficacy of not less than 40 lumens per watt, including ballast losses, in conjunction with a device that turns off the lights within 15 minutes when the space is not occupied.

C403.2.16 Walk-in coolers and walk-in freezers. Site-assembled or site-constructed *walk-in coolers* and *walk-in freezers* shall comply with the following:

1. Automatic door closers shall be provided that fully close walk-in doors that have been closed to within 1 inch (25 mm) of full closure.

   Exception: Closers are not required for doors more than 45 inches (1143 mm) in width or more than 7 feet (2134 mm) in height.

2. Doorways shall be provided with strip doors, curtains, spring-hinged doors or other method of minimizing infiltration when the doors are open.

TABLE C403.2.14(1)
MINIMUM EFFICIENCY REQUIREMENTS: COMMERCIAL REFRIGERATION

EQUIPMENT TYPE	APPLICATION	ENERGY USE LIMITS (kWh per day)[a]	TEST PROCEDURE
Refrigerator with solid doors	Holding Temperature	0.10 · V + 2.04	AHRI 1200
Refrigerator with transparent doors		0.12 · V + 3.34	
Freezers with solid doors		0.40 · V + 1.38	
Freezers with transparent doors		0.75 · V + 4.10	
Refrigerators/freezers with solid doors		the greater of 0.12 · V + 3.34 or 0.70	
Commercial refrigerators	Pulldown	0.126 · V + 3.51	

a. V = volume of the chiller or frozen compartment as defined in AHAM-HRF-1.

TABLE C403.2.14(2)
MINIMUM EFFICIENCY REQUIREMENTS: COMMERCIAL REFRIGERATORS AND FREEZERS

EQUIPMENT TYPE				ENERGY USE LIMITS (kWh/day)[a,b]	TEST PROCEDURE
Equipment Classc	Family Code	Operating Mode	Rating Temperature		
VOP.RC.M	Vertical open	Remote condensing	Medium	0.82 · TDA + 4.07	AHRI 1200
SVO.RC.M	Semivertical open	Remote condensing	Medium	0.83 · TDA + 3.18	
HZO.RC.M	Horizontal open	Remote condensing	Medium	0.35 · TDA + 2.88	
VOP.RC.L	Vertical open	Remote condensing	Low	2.27 · TDA + 6.85	
HZO.RC.L	Horizontal open	Remote condensing	Low	0.57 · TDA + 6.88	
VCT.RC.M	Vertical transparent door	Remote condensing	Medium	0.22 TDA + 1.95	
VCT.RC.L	Vertical transparent door	Remote condensing	Low	0.56 · TDA + 2.61	
SOC.RC.M	Service over counter	Remote condensing	Medium	0.51 · TDA + 0.11	
VOP.SC.M	Vertical open	Self-contained	Medium	1.74 · TDA + 4.71	
SVO.SC.M	Semivertical open	Self-contained	Medium	1.73 · TDA + 4.59	
HZO.SC.M	Horizontal open	Self-contained	Medium	0.77 · TDA + 5.55	
HZO.SC.L	Horizontal open	Self-contained	Low	1.92 · TDA + 7.08	
VCT.SC.I	Vertical transparent door	Self-contained	Ice cream	0.67 · TDA + 3.29	
VCS.SC.I	Vertical solid door	Self-contained	Ice cream	0.38 · V + 0.88	
HCT.SC.I	Horizontal transparent door	Self-contained	Ice cream	0.56 · TDA + 0.43	
SVO.RC.L	Semivertical open	Remote condensing	Low	2.27 · TDA + 6.85	
VOP.RC.I	Vertical open	Remote condensing	Ice cream	2.89 · TDA + 8.7	
SVO.RC.I	Semivertical open	Remote condensing	Ice cream	2.89 · TDA + 8.7	
HZO.RC.I	Horizontal open	Remote condensing	Ice cream	0.72 · TDA + 8.74	
VCT.RC.I	Vertical transparent door	Remote condensing	Ice cream	0.66 · TDA + 3.05	
HCT.RC.M	Horizontal transparent door	Remote condensing	Medium	0.16 · TDA + 0.13	

(continued)

TABLE C403.2.14(2)—continued
MINIMUM EFFICIENCY REQUIREMENTS: COMMERCIAL REFRIGERATORS AND FREEZERS

EQUIPMENT TYPE				ENERGY USE LIMITS (kWh/day)[a,b]	TEST PROCEDURE
Equipment Class[c]	Family Code	Operating Mode	Rating Temperature		
HCT.RC.L	Horizontal transparent door	Remote condensing	Low	0.34 · TDA + 0.26	AHRI 1200
HCT.RC.I	Horizontal transparent door	Remote condensing	Ice cream	0.4 · TDA + 0.31	
VCS.RC.M	Vertical solid door	Remote condensing	Medium	0.11 · V + 0.26	
VCS.RC.L	Vertical solid door	Remote condensing	Low	0.23 · V + 0.54	
VCS.RC.I	Vertical solid door	Remote condensing	Ice cream	0.27 · V + 0.63	
HCS.RC.M	Horizontal solid door	Remote condensing	Medium	0.11 · V + 0.26	
HCS.RC.L	Horizontal solid door	Remote condensing	Low	0.23 · V + 0.54	
HCS.RC.I	Horizontal solid door	Remote condensing	Ice cream	0.27 · V + 0.63	
HCS.RC.I	Horizontal solid door	Remote condensing	Ice cream	0.27 · V + 0.63	
SOC.RC.L	Service over counter	Remote condensing	Low	1.08 · TDA + 0.22	
SOC.RC.I	Service over counter	Remote condensing	Ice cream	1.26 · TDA + 0.26	
VOP.SC.L	Vertical open	Self-contained	Low	4.37 · TDA + 11.82	
VOP.SC.I	Vertical open	Self-contained	Ice cream	5.55 · TDA + 15.02	
SVO.SC.L	Semivertical open	Self-contained	Low	4.34 · TDA + 11.51	
SVO.SC.I	Semivertical open	Self-contained	Ice cream	5.52 · TDA + 14.63	
HZO.SC.I	Horizontal open	Self-contained	Ice cream	2.44 · TDA + 9.0	
SOC.SC.I	Service over counter	Self-contained	Ice cream	1.76 · TDA + 0.36	
HCS.SC.I	Horizontal solid door	Self-contained	Ice cream	0.38 · V + 0.88	

a. V = Volume of the case, as measured in accordance with Appendix C of AHRI 1200.

b. TDA = Total display area of the case, as measured in accordance with Appendix D of AHRI 1200.

c. Equipment class designations consist of a combination [(in sequential order separated by periods (AAA).(BB).(C))] of:

(AAA) An equipment family code where:
- VOP = vertical open
- SVO = semivertical open
- HZO = horizontal open
- VCT = vertical transparent doors
- VCS = vertical solid doors
- HCT = horizontal transparent doors
- HCS = horizontal solid doors
- SOC = service over counter

(BB) An operating mode code:
- RC = remote condensing
- SC = self-contained

(C) A rating temperature code:
- M = medium temperature (38°F)
- L = low temperature (0°F)
- I = ice-cream temperature (15°F)

For example, "VOP.RC.M" refers to the "vertical-open, remote-condensing, medium-temperature" equipment class.

3. Walls shall be provided with insulation having a thermal resistance of not less than R-25, ceilings shall be provided with insulation having a thermal resistance of not less than R-25 and doors of *walk-in coolers* and *walk-in freezers* shall be provided with insulation having a thermal resistance of not less than R-32.

   Exception: Insulation is not required for glazed portions of doors or at structural members associated with the walls, ceiling or door frame.

4. The floor of *walk-in freezers* shall be provided with insulation having a thermal resistance of not less than R-28.
5. Transparent reach-in doors for and windows in opaque *walk-in freezer* doors shall be provided with triple-pane glass having the interstitial spaces filled with inert gas or provided with heat-reflective treated glass.
6. Transparent reach-in doors for and windows in opaque *walk-in cooler* doors shall be double-pane heat-reflective treated glass having the interstitial space gas filled.
7. Evaporator fan motors that are less than 1 hp (0.746 kW) and less than 460 volts shall be electronically commutated motors or 3-phase motors.
8. Condenser fan motors that are less than 1 hp (0.746 kW) in capacity shall be of the electronically commutated or permanent split capacitor-type or shall be 3-phase motors.

   Exception: Fan motors in *walk-in coolers* and *walk-in freezers* combined in a single enclosure greater than 3,000 square feet (279 m^2) in floor area are exempt.

9. Antisweat heaters that are not provided with antisweat heater controls shall have a total door rail, glass and frame heater power draw not greater than 7.1 W/ft^2 (76 W/m^2) of door opening for *walk-in freezers*, and not greater than 3.0 W/ft^2 (32 W/m^2) of door opening for *walk-in coolers*.
10. Antisweat heater controls shall be capable of reducing the energy use of the antisweat heater as a function of the relative humidity in the air outside the door or to the condensation on the inner glass pane.
11. Light sources shall have an efficacy of not less than 40 lumens per Watt, including any ballast losses, or shall be provided with a device that automatically turns off the lights within 15 minutes of when the *walk-in cooler* or *walk-in freezer* was last occupied.

C403.2.17 Refrigerated display cases. Site-assembled or site-constructed refrigerated display cases shall comply with the following:

1. Lighting and glass doors in refrigerated display cases shall be controlled by one of the following:
   1.1. Time switch controls to turn off lights during nonbusiness hours. Timed overrides for display cases shall turn the lights on for up to 1 hour and shall automatically time out to turn the lights off.
   1.2. Motion sensor controls on each display case section that reduce lighting power by at least 50 percent within 3 minutes after the area within the sensor range is vacated.
2. Low-temperature display cases shall incorporate temperature-based defrost termination control with a time-limit default. The defrost cycle shall terminate first on an upper temperature limit breach and second upon a time limit breach.
3. Antisweat heater controls shall reduce the energy use of the antisweat heater as a function of the relative humidity in the air outside the door or to the condensation on the inner glass pane.

C403.3 Economizers (Prescriptive). Each cooling system shall include either an air or water economizer complying with Sections C403.3.1 through C403.3.4.

Exceptions: Economizers are not required for the systems listed below.

1. In cooling systems for buildings located in *Climate Zones* 1A and 1B.
2. In *climate zones* other than 1A and 1B, where individual fan cooling units have a capacity of less than 54,000 Btu/h (15.8 kW) and meet one of the following:
   2.1. Have direct expansion cooling coils.
   2.2. The total chilled water system capacity less the capacity of fan units with air economizers is less than the minimum specified in Table C403.3(1).

   The total supply capacity of all fan-cooling units not provided with economizers shall not exceed 20 percent of the total supply capacity of all fan-cooling units in the building or 300,000 Btu/h (88 kW), whichever is greater.
3. Where more than 25 percent of the air designed to be supplied by the system is to spaces that are designed to be humidified above 35°F (1.7°C) dew-point temperature to satisfy process needs.
4. Systems that serve *residential* spaces where the system capacity is less than five times the requirement listed in Table C403.3(1).
5. Systems expected to operate less than 20 hours per week.

TABLE C403.3(1)
MINIMUM CHILLED-WATER SYSTEM COOLING CAPACITY FOR DETERMINING ECONOMIZER COOLING REQUIREMENTS

CLIMATE ZONES (COOLING)	TOTAL CHILLED-WATER SYSTEM CAPACITY LESS CAPACITY OF COOLING UNITS WITH AIR ECONOMIZERS	
	Local Water-cooled Chilled-water Systems	Air-cooled Chilled-water Systems or District Chilled-Water Systems
1a	No economizer requirement	No economizer requirement
1b, 2a, 2b	960,000 Btu/h	1,250,000 Btu/h
3a, 3b, 3c, 4a, 4b, 4c	720,000 Btu/h	940,000 Btu/h
5a, 5b, 5c, 6a, 6b, 7, 8	1,320,000 Btu/h	1,720,000 Btu/h

For SI: 1 British thermal unit per hour = 0.2931 W.

6. Where the use of *outdoor air* for cooling will affect supermarket open refrigerated casework systems.
7. The required air or water economizer may be eliminated if the minimum code required cooling efficiency of the HVAC unit rated with an IPLV, IEER or SEER is increased by at least 17 percent. If the HVAC unit is only rated with a full-load metric like EER cooling, then it must be increased by at least 17 percent.
8. Chilled-water cooling systems that are passive (without a fan) or use induction where the total chilled water system capacity less the capacity of fan units with air economizers is less than the minimum specified in Table C403.3(1).
9. Systems that include a heat recovery system in accordance with Section C403.4.5.

Table C403.3(2) Equipment Efficiency Performance Exception for Economizers. Reserved.

C403.3.1 Integrated economizer control. Economizer systems shall be integrated with the mechanical cooling system and be capable of providing partial cooling even where additional mechanical cooling is required to provide the remainder of the cooling load. Controls shall not be capable of creating a false load in the mechanical cooling systems by limiting or disabling the economizer or any other means, such as hot gas bypass, except at the lowest stage of mechanical cooling.

Units that include an air economizer shall comply with the following:

1. Unit controls shall have the mechanical cooling capacity control interlocked with the air economizer controls such that the outdoor air damper is at the 100-percent open position when mechanical cooling is on and the outdoor air damper does not begin to close to prevent coil freezing due to minimum compressor run time until the leaving air temperature is less than 45°F (7°C).
2. Direct expansion (DX) units that control 75,000 Btu/h (22 kW) or greater of rated capacity of the capacity of the mechanical cooling directly based on occupied space temperature shall have not fewer than two stages of mechanical cooling capacity.
3. Other DX units, including those that control space temperature by modulating the airflow to the space, shall be in accordance with Table C403.3.1.

C403.3.2 Economizer heating system impact. HVAC system design and economizer controls shall be such that economizer operation does not increase building heating energy use during normal operation.

Exception: Economizers on variable air volume (VAV) systems that cause *zone* level heating to increase due to a reduction in supply air temperature.

C403.3.3 Air economizers. Air economizers shall comply with Sections C403.3.3.1 through C403.3.3.5.

C403.3.3.1 Design capacity. Air economizer systems shall be capable of modulating *outdoor air* and return air dampers to provide up to 100 percent of the design supply air quantity as *outdoor air* for cooling.

C403.3.3.2 Control signal. Economizer dampers shall be capable of being sequenced with the mechanical cooling equipment and shall not be controlled by only mixed-air temperature.

Exception: The use of mixed-air temperature limit control shall be permitted for systems controlled from space temperature (such as single-*zone* systems).

C403.3.3.3 High-limit shutoff. Air economizers shall be capable of automatically reducing *outdoor air* intake to the design minimum *outdoor air* quantity when *outdoor air* intake will no longer reduce cooling energy usage. High-limit shutoff control types for specific climates shall be chosen from Table C403.3.3.3. High-limit shutoff control settings for these control types shall be those specified in Table C403.3.3.3.

C403.3.3.4 Relief of excess outdoor air. Systems shall be capable of relieving excess *outdoor air* during air economizer operation to prevent overpressurizing the building. The relief air outlet shall be located to avoid recirculation into the building.

C403.3.3.5 Economizer dampers. Return, exhaust/relief and outdoor air dampers used in economizers shall comply with Section C403.2.4.3.

TABLE C403.3.1
DX COOLING STAGE REQUIREMENTS FOR MODULATING AIRFLOW UNITS

RATING CAPACITY	MINIMUM NUMBER OF MECHANICAL COOLING STAGES	MINIMUM COMPRESSOR DISPLACEMENT[a]
≥ 65,000 Btu/h and < 240,000 Btu/h	3 stages	≤ 35% of full load
≥ 240,000 Btu/h	4 stages	≤ 25% full load

For SI: 1 British thermal unit per hour = 0.2931 W.

a. For *mechanical cooling* stage control that does not use variable compressor displacement, the percent displacement shall be equivalent to the mechanical cooling capacity reduction evaluated at the full load rating conditions for the compressor.

TABLE C403.3.3.3
HIGH-LIMIT SHUTOFF CONTROL SETTING FOR AIR ECONOMIZERS[b]

DEVICE TYPE	CLIMATE ZONE	REQUIRED HIGH LIMIT (ECONOMIZER OFF WHEN):	
		Equation	Description
Fixed dry bulb	1B, 2B, 3B, 3C, 4B, 4C, 5B, 5C, 6B, 7, 8	$T_{OA} > 75°F$	Outdoor air temperature exceeds 75°F
	5A, 6A	$T_{OA} > 70°F$	Outdoor air temperature exceeds 70°F
	1A, 2A, 3A, 4A	$T_{OA} > 65°F$	Outdoor air temperature exceeds 65°F
Differential dry bulb	1B, 2B, 3B, 3C, 4B, 4C, 5A, 5B, 5C, 6A, 6B, 7, 8	$T_{OA} > T_{RA}$	Outdoor air temperature exceeds return air temperature
Fixed enthalpy with fixed dry-bulb temperatures	All	$h_{OA} > 28$ Btu/lb[a] or $T_{OA} > 75°F$	Outdoor air enthalpy exceeds 28 Btu/lb of dry air[a] or Outdoor air temperature exceeds 75°F
Differential enthalpy with fixed dry-bulb temperature	All	$h_{OA} > h_{RA}$ or $T_{OA} > 75°F$	Outdoor air enthalpy exceeds return air enthalpy or Outdoor air temperature exceeds 75°F

For SI: 1 foot = 305 mm, °C = (°F - 32)/1.8, 1 Btu/lb = 2.33 kJ/kg.

a. At altitudes substantially different than sea level, the fixed enthalpy limit shall be set to the enthalpy value at 75°F and 50-percent relative humidity. As an example, at approximately 6,000 feet elevation, the fixed enthalpy limit is approximately 30.7 Btu/lb.

b. Devices with selectable setpoints shall be capable of being set to within 2°F and 2 Btu/lb of the setpoint listed.

C403.3.4 Water-side economizers. Water-side economizers shall comply with Sections C403.3.4.1 and C403.3.4.2.

C403.3.4.1 Design capacity. Water economizer systems shall be capable of cooling supply air by indirect evaporation and providing up to 100 percent of the expected system cooling load at *outdoor air* temperatures of not greater than 50°F (10°C) dry bulb/45°F (7°C) wet bulb.

Exceptions:

1. Systems primarily serving computer rooms in which 100 percent of the expected system cooling load at 40°F (4°C) dry bulb/35°F (1.7°C) wet bulb is met with evaporative water economizers.
2. Systems primarily serving computer rooms with dry cooler water economizers which satisfy 100 percent of the expected system cooling load at 35°F (1.7°C) dry bulb.
3. Systems where dehumidification requirements cannot be met using outdoor air temperatures of 50°F (10°C) dry bulb/45°F (7°C) wet bulb and where 100 percent of the expected system cooling load at 45°F (7°C) dry bulb/40°F (4°C) wet bulb is met with evaporative water economizers.

C403.3.4.2 Maximum pressure drop. Precooling coils and water-to-water heat exchangers used as part of a water economizer system shall either have a water-side pressure drop of less than 15 feet (45 kPa) of water or a secondary loop shall be created so that the coil or heat exchanger pressure drop is not seen by the circulating pumps when the system is in the normal cooling (noneconomizer) mode.

C403.4 Hydronic and multiple-zone HVAC systems controls and equipment. (Prescriptive). Hydronic and multiple-zone HVAC system controls and equipment shall comply with this section.

C403.4.1 Fan control. Controls shall be provided for fans in accordance with Sections C403.4.1.1 through C403.4.1.3.

C403.4.1.1 Fan airflow control. Each cooling system listed in Table C403.4.1.1 shall be designed to vary the indoor fan airflow as a function of load and shall comply with the following requirements:

1. Direct expansion (DX) and chilled water cooling units that control the capacity of the mechanical cooling directly based on space temperature shall have not fewer than two stages of fan control. Low or minimum speed shall not be greater than 66 percent of full speed. At low or minimum speed, the fan system shall draw not more than 40 percent of the fan power at full fan speed. Low or minimum speed shall be used during periods of low cooling load and ventilation-only operation.
2. Other units including DX cooling units and chilled water units that control the space temperature by modulating the airflow to the space shall have modulating fan control. Minimum speed shall be not greater than 50 percent of full speed. At minimum speed the fan system shall draw not more than 30 percent of the power at full fan speed. Low or minimum speed shall be used during periods of low cooling load and ventilation-only operation.
3. Units that include an airside economizer in accordance with Section C403.3 shall have not fewer than two speeds of fan control during economizer operation.

Exceptions:

1. Modulating fan control is not required for chilled water and evaporative cooling units with fan motors of less than 1 hp (0.746 kW) where the units are not used to provide *ventilation* air and the indoor fan cycles with the load.
2. Where the volume of outdoor air required to comply with the *ventilation* requirements of the *Florida Building Code, Mechanical,* at low speed exceeds the air that would be delivered at the speed defined in Section C403.4.1, the minimum speed shall be selected to provide the required *ventilation air.*

TABLE C403.4.1.1
EFFECTIVE DATES FOR FAN CONTROL

COOLING SYSTEM TYPE	FAN MOTOR SIZE	MECHANICAL COOLING CAPACITY
DX cooling	Any	≥ 75,000 Btu/h (before 1/1/2016)
		≥ 65,000 Btu/h (after 1/1/2016)
Chilled water and evaporative cooling	≥ 5 hp	Any
	≥ $^{1}/_{4}$ hp	Any

For SI: 1 British thermal unit per hour = 0.2931 W; 1 hp = 0.746 kW.

C403.4.1.2 Static pressure sensor location. Static pressure sensors used to control VAV fans shall be located such that the controller set point is not greater than 1.2 inches w.c. (299 Pa). Where this results in one or more sensors being located downstream of major duct splits, not less than one sensor shall be located on each major branch to ensure that static pressure can be maintained in each branch.

C403.4.1.3 Set points for direct digital control. For systems with direct digital control of individual zones reporting to the central control panel, the static pressure set point shall be reset based on the *zone* requiring the most pressure. In such case, the set point is reset lower until one *zone* damper is nearly wide open. The direct digital controls shall be capable of monitoring *zone* damper positions or shall have an alternative method of indicating the need for static pressure that is capable of all of the following:

1. Automatically detecting any *zone* that excessively drives the reset logic.
2. Generating an alarm to the system operational location.
3. Allowing an operator to readily remove one or more *zones* from the reset algorithm.

C403.4.2 Hydronic systems controls. The heating of fluids that have been previously mechanically cooled and the cooling of fluids that have been previously mechanically heated shall be limited in accordance with Sections C403.4.2.1 through C403.4.2.3. Hydronic heating systems comprised of multiple-packaged boilers and designed to deliver conditioned water or steam into a common distribution system shall include automatic controls capable of sequencing operation of the boilers. Hydronic heating systems comprised of a single boiler and greater than 500,000 Btu/h (146.5 kW) input design capacity shall include either a multistaged or modulating burner.

C403.4.2.1 Three-pipe system. Hydronic systems that use a common return system for both hot water and chilled water are prohibited.

C403.4.2.2 Two-pipe changeover system. Systems that use a common distribution system to supply both heated and chilled water shall be designed to allow a dead band between changeover from one mode to the other of not less than 15°F (8.3°C) outside air temperatures; be designed to and provided with controls that will allow operation in one mode for not less than 4 hours before changing over to the other mode; and be provided with controls that allow heating and cooling supply temperatures at the changeover point to be not more than 30°F (16.7°C) apart.

C403.4.2.3 Hydronic (water loop) heat pump systems. Hydronic heat pump systems shall comply with Sections C403.4.2.3.1 through C403.4.2.3.2.

C403.4.2.3.1 Temperature dead band. Hydronic heat pumps connected to a common heat pump water loop with central devices for heat rejection and heat addition shall have controls that are capable of providing a heat pump water supply temperature dead band of not less than 20°F (11°C) between initiation of heat rejection and heat addition by the central devices.

Exception: Where a system loop temperature optimization controller is installed and can determine the most efficient operating temperature based on realtime conditions of demand and capacity, dead bands of less than 20°F (11°C) shall be permitted.

C403.4.2.3.2 Heat rejection. Heat rejection equipment shall comply with Sections C403.4.2.3.2.1 and C403.4.2.3.2.2.

Exception: Where it can be demonstrated that a heat pump system will be required to reject heat throughout the year.

C403.4.2.3.2.1 Climate Zones 3 and 4. For *Climate Zones* 3 and 4:

1. Where a closed-circuit cooling tower is used directly in the heat pump loop, either an automatic valve shall be installed to bypass all but a minimal flow of water around the tower, or lower leakage positive closure dampers shall be provided.
2. Where an open-circuit tower is used directly in the heat pump loop, an automatic valve shall be installed to bypass all heat pump water flow around the tower.
3. Where an open- or closed-circuit cooling tower is used in conjunction with a separate heat exchanger to isolate the cooling tower from the heat pump loop, then heat loss shall be controlled by shutting down the circulation pump on the cooling tower loop.

C403.4.2.3.2.2 Climate Zones 5 through 8. For *Climate Zones* 5 through 8, where an open- or closed-circuit cooling tower is used, a separate heat exchanger shall be provided to isolate the cooling tower from the heat pump loop, and heat loss shall be controlled by shutting down the circulation pump on the cooling tower loop and providing an automatic valve to stop the flow of fluid.

C403.4.2.3.3 Two-position valve. Each hydronic heat pump on the hydronic system having a total pump system power exceeding 10 hp (7.5 kW) shall have a two-position valve.

C403.4.2.4 Part-load controls. Hydronic systems greater than or equal to 500,000 Btu/h (146.5 kW) in design output capacity supplying heated or chilled water to comfort conditioning systems shall include controls that have the capability to do all of the following:

1. Automatically reset the supply-water temperatures in response to varying building heating and cooling demand using coil valve position, zone-return water temperature, building-return water temperature or outside air temperature. The temperature shall be capable of being reset by not less than 25 percent of the design supply-to-return water temperature difference.
2. Automatically vary fluid flow for hydronic systems with a combined motor capacity of 10 hp (7.5 kW) or larger with three or more control valves or other devices by reducing the system design flow rate by not less than 50 percent by designed valves that modulate or step open and close, or pumps that modulate or turn on and off as a function of load.
3. Automatically vary pump flow on chilled-water systems and heat rejection loops serving water-cooled unitary air conditioners with a combined motor capacity of 10 hp (7.5 kW) or larger by reducing pump design flow by not less than 50 percent, utilizing adjustable speed drives on pumps, or multiple-staged pumps where not less than one-half of the total pump horsepower is capable of being automatically turned off. Pump flow shall be controlled to maintain one control valve nearly wide open or to satisfy the minimum differential pressure.

Exceptions:

1. Supply-water temperature reset for chilled-water systems supplied by off-site district chilled water or chilled water from ice storage systems.
2. Minimum flow rates other than 50 percent as required by the equipment manufacturer for proper operation of equipment where using flow bypass or end-of-line 3-way valves.
3. Variable pump flow on dedicated equipment circulation pumps where configured in primary/secondary design to provide the minimum flow requirements of the equipment manufacturer for proper operation of equipment.

C403.4.2.5 Boiler turndown. *Boiler systems* with design input of greater than 1,000,000 Btu/h (293 kW) shall comply with the turndown ratio specified in Table C403.4.2.5.

The system turndown requirement shall be met through the use of multiple single input boilers, one or more *modulating boilers* or a combination of single input and *modulating boilers*.

C403.4.2.6 Pump isolation. Chilled water plants including more than one chiller shall have the capability to reduce flow automatically through the chiller plant when a chiller is shut down. Chillers piped in series for the purpose of increased temperature differential shall be considered as one chiller.

Boiler plants including more than one boiler shall have the capability to reduce flow automatically through the boiler plant when a boiler is shut down.

TABLE C403.4.2.5
BOILER TURNDOWN

BOILER SYSTEM DESIGN INPUT (Btu/h)	MINIMUM TURNDOWN RATIO
≥ 1,000,000 and less than or equal to 5,000,000	3 to 1
> 5,000,000 and less than or equal to 10,000,000	4 to 1
> 10,000,000	5 to 1

For SI: 1 British thermal unit per hour = 0.2931 W.

C403.4.3 Heat rejection equipment. Each fan powered by a motor of 7.5 hp (5.6 kW) or larger shall have the capability to operate that fan at two-thirds of full speed or less, and shall have controls that automatically change the fan speed to control the leaving fluid temperature or condensing temperature/pressure of the heat rejection device.

Exception: Factory-installed heat rejection devices within HVAC equipment tested and rated in accordance with Tables C403.2.3(6) and C403.2.3(7).

C403.4.3.1 General. Heat rejection equipment such as air-cooled condensers, dry coolers, open-circuit cooling towers, closed-circuit cooling towers and evaporative condensers used for comfort cooling applications shall comply with this section.

Exception: Heat rejection devices where energy usage is included in the equipment efficiency ratings listed in Tables C403.2.3(6) and C403.2.3(7).

C403.4.3.2 Fan speed control. The fan speed shall be controlled as provided in Sections C403.4.3.2.1 and C403.4.3.2.2.

C403.4.3.2.1 Fan motors not less than 7.5 hp. Each fan powered by a motor of 7.5 hp (5.6 kW) or larger shall have the capability to operate that fan at two-thirds of full speed or less, and shall have controls that automatically change the fan speed to control the leaving fluid temperature or condensing temperature/pressure of the heat rejection device.

Exception: The following fan motors over 7.5 hp (5.6 kW) are exempt:

1. Condenser fans serving multiple refrigerant circuits.
2. Condenser fans serving flooded condensers.
3. Installations located in *Climate Zones* 1 and 2.

C403.4.3.2.2 Multiple-cell heat rejection equipment. Multiple-cell heat rejection equipment with variable speed fan drives shall be controlled in both of the following manners:

1. To operate the maximum number of fans allowed that comply with the manufacturer's requirements for all system components.
2. So all fans can operate at the same fan speed required for the instantaneous cooling duty, as opposed to staged (on/off) operation.

Minimum fan speed shall be the minimum allowable speed of the fan drive system in accordance with the manufacturer's recommendations.

C403.4.3.3 Limitation on centrifugal fan open-circuit cooling towers. Centrifugal fan open-circuit cooling towers with a combined rated capacity of 1,100 gpm (4164 L/m) or greater at 95°F (35°C) condenser water return, 85°F (29°C) condenser water supply, and 75°F (24°C) outdoor air wet-bulb temperature shall meet the energy efficiency requirement for axial fan open-circuit cooling towers listed in Table C403.2.3(8).

Exception: Centrifugal open-circuit cooling towers that are designed with inlet or discharge ducts or require external sound attenuation.

C403.4.3.4 Tower flow turndown. Open-circuit cooling towers used on water-cooled chiller systems that are configured with multiple- or variable-speed condenser water pumps shall be designed so that all open-circuit cooling tower cells can be run in parallel with the larger of the flow that is produced by the smallest pump at its minimum expected flow rate or at 50 percent of the design flow for the cell.

C403.4.4 Requirements for complex mechanical systems serving multiple zones. Sections C403.4.4.1 through C403.4.6.4 shall apply to complex mechanical systems serving multiple zones. Supply air systems serving multiple zones shall be variable air volume (VAV) systems that, during periods of occupancy, are designed and capable of being controlled to reduce primary air supply to each *zone* to one of the following before reheating, recooling or mixing takes place:

1. Thirty percent of the maximum supply air to each *zone*.
2. Three hundred cfm (142 L/s) or less where the maximum flow rate is less than 10 percent of the total fan system supply airflow rate.
3. The minimum ventilation requirements of Chapter 4 of the *Florida Building Code, Mechanical.*
4. Any higher rate that can be demonstrated to reduce overall system annual energy use by offsetting reheat/recool energy losses through a reduction in *outdoor* air intake for the system, as *approved* by the *code official.*
5. The airflow rate required to comply with applicable codes or accreditation standards, such as pressure relationships or minimum air change rates.

Exception: The following individual *zones* or entire air distribution systems are exempted from the requirement for VAV control:

1. *Zones* or supply air systems where not less than 75 percent of the energy for reheating or for providing warm air in mixing systems is provided from a site-recovered or site-solar energy source.
2. *Zones* where special humidity levels are required to satisfy process needs.
3. *Zones* with a peak supply air quantity of 300 cfm (142 L/s) or less and where the flow rate is less

than 10 percent of the total fan system supply airflow rate.

4. *Zones* where the volume of air to be reheated, recooled or mixed is not greater than the volume of outside air required to provide the minimum ventilation requirements of Chapter 4 of the *Florida Building Code, Mechanical.*

5. *Zones* or supply air systems with thermostatic and humidistatic controls capable of operating in sequence the supply of heating and cooling energy to the *zones* and which are capable of preventing reheating, recooling, mixing or simultaneous supply of air that has been previously cooled, either mechanically or through the use of economizer systems, and air that has been previously mechanically heated.

C403.4.4.1 Single-duct VAV systems, terminal devices. Single-duct VAV systems shall use terminal devices capable of reducing the supply of primary supply air before reheating or recooling takes place.

C403.4.4.2 Dual-duct and mixing VAV systems, terminal devices. Systems that have one warm air duct and one cool air duct shall use terminal devices that are capable of reducing the flow from one duct to a minimum before mixing of air from the other duct takes place.

C403.4.4.3 Single-fan dual-duct and mixing VAV systems, economizers. Individual dual-duct or mixing heating and cooling systems with a single fan and with total capacities greater than 90,000 Btu/h [(26.4 kW) 7.5 tons] shall not be equipped with air economizers.

C403.4.4.4 Fractional hp fan motors. Motors for fans that are not less than $^{1}/_{12}$ hp (0.082 kW) and less than 1 hp (0.746 kW) shall be electronically commutated motors or shall have a minimum motor efficiency of 70 percent, rated in accordance with DOE 10 CFR 431. These motors shall also have the means to adjust motor speed for either balancing or remote control. The use of belt-driven fans to sheave adjustments for airflow balancing instead of a varying motor speed shall be permitted.

Exceptions: The following motors are not required to comply with this section:

1. Motors in the airstream within fan coils and terminal units that only provide heating to the space served.
2. Motors in space-conditioning equipment that comply with Section 403.2.3 or C403.2.12.
3. Motors that comply with Section C405.8.

C403.4.4.5 Supply-air temperature reset controls. Multiple-*zone* HVAC systems shall include controls that automatically reset the supply-air temperature in response to representative building loads, or to outdoor air temperature. The controls shall be capable of resetting the supply air temperature not less than 25 percent of the difference between the design supply-air temperature and the design room air temperature.

Exceptions:

1. Systems that prevent reheating, recooling or mixing of heated and cooled supply air.
2. Seventy-five percent of the energy for reheating is from site-recovered or site-solar energy sources.
3. *Zones* with peak supply air quantities of 300 cfm (142 L/s) or less.

C403.4.4.6 Multiple-zone VAV system ventilation optimization control. Multiple-zone VAV systems with direct digital control of individual zone boxes reporting to a central control panel shall have automatic controls configured to reduce outdoor air intake flow below design rates in response to changes in system ventilation efficiency (E_v) as defined by the *Florida Building Code, Mechanical.*

Exceptions:

1. VAV systems with zonal transfer fans that recirculate air from other zones without directly mixing it with outdoor air, dual-duct dual-fan VAV systems, and VAV systems with fan-powered terminal units.
2. Systems having exhaust air energy recovery complying with Section C403.2.7.
3. Systems where total design exhaust airflow is more than 70 percent of total design outdoor air intake flow requirements.

C403.4.5 Heat recovery for service water heating. Condenser heat recovery shall be installed for heating or reheating of service hot water provided that the facility operates 24 hours a day, the total installed heat capacity of water-cooled systems exceeds 6,000,000 Btu/hr (1 758 kW) of heat rejection, and the design service water heating load exceeds 1,000,000 Btu/h (293 kW).

The required heat recovery system shall have the capacity to provide the smaller of the following:

1. Sixty percent of the peak heat rejection load at design conditions.
2. The preheating required to raise the peak service hot water draw to 85°F (29°C).

Exceptions:

1. Facilities that employ condenser heat recovery for space heating or reheat purposes with a heat recovery design exceeding 30 percent of the peak water-cooled condenser load at design conditions.
2. Facilities that provide 60 percent of their service water heating from site solar or site recovered energy or from other sources.

C403.4.6 Hot gas bypass limitation. Cooling systems shall not use hot gas bypass or other evaporator pressure control systems unless the system is designed with multiple steps of unloading or continuous capacity modulation. The capacity of the hot gas bypass shall be limited as indicated in Table C403.4.6, as limited by Section C403.3.1.

TABLE C403.4.6
MAXIMUM HOT GAS BYPASS CAPACITY

RATED CAPACITY	MAXIMUM HOT GAS BYPASS CAPACITY (% of total capacity)
≤ 240,000 Btu/h	50
> 240,000 Btu/h	25

For SI: 1 British thermal unit per hour = 0.2931 W.

C403.5 Refrigeration systems. Refrigerated display cases, *walk-in coolers or walk-in freezers* that are served by remote compressors and remote condensers not located in a *condensing unit*, shall comply with Sections C403.5.1 and C403.5.2.

Exception: Systems where the working fluid in the refrigeration cycle goes through both subcritical and supercritical states (transcritical) or that use ammonia refrigerant are exempt.

C403.5.1 Condensers serving refrigeration systems. Fan-powered condensers shall comply with the following:

1. The design *saturated condensing temperatures* for air-cooled condensers shall not exceed the design dry-bulb temperature plus 10°F (5.6°C) for low-*temperature refrigeration systems*, and the design dry-bulb temperature plus 15°F (8°C) for *medium temperature refrigeration systems* where the *saturated condensing temperature* for blend refrigerants shall be determined using the average of liquid and vapor temperatures as converted from the condenser drain pressure.
2. Condenser fan motors that are less than 1 hp (0.75 kW) shall use electronically commutated motors, permanent split-capacitor-type motors or 3-phase motors.
3. Condenser fans for air-cooled condensers, evaporatively cooled condensers, air- or water-cooled fluid coolers or cooling towers shall reduce fan motor demand to not more than 30 percent of design wattage at 50 percent of design air volume, and incorporate one of the following continuous variable speed fan control approaches:
   3.1. Refrigeration system condenser control for air-cooled condensers shall use variable setpoint control logic to reset the condensing temperature setpoint in response to ambient dry-bulb temperature.
   3.2. Refrigeration system condenser control for evaporatively cooled condensers shall use variable setpoint control logic to reset the condensing temperature setpoint in response to ambient wet-bulb temperature.
4. Multiple fan condensers shall be controlled in unison.
5. The minimum condensing temperature setpoint shall be not greater than 70°F (21°C).

C403.5.2 Compressor systems. Refrigeration compressor systems shall comply with the following:

1. Compressors and multiple-compressor system suction groups shall include control systems that use floating suction pressure control logic to reset the target suction pressure temperature based on the temperature requirements of the attached refrigeration display cases or walk-ins.

   Exception: Controls are not required for the following:

   1. Single-compressor systems that do not have variable capacity capability.
   2. Suction groups that have a design saturated suction temperature of 30°F (-1.1°C) or higher, suction groups that comprise the high stage of a two-stage or cascade system, or suction groups that primarily serve chillers for secondary cooling fluids.
2. Liquid subcooling shall be provided for all low-temperature compressor systems with a design cooling capacity equal to or greater than 100,000 Btu/hr (29.3 kW) with a design-saturated suction temperature of -10°F (-23°C) or lower. The sub-cooled liquid temperature shall be controlled at a maximum temperature setpoint of 50°F (10°C) at the exit of the subcooler using either compressor economizer (interstage) ports or a separate compressor suction group operating at a saturated suction temperature of 18°F (-7.8°C) or higher.

   2.1. Insulation for liquid lines with a fluid operating temperature less than 60°F (15.6°C) shall comply with Table C403.2.10.
3. Compressors that incorporate internal or external crankcase heaters shall provide a means to cycle the heaters off during compressor operation.

C403.5.3 Condensing coils installed in cool air stream of another air-conditioning unit. The condensing coil of one air-conditioning unit shall not be installed in the cool air stream of another air-conditioning unit.

Exceptions:

1. Where condenser heat reclaim is used in a properly designed system including enthalpy control devices to achieve requisite humidity control for process, special storage or equipment spaces and occupant comfort within the criteria of ASHRAE Standard 55. Such systems shall result in less energy use than other appropriate options.
2. For computer or clean rooms whose location precludes the use of systems that would not reject heat into conditioned spaces.

SECTION C404
SERVICE WATER HEATING (MANDATORY)

C404.1 General. This section covers the minimum efficiency of, and controls for, service water-heating equipment and insulation of service hot water piping.

C404.2 Service water-heating equipment performance efficiency. Water-heating equipment and hot water storage tanks shall meet the requirements of Table C404.2. The efficiency shall be verified through data furnished by the manufacturer of the equipment or through certification under an *approved* certification program. Water-heating equipment also intended to be used to provide space heating shall meet the applicable provisions of Table C404.2.

C404.2.1 High input-rated service water-heating systems. Gas-fired water-heating equipment installed in new buildings shall be in compliance with this section. Where a singular piece of water-heating equipment serves the entire building and the input rating of the equipment is 1,000,000 Btu/h (293 kW) or greater, such equipment shall have a thermal efficiency, E_t, of not less than 90 percent. Where multiple pieces of water-heating equipment serve the building and the combined input rating of the water-heating equipment is 1,000,000 Btu/h (293 kW) or greater, the combined input-capacity-weighted-average thermal efficiency, E_t, shall be not less than 90 percent.

Exceptions:

1. Where 25 percent of the annual *service water-heating* requirement is provided by site-solar or site-recovered energy, the minimum thermal efficiency requirements of this section shall not apply.
2. The input rating of water heaters installed in individual dwelling units shall not be required to be included in the total input rating of *service water-heating* equipment for a building.
3. The input rating of water heaters with an input rating of not greater than 100,000 Btu/h (29.3 kW) shall not be required to be included in the total input rating of *service water-heating* equipment for a building.

C404.3 Heat traps. Water-heating equipment not supplied with integral heat traps and serving noncirculating systems shall be provided with heat traps on the supply and discharge piping associated with the equipment.

C404.4 Insulation of piping. Piping from a water heater to the termination of the heated water fixture supply pipe shall be insulated in accordance with Table C403.2.10. On both the inlet and outlet piping of a storage water heater or heated water storage tank, the piping to a heat trap or the first 8 feet (2438 mm) of piping, whichever is less, shall be insulated. Piping that is heat traced shall be insulated in accordance with Table C403.2.10 or the heat trace manufacturer's instructions. Tubular pipe insulation shall be installed in accordance with the insulation manufacturer's instructions. Pipe insulation shall be continuous except where the piping passes through a framing member. The minimum insulation thickness requirements of this section shall not supersede any greater insulation thickness requirements necessary for the protection of piping from freezing temperatures or the protection of personnel against external surface temperatures on the insulation.

Exception: Tubular pipe insulation shall not be required on the following:

1. The tubing from the connection at the termination of the fixture supply piping to a plumbing fixture or plumbing appliance.
2. Valves, pumps, strainers and threaded unions in piping that is 1 inch (25 mm) or less in nominal diameter.
3. Piping from user-controlled shower and bath mixing valves to the water outlets.
4. Cold-water piping of a demand recirculation water system.
5. Tubing from a hot drinking-water heating unit to the water outlet.
6. Piping at locations where a vertical support of the piping is installed.
7. Piping surrounded by building insulation with a thermal resistance (*R*-value) of not less than R-3.

C404.5 Efficient heated water supply piping. Heated water supply piping shall be in accordance with Section C404.5.1 or C404.5.2. The flow rate through $^1/_4$-inch (6.4 mm) piping shall be not greater than 0.5 gpm (1.9 L/m). The flow rate through $^5/_{16}$-inch (7.9 mm) piping shall be not greater than 1 gpm (3.8 L/m). The flow rate through $^3/_8$-inch (9.5 mm) piping shall be not greater than 1.5 gpm (5.7 L/m).

C404.5.1 Maximum allowable pipe length method. The maximum allowable piping length from the nearest source of heated water to the termination of the fixture supply pipe shall be in accordance with the following. Where the piping contains more than one size of pipe, the largest size of pipe within the piping shall be used for determining the maximum allowable length of the piping in Table C404.5.1.

1. For a public lavatory faucet, use the "Public lavatory faucets" column in Table C404.5.1.
2. For all other plumbing fixtures and plumbing appliances, use the "Other fixtures and appliances" column in Table C404.5.1.

C404.5.2 Maximum allowable pipe volume method. The water volume in the piping shall be calculated in accordance with Section C404.5.2.1. Water heaters, circulating water systems and heat trace temperature maintenance systems shall be considered sources of heated water.

The volume from the nearest source of heated water to the termination of the fixture supply pipe shall be as follows:

1. For a public lavatory faucet: not more than 2 ounces (0.06 L).
2. For other plumbing fixtures or plumbing appliances; not more than 0.5 gallon (1.89 L).

TABLE C404.2
MINIMUM PERFORMANCE OF WATER-HEATING EQUIPMENT

EQUIPMENT TYPE	SIZE CATEGORY (input)	SUBCATEGORY OR RATING CONDITION	PERFORMANCE REQUIRED[a, b]	TEST PROCEDURE
Water heaters, electric	≤ 12 kW[d]	Resistance	0.97 - 0.00 132V, EF	DOE 10 CFR Part 430
	> 12 kW	Resistance	$(0.3 + 27/V_m)$, %/h	ANSI Z21.10.3
	≤ 24 amps and ≤ 250 volts	Heat pump	0.93 - 0.00 132V, EF	DOE 10 CFR Part 430
Storage water heaters, gas	≤ 75,000 Btu/h	≥ 20 gal	0.67 - 0.0019V, EF	DOE 10 CFR Part 430
	> 75,000 Btu/h and ≤ 155,000 Btu/h	< 4,000 Btu/h/gal	80% E_t $(Q/800 + 110\sqrt{V})$SL, Btu/h	ANSI Z21.10.3
	> 155,000 Btu/h	< 4,000 Btu/h/gal	80% E_t $(Q/800 + 110\sqrt{V})$SL, Btu/h	
Instantaneous water heaters, gas	> 50,000 Btu/h and < 200,000 Btu/h[c]	≥ 4,000 (Btu/h)/gal and < 2 gal	0.62 - 0.00 19V, EF	DOE 10 CFR Part 430
	≥ 200,000 Btu/h	≥ 4,000 Btu/h/gal and < 10 gal	80% E_t	ANSI Z21.10.3
	≥ 200,000 Btu/h	≥ 4,000 Btu/h/gal and ≥ 10 gal	80% E_t $(Q/800 + 110\sqrt{V})$SL, Btu/h	
Storage water heaters, oil	≤ 105,000 Btu/h	≥ 20 gal	0.59 - 0.0019V, EF	DOE 10 CFR Part 430
	≥ 105,000 Btu/h	< 4,000 Btu/h/gal	80% E_t $(Q/800 + 110\sqrt{V})$SL, Btu/h	ANSI Z21.10.3
Instantaneous water heaters, oil	≤ 210,000 Btu/h	≥ 4,000 Btu/h/gal and < 2 gal	0.59 - 0.0019V, EF	DOE 10 CFR Part 430
	> 210,000 Btu/h	≥ 4,000 Btu/h/gal and < 10 gal	80% E_t	ANSI Z21.10.3
	> 210,000 Btu/h	≥ 4,000 Btu/h/gal and ≥ 10 gal	78% E_t $(Q/800 + 110\sqrt{V})$SL, Btu/h	
Hot water supply boilers, gas and oil	≥ 300,000 Btu/h and < 12,500,000 Btu/h	≥ 4,000 Btu/h/gal and < 10 gal	80% E_t	ANSI Z21.10.3
Hot water supply boilers, gas	≥ 300,000 Btu/h and < 12,500,000 Btu/h	≥ 4,000 Btu/h/gal and ≥ 10 gal	80% E_t $(Q/800 + 110\sqrt{V})$SL, Btu/h	
Hot water supply boilers, oil	> 300,000 Btu/h and < 12,500,000 Btu/h	> 4,000 Btu/h/gal and > 10 gal	78% E_t $(Q/800 + 110\sqrt{V})$SL, Btu/h	
Pool heaters, gas and oil	All	—	82% E_t	ASHRAE 146
Heat pump pool heaters	All	—	4.0 COP At low air temperature	AHRI 1160[e, f]
Unfired storage tanks	All	—	Minimum insulation requirement R-12.5 (h • ft^2 • °F)/Btu	(none)

For SI: °C = [(°F) - 32]/1.8, 1 British thermal unit per hour = 0.2931 W, 1 gallon = 3.785 L, 1 British thermal unit per hour per gallon = 0.078 W/L.

a. Energy factor (EF) and thermal efficiency (E_t) are minimum requirements. In the EF equation, V is the rated volume in gallons.

b. Standby loss (SL) is the maximum Btu/h based on a nominal 70°F temperature difference between stored water and ambient requirements. In the SL equation, Q is the nameplate input rate in Btu/h. In the equations for electric water heaters, V is the rated volume in gallons and V_m is the measured volume in gallons. In the SL equation for oil and gas water heaters and boilers, V is the rated volume in gallons.

c. Instantaneous water heaters with input rates below 200,000 Btu/h shall comply with these requirements where the water heater is designed to heat water to temperatures 180°F or higher.

d. Electric water heaters with an input rating of 12 kW (40,950 Btu/hr) or less that are designed to heat water to temperatures of 180°F or greater shall comply with the requirements for electric water heaters that have an input rating greater than 12 kW (40,950 Btu/h).

e. Test report from independent laboratory is required to verify procedure compliance.

f. Geothermal swimming pool heat pumps are not required to meet this standard.

TABLE C404.5.1
PIPING VOLUME AND MAXIMUM PIPING LENGTHS

NOMINAL PIPE SIZE (inches)	VOLUME (liquid ounces per foot length)	MAXIMUM PIPING LENGTH (feet)	
		Public lavatory faucets	Other fixtures and appliances
1/4	0.33	6	50
5/16	0.5	4	50
3/8	0.75	3	50
1/2	1.5	2	43
5/8	2	1	32
3/4	3	0.5	21
7/8	4	0.5	16
1	5	0.5	13
1 1/4	8	0.5	8
1 1/2	11	0.5	6
2 or larger	18	0.5	4

For SI: 1 inch = 25.4 mm, 1 foot = 304.8 mm, 1 liquid ounce = 0.030 L, 1 gallon = 128 ounces.

C404.5.2.1 Water volume determination. The volume shall be the sum of the internal volumes of pipe, fittings, valves, meters and manifolds between the nearest source of heated water and the termination of the fixture supply pipe. The volume in the piping shall be determined from the "Volume" column in Table C404.5.1. The volume contained within fixture shutoff valves, within flexible water supply connectors to a fixture fitting and within a fixture fitting shall not be included in the water volume determination. Where heated water is supplied by a recirculating system or heat-traced piping, the volume shall include the portion of the fitting on the branch pipe that supplies water to the fixture.

C404.6 Heated-water circulating and temperature maintenance systems. Heated-water circulation systems shall be in accordance with Section C404.6.1. Heat trace temperature maintenance systems shall be in accordance with Section C404.6.2. Controls for hot water storage shall be in accordance with Section C404.6.3. Automatic controls, temperature sensors and pumps shall be *accessible*. Manual controls shall be *readily accessible*.

C404.6.1 Circulation systems. Heated-water circulation systems shall be provided with a circulation pump. The system return pipe shall be a dedicated return pipe or a cold water supply pipe. Gravity and thermo-syphon circulation systems shall be prohibited. Controls for circulating hot water system pumps shall start the pump based on the identification of a demand for hot water within the occupancy. The controls shall automatically turn off the pump when the water in the circulation loop is at the desired temperature and when there is no demand for hot water.

C404.6.2 Heat trace systems. Electric heat trace systems shall comply with IEEE 515.1. Controls for such systems shall be able to automatically adjust the energy input to the heat tracing to maintain the desired water temperature in the piping in accordance with the times when heated water is used in the occupancy. Heat trace shall be arranged to be turned off automatically when there is no hot water demand.

C404.6.3 Controls for hot water storage. The controls on pumps that circulate water between a water heater and a heated-water storage tank shall limit operation of the pump from heating cycle startup to not greater than 5 minutes after the end of the cycle.

C404.7 Demand recirculation controls. A water distribution system having one or more recirculation pumps that pump water from a heated-water supply pipe back to the heated-water source through a cold-water supply pipe shall be a *demand recirculation water system*. Pumps shall have controls that comply with both of the following:

1. The control shall start the pump upon receiving a signal from the action of a user of a fixture or appliance, sensing the presence of a user of a fixture or sensing the flow of hot or tempered water to a fixture fitting or appliance.
2. The control shall limit the temperature of the water entering the cold-water piping to 104°F (40°C).

C404.8 Drain water heat recovery units. Drain water heat recovery units shall comply with CSA B55.2. Potable water-side pressure loss shall be less than 10 psi (69 kPa) at maximum design flow. For Group R occupancies, the efficiency of drain water heat recovery unit efficiency shall be in accordance with CSA B55.1.

C404.9 Energy consumption of pools and permanent spas. (Mandatory). The energy consumption of pools and permanent spas shall be controlled by the requirements in Sections C404.9.1 through C404.9.3.

C404.9.1 Heaters. The electric power to all heaters shall be controlled by a readily accessible on-off switch that is an integral part of the heater, mounted on the exterior of the heater, or external to and within 3 feet (914 mm) of the heater. Operation of such switch shall not change the setting of the heater thermostat. Such switches shall be in addition to a circuit breaker for the power to the heater.

Gas-fired heaters shall not be equipped with continuously burning ignition pilots.

C404.9.2 Time switches. Time switches or other control methods that can automatically turn off and on heaters and pump motors according to a preset schedule shall be installed for heaters and pump motors. Heaters and pump motors that have built-in time switches shall be in compliance with this section.

Exceptions:

1. Where public health standards require 24-hour pump operation.
2. Pumps that operate solar- and waste-heat-recovery pool heating systems.

C404.9.3 Covers. Outdoor heated swimming pools and outdoor permanent spas shall be equipped with a vapor-retardant cover on or at the water surface or a liquid cover or other means proven to reduce heat loss.

Exception: Where more than 70 percent of the energy for heating, computed over an operating season, is from site-recovered energy such as from a heat pump or solar energy source, covers or other vapor-retardant means shall not be required.

C404.10 Energy consumption of portable spas (Mandatory). The energy consumption of electric-powered portable spas shall be controlled by the requirements of APSP 14.

C404.11 Service water-heating system commissioning and completion requirements. *Service water-heating systems,* swimming pool water-heating systems, spa water-heating systems and the controls for those systems shall be commissioned and completed in accordance with Section C408.2.

C404.12 Water flow rate controls.

C404.12.1 Showers. Showers used for other than safety reasons shall be equipped with flow control devices to limit the water discharge to a maximum of 2.5 gpm (.16 L/S) per showerhead at a distribution pressure of 80 psig (552 kPa) when tested in accordance with the procedures of ANSI A112.18.1M. Flow restricting inserts used as a component part of a showerhead shall be mechanically retained at the point of manufacture.

C404.12.2 Lavatories or restrooms of public facilities. Lavatories or restrooms of public facilities shall:

1. Be equipped with outlet devices that limit the flow of hot water to a maximum of 0.5 gpm (.03 L/S) or be equipped with self-closing valves that limit delivery to a per cycle maximum of 0.25 gallons (.95 L) of hot water for recirculating systems and to a maximum of 0.50 gallons (1.9 L) for non-recirculating systems.

   Exception: Separate lavatories for physically handicapped persons shall not be equipped with self-closing valves.

2. Be equipped with devices that limit the outlet temperature to a maximum of 110°F (43°C).
3. Meet the provisions of 42 CFR 6295 (k), Standards for Water Closets and Urinals.

SECTION C405
ELECTRICAL POWER AND LIGHTING SYSTEMS

C405.1 General (Mandatory). This section covers lighting system controls, the maximum lighting power for interior and exterior applications and electrical energy consumption.

Exception: Dwelling units within commercial buildings shall not be required to comply with Sections C405.2 through C405.5, provided that they comply with Section R404.1.

Walk-in coolers, walk-in freezers, refrigerated warehouse coolers and refrigerated warehouse freezers shall comply with Section C403.2.15 or C403.2.16.

C405.2 Lighting controls (Mandatory). Lighting systems shall be provided with controls as specified in Sections C405.2.1, C405.2.2, C405.2.3, C405.2.4 and C405.2.5.

Exceptions: Lighting controls are not required for the following:

1. Areas designated as security or emergency areas that are required to be continuously lighted.
2. Interior exit stairways, interior exit ramps and exit passageways.
3. Emergency egress lighting that is normally off.

C405.2.1 Occupant sensor controls. Occupant *sensor controls* shall be installed to control lights in the following space types:

1. Classrooms/lecture/training rooms.
2. Conference/meeting/multipurpose rooms.
3. Copy/print rooms.
4. Lounges.
5. Employee lunch and break rooms.
6. Private offices.
7. Restrooms.
8. Storage rooms.
9. Janitorial closets.
10. Locker rooms.
11. Other spaces 300 square feet (28 m^2) or less that are enclosed by floor-to-ceiling height partitions.
12. Warehouses.

C405.2.1.1 Occupant sensor control function. Occupant sensor controls in spaces other than warehouses specified in Section C405.2.1 shall comply with the following:

1. Automatically turn off lights within 30 minutes of all occupants leaving the space.
2. Be manual on or controlled to automatically turn the lighting on to not more than 50 percent power.

   Exception: Full automatic-on controls shall be permitted to control lighting in public corridors, stairways, restrooms, primary building entrance areas and lobbies, and areas where manual-on operation would endanger the safety or security of the room or building occupants.

3. Shall incorporate a *manual control* to allow occupants to turn lights off.

C405.2.1.2 Occupant sensor control function in warehouses. In warehouses, the lighting in aisleways and open areas shall be controlled with occupant sensors that automatically reduce lighting power by not less than 50 percent when the areas are unoccupied. The occupant sensors shall control lighting in each aisleway independently and shall not control lighting beyond the aisleway being controlled by the sensor.

C405.2.2 Time-switch controls. Each area of the building that is not provided with *occupant sensor controls* complying with Section C405.2.1.1 shall be provided with *time switch controls* complying with Section C405.2.2.1.

Exception: Where a *manual control* provides light reduction in accordance with Section C405.2.2.2, automatic controls shall not be required for the following:

1. *Sleeping units.*
2. Spaces where patient care is directly provided.
3. Spaces where an automatic shutoff would endanger occupant safety or security.
4. Lighting intended for continuous operation.
5. Shop and laboratory classrooms.

C405.2.2.1 Time-switch control function. Each space provided with *time-switch controls* shall also be provided with a *manual control* for light reduction in accordance with Section C405.2.2.2. Time-switch *controls* shall include an override switching device that complies with the following:

1. Have a minimum 7-day clock.
2. Be capable of being set for seven different day types per week.
3. Incorporate an automatic holiday "shutoff" feature, which turns off all controlled lighting loads for at least 24 hours and then resumes normally scheduled operations.
4. Have program backup capabilities, which prevent the loss of program and time settings for at least 10 hours, if power is interrupted.
5. Include an override switch that complies with the following:
   - 5.1. The override switch shall be a manual control.
   - 5.2. The override switch, when initiated, shall permit the controlled lighting to remain on for not more than 2 hours.
   - 5.3. Any individual override switch shall control the lighting for an area not larger than 5,000 square feet (465 m^2).

Exceptions:

1. Within malls, arcades, auditoriums, single-tenant retail spaces, industrial facilities and arenas:
   - 1.1. The time limit shall be permitted to be greater than 2 hours, provided that the override switch is a captive key device.
   - 1.2. The area controlled by the override switch is permitted to be greater than 5,000 square feet (465 m^2), but shall not be greater than 20,000 square feet (1860 m^2).
2. Where provided with *manual control*, the following areas are not required to have light reduction control:
   - 2.1. Spaces that have only one luminaire with a rated power of less than 100 watts.
   - 2.2. Spaces that use less than 0.6 watts per square foot (6.5 W/m^2).
   - 2.3. Corridors, equipment rooms, public lobbies, electrical or mechanical rooms.

C405.2.2.2 Light-reduction controls. Spaces required to have light-reduction controls shall have a *manual control* that allows the occupant to reduce the connected lighting load in a reasonably uniform illumination pattern by at least 50 percent. Lighting reduction shall be achieved by one of the following or another *approved* method:

1. Controlling all lamps or luminaires.
2. Dual switching of alternate rows of luminaires, alternate luminaires or alternate lamps.
3. Switching the middle lamp luminaires independently of the outer lamps.
4. Switching each luminaire or each lamp.

Exception: Light reduction controls are not required in *daylight zones* with *daylight responsive controls* complying with Section C405.2.3.

C405.2.2.3 Manual controls. *Manual controls* for lights shall comply with the following:

1. Shall be readily accessible to occupants.
2. Shall be located where the controlled lights are visible, or shall identify the area served by the lights and indicate their status.

C405.2.3 Daylight-responsive controls. *Daylight-responsive controls* complying with Section C405.2.3.1 shall be provided to control the electric lights within *daylight zones* in the following spaces:

1. Spaces with a total of more than 150 watts of *general lighting* within sidelight *daylight zones* complying with Section C405.2.3.2. *General lighting* does not include lighting that is required to have specific application control in accordance with Section C405.2.4.
2. Spaces with a total of more than 150 watts of *general lighting* within toplight *daylight zones* complying with Section C405.2.3.3.

Exceptions: Daylight responsive controls are not required for the following:

1. Spaces in health care facilities where patient care is directly provided.
2. Dwelling units and sleeping units.
3. Lighting that is required to have specific application control in accordance with Section C405.2.4.
4. Sidelight daylight zones on the first floor above grade in Group A-2 and Group M occupancies.

C405.2.3.1 Daylight-responsive control function. Where required, *daylight-responsive controls* shall be provided within each space for control of lights in that space and shall comply with all of the following:

1. Lights in toplight *daylight zones* in accordance with Section C405.2.3.3 shall be controlled independently of lights in sidelight *daylight zones* in accordance with Section C405.2.3.2.
2. *Daylight responsive controls* within each space shall be configured so that they can be calibrated from within that space by authorized personnel.
3. Calibration mechanisms shall be *readily accessible.*
4. Where located in offices, classrooms, laboratories and library reading rooms, *daylight responsive controls* shall dim lights continuously from full light output to 15 percent of full light output or lower.
5. *Daylight responsive controls* shall be capable of a complete shutoff of all controlled lights.
6. Lights in sidelight *daylight zones* in accordance with Section C405.2.3.2 facing different cardinal orientations [i.e., within 45 degrees (0.79 rad) of due north, east, south, west] shall be controlled independently of each other.

Exception: Up to 150 watts of lighting in each space is permitted to be controlled together with lighting in a daylight zone facing a different cardinal orientation.

C405.2.3.2 Sidelight daylight zone. The sidelight *daylight zone* is the floor area adjacent to vertical *fenestration* which complies with all of the following:

1. Where the fenestration is located in a wall, the daylight zone shall extend laterally to the nearest full-height wall, or up to 1.0 times the height from the floor to the top of the fenestration, and longitudinally from the edge of the fenestration to the nearest full-height wall, or up to 2 feet (610 mm), whichever is less, as indicated in Figure C405.2.3.2(1).
2. Where the *fenestration* is located in a rooftop monitor, the *daylight zone* shall extend laterally to the nearest obstruction that is taller than 0.7 times the ceiling height, or up to 1.0 times the height from the floor to the bottom of the *fenestration,* whichever is less, and longitudinally from the edge of the *fenestration* to the nearest obstruction that is taller than 0.7 times the ceiling height, or up to 0.25 times the height from the floor to the bottom of the *fenestration*, whichever is less, as indicated in Figures C405.2.3.2(2) and C405.2.3.2(3).
3. The area of the *fenestration* is not less than 24 square feet (2.23 m^2).
4. The distance from the *fenestration* to any building or geological formation which would block access to daylight is greater than the height from the bottom of the *fenestration* to the top of the building or geologic formation.
5. Where located in existing buildings, the *visible transmittance* of the *fenestration* is not less than 0.20.

C405.2.3.3 Toplight daylight zone. The toplight *daylight zone* is the floor area underneath a roof fenestration assembly which complies with all of the following:

1. The *daylight zone* shall extend laterally and longitudinally beyond the edge of the roof *fenestration* assembly to the nearest obstruction that is taller than 0.7 times the ceiling height, or up to 0.7 times the ceiling height, whichever is less, as indicated in Figure C405.2.3.3.
2. No building or geological formation blocks direct sunlight from hitting the roof *fenestration* assembly at the peak solar angle on the summer solstice.
3. Where located in existing buildings, the product of the *visible transmittance* of the roof *fenestration* assembly and the area of the rough opening of the roof *fenestration* assembly divided by the area of the *daylight zone* is not less than 0.008.

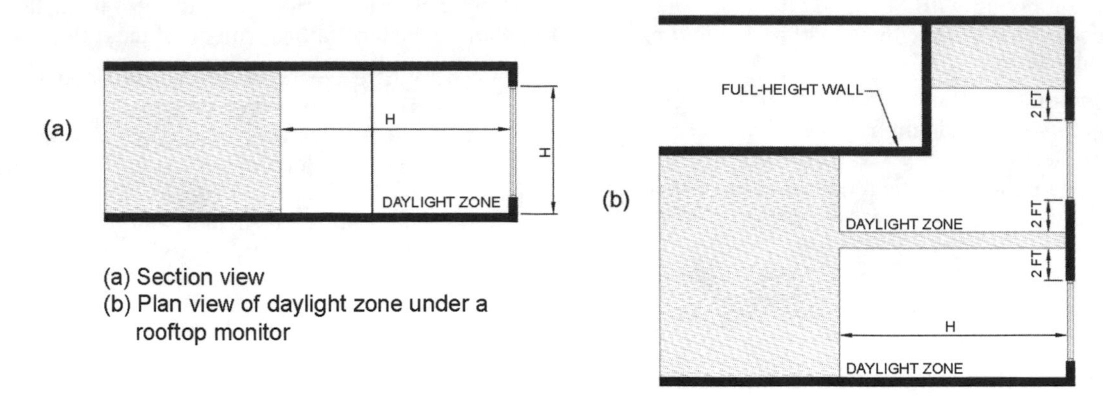

FIGURE C405.2.3.2(1)
DAYLIGHT ZONE ADJACENT TO FENESTRATION IN A WALL

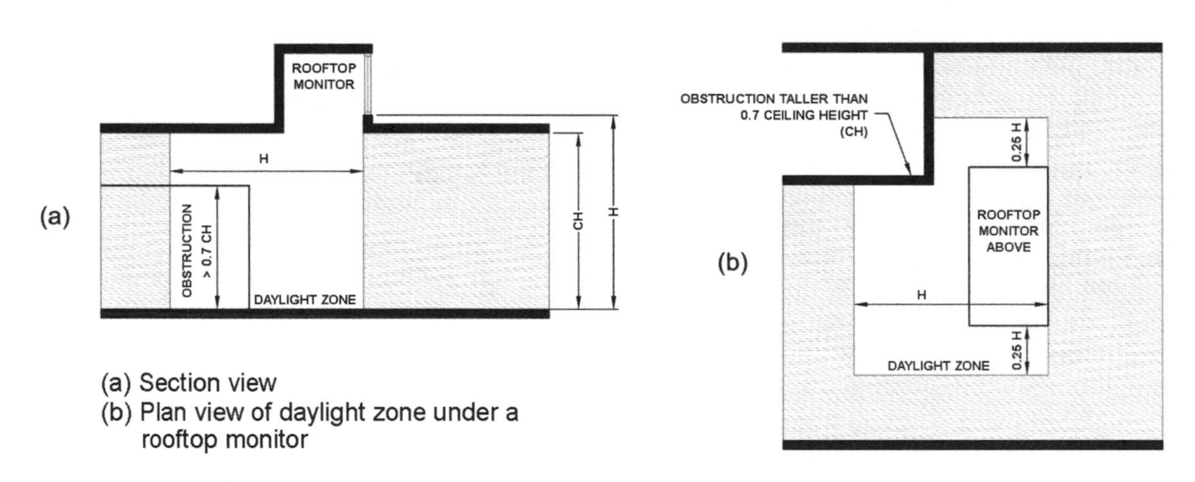

FIGURE C405.2.3.2(2)
DAYLIGHT ZONE UNDER A ROOFTOP MONITOR

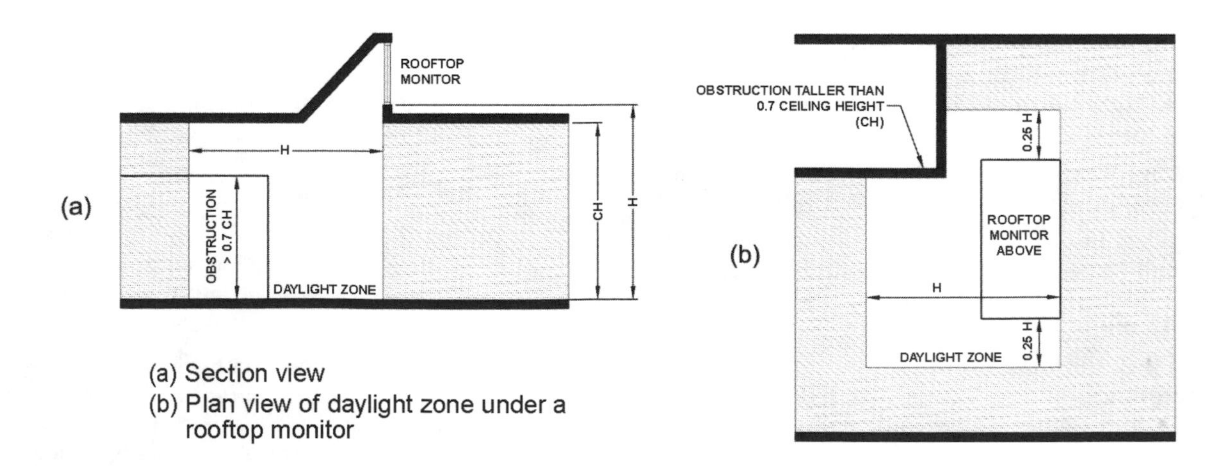

FIGURE C405.2.3.2(3)
DAYLIGHT ZONE UNDER A SLOPED ROOFTOP MONITOR

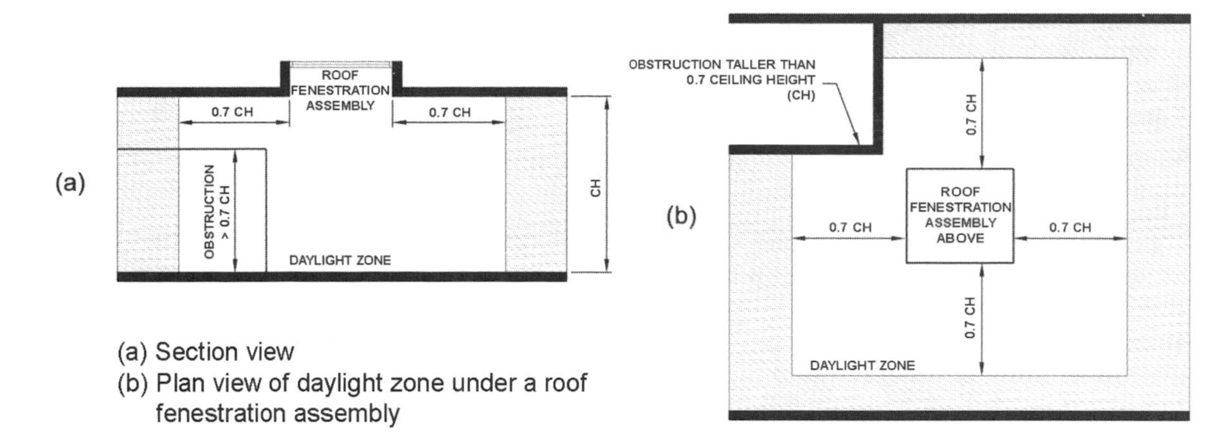

FIGURE C405.2.3.3
DAYLIGHT ZONE UNDER A ROOF FENESTRATION ASSEMBLY

C405.2.4 Specific application controls. Specific application controls shall be provided for the following:

1. Display and accent light shall be controlled by a dedicated control that is independent of the controls for other lighting within the room or space.
2. Lighting in cases used for display case purposes shall be controlled by a dedicated control that is independent of the controls for other lighting within the room or space.
3. Hotel and motel sleeping units and guest suites shall have a master control device that is capable of automatically switching off all installed luminaires and switched receptacles within 20 minutes after all occupants leave the room.

   Exception: Lighting and switched receptacles controlled by captive key systems.
4. Supplemental task lighting, including permanently installed under-shelf or under-cabinet lighting, shall have a control device integral to the luminaires or be controlled by a wall-mounted control device provided that the control device is readily accessible.
5. Lighting for nonvisual applications, such as plant growth and food warming, shall be controlled by a dedicated control that is independent of the controls for other lighting within the room or space.
6. Lighting equipment that is for sale or for demonstrations in lighting education shall be controlled by a dedicated control that is independent of the controls for other lighting within the room or space.

C405.2.5 Exterior lighting controls. Lighting for exterior applications other than emergency lighting that is intended to be automatically off during building operation, lighting specifically required to meet health and life safety requirements or decorative gas lighting systems shall:

1. Be provided with a control that automatically turns off the lighting as a function of available daylight.
2. Where lighting the building façade or landscape, the lighting shall have controls that automatically shut off the lighting as a function of dawn/dusk and a set opening and closing time.
3. Where not covered in Item 2, the lighting shall have controls configured to automatically reduce the connected lighting power by not less than 30 percent from not later than midnight to 6 a.m., from one hour after business closing to one hour before business opening or during any period when activity has not been detected for a time of longer than 15 minutes.

All time switches shall be able to retain programming and the time setting during loss of power for a period of at least 10 hours.

Exception: Lighting for covered vehicle entrances or exits from buildings or parking structures where required for safety, security or eye adaptation.

C405.3 Exit signs (Mandatory). Internally illuminated exit signs shall not be more than 5 watts per side.

C405.4 Interior lighting power requirements (Prescriptive). A building complies with this section where its total connected lighting power calculated under Section C405.4.1 is not greater than the interior lighting power calculated under Section C405.4.2.

C405.4.1 Total connected interior lighting power. The total connected interior lighting power shall be determined in accordance with Equation 4-9.

$$TCLP = [SL + LV + LTPB + \text{Other}] \quad \textbf{(Equation 4-9)}$$

where:

TCLP = Total connected lighting power (watts).

SL = Labeled wattage of luminaires for screw-in lamps.

LV = Wattage of the transformer supplying low-voltage lighting.

LTPB = Wattage of line-voltage lighting tracks and plug-in busways as the specified wattage of the luminaires, but at least 30 W/lin. ft. (100 W/lin m), or the wattage limit of the system's circuit breaker, or the wattage limit of other permanent current-limiting devices on the system.

Other = The wattage of all other luminaires and lighting sources not covered previously and associated with interior lighting verified by data supplied by the manufacturer or other *approved* sources.

Exceptions:

1. The connected power associated with the following lighting equipment is not included in calculating total connected lighting power.
   - 1.1. Professional sports arena playing field lighting.
   - 1.2. Lighting in sleeping units, provided that the lighting complies with Section R404.1.
   - 1.3. Emergency lighting automatically off during normal building operation.
   - 1.4. Lighting in spaces specifically designed for use by occupants with special lighting needs, including those with visual impairment and other medical and age-related issues.
   - 1.5. Lighting in interior spaces that have been specifically designated as a registered interior historic landmark.
   - 1.6. Casino gaming areas.
   - 1.7. Mirror lighting in dressing rooms.
2. Lighting equipment used for the following shall be exempt provided that it is in addition to general lighting and is controlled by an independent control device:
   - 2.1. Task lighting for medical and dental purposes.
   - 2.2. Display lighting for exhibits in galleries, museums and monuments.
3. Lighting for theatrical purposes, including performance, stage, film production and video production.
4. Lighting for photographic processes.
5. Lighting integral to equipment or instrumentation and installed by the manufacturer.
6. Task lighting for plant growth or maintenance.
7. Advertising signage or directional signage.
8. In restaurant buildings and areas, lighting for food warming or integral to food preparation equipment.
9. Lighting equipment that is for sale.
10. Lighting demonstration equipment in lighting education facilities.
11. Lighting *approved* because of safety or emergency considerations, inclusive of exit lights.
12. Lighting integral to both open and glass-enclosed refrigerator and freezer cases.
13. Lighting in retail display windows, provided the display area is enclosed by ceiling-height partitions.
14. Furniture-mounted supplemental task lighting that is controlled by automatic shutoff.
15. Exit signs.

C405.4.2 Interior lighting power. The total interior lighting power allowance (watts) is determined according to Table C405.4.2(1) using the Building Area Method, or Table C405.4.2(2) using the Space-by-Space Method, for all areas of the building covered in this permit.

C405.4.2.1 Building Area Method. For the Building Area Method, the interior lighting power allowance is the floor area for each building area type listed in Table C405.4.2(1) times the value from Table C405.4.2(1) for that area. For the purposes of this method, an "area" shall be defined as all contiguous spaces that accommodate or are associated with a single building area type, as listed in Table C405.4.2(1). Where this method is used to calculate the total interior lighting power for an entire building, each building area type shall be treated as a separate area.

TABLE C405.4.2(1)
INTERIOR LIGHTING POWER ALLOWANCES: BUILDING AREA METHOD

BUILDING AREA TYPE	LPD (w/ft^2)
Automotive facility	0.80
Convention center	1.01
Courthouse	1.01
Dining: bar lounge/leisure	1.01
Dining: cafeteria/fast food	0.9
Dining: family	0.95
Dormitory	0.57
Exercise center	0.84
Fire station	0.67
Gymnasium	0.94
Health care clinic	0.90
Hospital	1.05
Hotel/Motel	0.87
Library	1.19
Manufacturing facility	1.17
Motion picture theater	0.76
Multifamily	0.51
Museum	1.02
Office	0.82
Parking garage	0.21
Penitentiary	0.81
Performing arts theater	1.39
Police station	0.87
Post office	0.87
Religious building	1.0
Retail	1.26
School/university	0.87
Sports arena	0.91
Town hall	0.89
Transportation	0.70
Warehouse	0.66
Workshop	1.19

TABLE C405.4.2(2)
INTERIOR LIGHTING POWER ALLOWANCES: SPACE-BY-SPACE METHOD

COMMON SPACE TYPES[a]	LPD (watts/sq.ft)
Atrium	
Less than 40 feet in height	0.03 per foot in total height
Greater than 40 feet in height	0.40 + 0.02 per foot in total height
Audience seating area	
In an auditorium	0.63
In a convention center	0.82
In a gymnasium	0.65
In a motion picture theater	1.14
In a penitentiary	0.28
In a performing arts theater	2.43
In a religious building	1.53
In a sports arena	0.43
Otherwise	0.43
Banking activity area	1.01
Breakroom (See Lounge/Breakroom)	
Classroom/lecture hall/training room	
In a penitentiary	1.34
Otherwise	1.24
Conference/meeting/multipurpose room	1.23
Copy/print room	0.72
Corridor	
In a facility for the visually impaired (and not used primarily by the staff)[b]	0.92
In a hospital	0.79
In a manufacturing facility	0.41
Otherwise	0.66
Courtroom	1.72
Computer room	1.71
Dining area	
In a penitentiary	0.96
In a facility for the visually impaired (and not used primarily by the staff)[b]	1.9
In bar/lounge or leisure dining	1.07
In cafeteria or fast food dining	0.65
In family dining	0.89
Otherwise	0.65
Electrical/mechanical room	0.95
Emergency vehicle garage	0.56

(continued)

TABLE C405.4.2(2)—continued
INTERIOR LIGHTING POWER ALLOWANCES: SPACE-BY-SPACE METHOD

COMMON SPACE TYPES[a]	LPD (watts/sq.ft)
Food preparation area	1.21
Guest room	0.47
Laboratory	
In or as a classroom	1.43
Otherwise	1.81
Laundry/washing area	0.6
Loading dock, interior	0.47
Lobby	
In a facility for the visually impaired (and not used primarily by the staff)[b]	1.8
For an elevator	0.64
In a hotel	1.06
In a motion picture theater	0.59
In a performing arts theater	2.0
Otherwise	0.9
Locker room	0.75
Lounge/breakroom	
In a healthcare facility	0.92
Otherwise	0.73
Office	
Enclosed	1.11
Open plan	0.98
Parking area, interior	0.19
Pharmacy area	1.68
Restroom	
In a facility for the visually impaired (and not used primarily by the staff[b]	1.21
Otherwise	0.98
Sales area	1.59
Seating area, general	0.54
Stairway (See space containing stairway)	
Stairwell	0.69
Storage room	0.63
Vehicular maintenance area	0.67
Workshop	1.59
BUILDING TYPE SPECIFIC SPACE TYPES[a]	**LPD (watts/sq.ft)**
Facility for the visually impaired[b]	
In a chapel (and not used primarily by the staff)	2.21
In a recreation room (and not used primarily by the staff)	2.41
Automotive (See Vehicular Maintenance Area above)	
Convention center—exhibit space	1.45
Dormitory—living quarters	0.38
Fire station—sleeping quarters	0.22
Gymnasium/fitness center	
In an exercise area	0.72
In a playing area	1.2

(continued)

TABLE C405.4.2(2)—continued
INTERIOR LIGHTING POWER ALLOWANCES: SPACE-BY-SPACE METHOD

BUILDING TYPE SPECIFIC SPACE TYPES[a]	LPD (watts/sq.ft)
Healthcare facility	
In an exam/treatment room	1.66
In an imaging room	1.51
In a medical supply room	0.74
In a nursery	0.88
In a nurse's station	0.71
In an operating room	2.48
In a patient room	0.62
In a physical therapy room	0.91
In a recovery room	1.15
Library	
In a reading area	1.06
In the stacks	1.71
Manufacturing facility	
In a detailed manufacturing area	1.29
In an equipment room	0.74
In an extra high bay area (greater than 50′ floor-to-ceiling height)	1.05
In a high bay area (25-50′ floor-to-ceiling height)	1.23
In a low bay area (less than 25' floor-to-ceiling height)	1.19
Museum	
In a general exhibition area	1.05
In a restoration room	1.02
Performing arts theater—dressing room	0.61
Post office—sorting area	0.94
Religious buildings	
In a fellowship hall	0.64
In a worship/pulpit/choir area	1.53
Retail facilities	
In a dressing/fitting room	0.71
In a mall concourse	1.1
Sports arena—playing area	
For a Class I facility	3.68
For a Class II facility	2.4
For a Class III facility	1.8
For a Class IV facility	1.2
Transportation facility	
In a baggage/carousel area	0.53
In an airport concourse	0.36
At a terminal ticket counter	0.8
Warehouse—storage area	
For medium to bulky, palletized items	0.58
For smaller, hand-carried items	0.95

a. In cases where both a common space type and a building area specific space type are listed, the building area specific space type shall apply.

b. A 'Facility for the Visually Impaired' is a facility that is licensed or will be licensed by local or state authorities for senior long-term care, adult daycare, senior support or people with special visual needs.

C405.4.2.2 Space-by-Space Method. For the Space-by-Space Method, the interior lighting power allowance is determined by multiplying the floor area of each space times the value for the space type in Table C405.4.2(2) that most closely represents the proposed use of the space, and then summing the lighting power allowances for all spaces. Trade-offs among spaces are permitted.

C405.4.2.2.1 Additional interior lighting power. Where using the Space-by-Space Method, an increase in the interior lighting power allowance is permitted for specific lighting functions. Additional power shall be permitted only where the specified lighting is installed and automatically controlled separately from the general lighting, to be turned off during nonbusiness hours. This additional power shall be used only for the specified luminaires and shall not be used for any other purpose. An increase in the interior lighting power allowance is permitted in the following cases:

1. For lighting equipment to be installed in sales areas specifically to highlight merchandise, the additional lighting power shall be determined in accordance with Equation 4-10.

   Additional interior lighting power allowance = 500 watts + (Retail Area 1 · 0.6 W/ft^2) + (Retail Area 2 · 0.6 W/ft^2) + (Retail Area 3 · 1.4 W/ft^2) + (Retail Area 4 · 2.5 W/ft^2)

   (Equation 4-10)

   where:

   Retail Area 1 = The floor area for all products not listed in Retail Area 2, 3 or 4.

   Retail Area 2 = The floor area used for the sale of vehicles, sporting goods and small electronics.

   Retail Area 3 = The floor area used for the sale of furniture, clothing, cosmetics and artwork.

   Retail Area 4 = The floor area used for the sale of jewelry, crystal and china.

   Exception: Other merchandise categories are permitted to be included in Retail Areas 2 through 4, provided that justification documenting the need for additional lighting power based on visual inspection, contrast, or other critical display is *approved* by the code official.

2. For spaces in which lighting is specified to be installed in addition to the general lighting for the purpose of decorative appearance or for highlighting art or exhibits, provided that the additional lighting power shall be not more than 1.0 w/ft^2 (10.7 w/m^2) of such spaces.

C405.5 Exterior lighting (Mandatory). Where the power for exterior lighting is supplied through the energy service to the building, all exterior lighting shall comply with Section C405.5.1.

Exception: Where *approved* because of historical, safety, signage or emergency considerations.

C405.5.1 Exterior building lighting power. The total exterior lighting power allowance for all exterior building applications is the sum of the base site allowance plus the individual allowances for areas that are to be illuminated and are permitted in Table C405.5.1(2) for the applicable lighting zone. Trade-offs are allowed only among exterior lighting applications listed in Table C405.5.1(2), in the Tradable Surfaces section. The lighting zone for the building exterior is determined from Table C405.5.1(1) unless otherwise specified by the local jurisdiction.

Exception: Lighting used for the following exterior applications is exempt where equipped with a control device independent of the control of the nonexempt lighting:

1. Specialized signal, directional and marker lighting associated with transportation.
2. Advertising signage or directional signage.
3. Integral to equipment or instrumentation and is installed by its manufacturer.
4. Theatrical purposes, including performance, stage, film production and video production.
5. Athletic playing areas.
6. Temporary lighting.
7. Industrial production, material handling, transportation sites and associated storage areas.
8. Theme elements in theme/amusement parks.
9. Used to highlight features of public monuments and registered historic landmark structures or buildings.

TABLE C405.5.1(1)
EXTERIOR LIGHTING ZONES

LIGHTING ZONE	DESCRIPTION
1	Developed areas of national parks, state parks, forest land, and rural areas
2	Areas predominantly consisting of residential zoning, neighborhood business districts, light industrial with limited nighttime use and residential mixed-use areas
3	All other areas not classified as lighting zone 1, 2 or 4
4	High-activity commercial districts in major metropolitan areas as designated by the local land use planning authority

TABLE C405.5.1(2)
INDIVIDUAL LIGHTING POWER ALLOWANCES FOR BUILDING EXTERIORS

		LIGHTING ZONES			
		Zone 1	**Zone 2**	**Zone 3**	**Zone 4**
Base Site Allowance (Base allowance is usable in tradable or nontradable surfaces.)		500 W	600 W	750 W	1300 W
Tradable Surfaces (Lighting power densities for uncovered parking areas, building grounds, building entrances and exits, canopies and overhangs and outdoor sales areas are tradable.)	**Uncovered Parking Areas**				
	Parking areas and drives	0.04 W/ft^2	0.06 W/ft^2	0.10 W/ft^2	0.13 W/ft^2
	Building Grounds				
	Walkways less than 10 feet wide	0.7 W/linear foot	0.7 W/linear foot	0.8 W/linear foot	1.0 W/linear foot
	Walkways 10 feet wide or greater, plaza areas special feature areas	0.14 W/ft^2	0.14 W/ft^2	0.16 W/ft^2	0.2 W/ft^2
	Stairways	0.75 W/ft^2	1.0 W/ft^2	1.0 W/ft^2	1.0 W/ft^2
	Pedestrian tunnels	0.15 W/ft^2	0.15 W/ft^2	0.2 W/ft^2	0.3 W/ft^2
	Building Entrances and Exits				
	Main entries	20 W/linear foot of door width	20 W/linear foot of door width	30 W/linear foot of door width	30 W/linear foot of door width
	Other doors	20 W/linear foot of door width	20 W/linear foot of door width	20 W/linear foot of door width	20 W/linear foot of door width
	Entry canopies	0.25 W/ft^2	0.25 W/ft^2	0.4 W/ft^2	0.4 W/ft^2
	Sales Canopies				
	Free-standing and attached	0.6 W/ft^2	0.6 W/ft^2	0.8 W/ft^2	1.0 W/ft^2
	Outdoor Sales				
	Open areas (including vehicle sales lots)	0.25 W/ft^2	0.25 W/ft^2	0.5 W/ft^2	0.7 W/ft^2
	Street frontage for vehicle sales lots in addition to "open area" allowance	No allowance	10 W/linear foot	10 W/linear foot	30 W/linear foot
Nontradable Surfaces (Lighting power density calculations for the following applications can be used only for the specific application and cannot be traded between surfaces or with other exterior lighting. The following allowances are in addition to any allowance otherwise permitted in the "Tradable Surfaces" section of this table.)	Building facades	No allowance	0.075 W/ft^2 of gross above-grade wall area	0.113 W/ft^2 of gross above-grade wall area	0.15 W/ft^2 of gross above-grade wall area
	Automated teller machines (ATM) and night depositories	270 W per location plus 90 W per additional ATM per location	270 W per location plus 90 W per additional ATM per location	270 W per location plus 90 W per additional ATM per location	270 W per location plus 90 W per additional ATM per location
	Entrances and gatehouse inspection stations at guarded facilities	0.75 W/ft^2 of covered and uncovered area	0.75 W/ft^2 of covered and uncovered area	0.75 W/ft^2 of covered and uncovered area	0.75 W/ft^2 of covered and uncovered area
	Loading areas for law enforcement, fire, ambulance and other emergency service vehicles	0.5 W/ft^2 of covered and uncovered area	0.5 W/ft^2 of covered and uncovered area	0.5 W/ft^2 of covered and uncovered area	0.5 W/ft^2 of covered and uncovered area
	Drive-up windows/doors	400 W per drive-through	400 W per drive-through	400 W per drive-through	400 W per drive-through
	Parking near 24-hour retail entrances	800 W per main entry	800 W per main entry	800 W per main entry	800 W per main entry

For SI: 1 foot = 304.8 mm, 1 watt per square foot = W/0.0929 m^2.
W = watts.

C405.6 Electrical power (Mandatory).

C405.6.1 Applicability. This section applies to all building power distribution systems. The provisions for electrical distribution for all sections of this code are subject to the design conditions in ASHRAE Standard 90.1.

C405.6.2 Electrical metering. In buildings having individual dwelling units, provisions shall be made to determine the electrical energy consumed by each tenant by separately metering individual dwelling units.

C405.6.3 Voltage drop. The conductors for feeders and branch circuits combined shall be sized for a maximum of 5 percent voltage drop total.

C405.6.4 Completion requirements.

C405.6.4.1 Drawings. Construction documents shall require that within 30 days after the date of system acceptance, record drawings of the actual installation shall be provided to the building owner, including:

1. a single-line diagram of the building electrical distribution system and
2. floor plans indicating location and area served for all distribution.

C405.6.4.2 Manuals. Construction documents shall require that an operating manual and maintenance manual be provided to the building owner. The manuals shall include, at a minimum, the following:

1. Submittal data stating equipment rating and selected options for each piece of equipment requiring maintenance.
2. Operation manuals and maintenance manuals for each piece of equipment requiring maintenance. Required routine maintenance actions shall be clearly identified.
3. Names and addresses of at least one qualified service agency.

Note: Enforcement agencies should only check to be sure that the construction documents require this information to be transmitted to the owner and should not expect copies of any of the materials.

C405.7 Electrical transformers (Mandatory). Electric transformers shall meet the minimum efficiency requirements of Table C405.7 as tested and rated in accordance with the test procedure listed in DOE 10 CFR 431. The efficiency shall be verified through certification under an approved certification program or, where a certification program does not exist, the equipment efficiency ratings shall be supported by data furnished by the transformer manufacturer.

Exceptions: The following transformers are exempt:

1. Transformers that meet the *Energy Policy Act of 2005* exclusions based on the DOE 10 CFR 431 definition of special purpose applications.
2. Transformers that meet the *Energy Policy Act of 2005* exclusions that are not to be used in general purpose applications based on information provided in DOE 10 CFR 431.
3. Transformers that meet the *Energy Policy Act of 2005* exclusions with multiple voltage taps where the highest tap is at least 20 percent more than the lowest tap.
4. Drive transformers.
5. Rectifier transformers.
6. Auto-transformers.
7. Uninterruptible power system transformers.
8. Impendance transformers.
9. Regulating transformers.
10. Sealed and nonventilating transformers.
11. Machine tool transformers.
12. Welding transformers.
13. Grounding transformers.
14. Testing transformers.

TABLE C405.7
MINIMUM NOMINAL EFFICIENCY LEVELS FOR 10 CFR 431 LOW-VOLTAGE DRY-TYPE DISTRIBUTION TRANSFORMERS

SINGLE-PHASE TRANSFORMERS		THREE-PHASE TRANSFORMERS	
kVA[a]	Efficiency (%)[b]	kVA[a]	Efficiency (%)[b]
15	97.7	15	97.0
25	98.0	30	97.5
37.5	98.2	45	97.7
50	98.3	75	98.0
75	98.5	112.5	98.2
100	98.6	150	98.3
167	98.7	225	98.5
250	98.8	300	98.6
333	98.9	500	98.7
		750	98.8
		1000	98.9

a. kiloVolt-Amp rating.

b. Nominal efficiencies shall be established in accordance with the DOE 10 CFR 431 test procedure for low-voltage dry-type transformers.

C405.8 Electrical motors (Mandatory). Electric motors shall meet the minimum efficiency requirements of Tables C405.8(1) through C405.8(4) when tested and rated in accordance with the DOE 10 CFR 431. The efficiency shall be verified through certification under an approved certification program or, where a certification program does not exist, the equipment efficiency ratings shall be supported by data furnished by the motor manufacturer.

C405.9 Vertical and horizontal transportation systems and equipment. Vertical and horizontal transportation systems and equipment shall comply with this section.

C405.9.1 Elevator cabs. For the luminaires in each elevator cab, not including signals and displays, the sum of the lumens divided by the sum of the watts shall be not less than 35 lumens per watt. Ventilation fans in elevators that do not have their own air-conditioning system shall not consume more than 0.33 watts/cfm at the maximum rated speed of the fan. Controls shall be provided that will de-energize ventilation fans and lighting systems when the elevator is stopped, unoccupied and with its doors closed for over 15 minutes.

C405.9.2 Escalators and moving walks. Escalators and moving walks shall comply with ASME A17.1/CSA B44 and shall have automatic controls configured to reduce speed to the minimum permitted speed in accordance with ASME A17.1/CSA B44 or applicable local code when not conveying passengers.

TABLE C405.8(1)
MINIMUM NOMINAL FULL-LOAD EFFICIENCY FOR 60 HZ NEMA GENERAL PURPOSE ELECTRIC MOTORS (SUBTYPE I) RATED 600 VOLTS OR LESS (Random Wound)[a]

MOTOR HORSEPOWER	NUMBER OF POLES	OPEN DRIP-PROOF MOTORS			TOTALLY ENCLOSED FAN-COOLED MOTORS		
		2	4	6	2	4	6
	Synchronous Speed (RPM)	3600	1800	1200	3600	1800	1200
1		77.0	85.5	82.5	77.0	85.5	82.5
1.5		84.0	86.5	86.5	84.0	86.5	87.5
2		85.5	86.5	87.5	85.5	86.5	88.5
3		85.5	89.5	88.5	86.5	89.5	89.5
5		86.5	89.5	89.5	88.5	89.5	89.5
7.5		88.5	91.0	90.2	89.5	91.7	91.0
10		89.5	91.7	91.7	90.2	91.7	91.0
15		90.2	93.0	91.7	91.0	92.4	91.7
20		91.0	93.0	92.4	91.0	93.0	91.7
25		91.7	93.6	93.0	91.7	93.6	93.0
30		91.7	94.1	93.6	91.7	93.6	93.0
40		92.4	94.1	94.1	92.4	94.1	94.1
50		93.0	94.5	94.1	93.0	94.5	94.1
60		93.6	95.0	94.5	93.6	95.0	94.5
75		93.6	95.0	94.5	93.6	95.4	94.5
100		93.6	95.4	95.0	94.1	95.4	95.0
125		94.1	95.4	95.0	95.0	95.4	95.0
150		94.1	95.8	95.4	95.0	95.8	95.8
200		95.0	95.8	95.4	95.4	96.2	95.8
250		95.0	95.8	95.4	95.8	96.2	95.8
300		95.4	95.8	95.4	95.8	96.2	95.8
350		95.4	95.8	95.4	95.8	96.2	95.8
400		95.8	95.8	95.8	95.8	96.2	95.8
450		95.8	96.2	96.2	95.8	96.2	95.8
500		95.8	96.2	96.2	95.8	96.2	95.8

a. Nominal efficiencies shall be established in accordance with DOE 10 CFR 431.

**TABLE C405.8(2)
MINIMUM NOMINAL FULL-LOAD EFFICIENCY OF
GENERAL PURPOSE ELECTRIC MOTORS (SUBTYPE II) AND ALL DESIGN B MOTORS GREATER THAN 200 HORSEPOWER[a]**

MOTOR HORSEPOWER	NUMBER OF POLES	OPEN DRIP-PROOF MOTORS				TOTALLY ENCLOSED FAN-COOLED MOTORS			
		2	4	6	8	2	4	6	8
	Synchronous Speed (RPM)	3600	1800	1200	900	3600	1800	1200	900
1		NR	82.5	80.0	74.0	75.5	82.5	80.0	74.0
1.5		82.5	84.0	84.0	75.5	82.5	84.0	85.5	77.0
2		84.0	84.0	85.5	85.5	84.0	84.0	86.5	82.5
3		84.0	86.5	86.5	86.5	85.5	87.5	87.5	84.0
5		85.5	87.5	87.5	87.5	87.5	87.5	87.5	84.0
7.5		87.5	88.5	88.5	88.5	88.5	89.5	89.5	85.5
10		88.5	89.5	90.2	89.5	89.5	89.5	89.5	88.5
15		89.5	91.0	90.2	89.5	90.2	91.0	90.2	88.5
20		90.2	91.0	91.0	90.2	90.2	91.0	90.2	89.5
25		91.0	91.7	91.7	90.2	91.0	92.4	91.7	89.5
30		91.0	92.4	92.4	91.0	91.0	92.4	91.7	91.0
40		91.7	93.0	93.0	91.0	91.7	93.0	93.0	91.0
50		92.4	93.0	93.0	91.7	92.4	93.0	93.0	91.7
60		93.0	93.6	93.6	92.4	93.0	93.6	93.6	91.7
75		93.0	94.1	93.6	93.6	93.0	94.1	93.6	93.0
100		93.0	94.1	94.1	93.6	93.6	94.5	94.1	93.0
125		93.6	94.5	94.1	93.6	94.5	94.5	94.1	93.6
150		93.6	95.0	94.5	93.6	94.5	95.0	95.0	93.6
200		94.5	95.0	94.5	93.6	95.0	95.0	95.0	94.1
250		94.5	95.4	95.4	94.5	95.4	95.0	95.0	94.5
300		95.0	95.4	95.4	NR	95.4	95.4	95.0	NR
350		95.0	95.4	95.4	NR	95.4	95.4	95.0	NR
400		95.4	95.4	NR	NR	95.4	95.4	NR	NR
450		95.8	95.8	NR	NR	95.4	95.4	NR	NR
500		95.8	95.8	NR	NR	95.4	95.8	NR	NR

NR = No requirement.

a. Nominal efficiencies shall be established in accordance with DOE 10 CFR 431.

TABLE C405.8(3)
MINIMUM AVERAGE FULL-LOAD EFFICIENCY POLYPHASE SMALL ELECTRIC MOTORS[a]

MOTOR HORSEPOWER	OPEN MOTORS			
	Number of Poles	2	4	6
	Synchronous Speed (RPM)	3600	1800	1200
0.25		65.6	69.5	67.5
0.33		69.5	73.4	71.4
0.50		73.4	78.2	75.3
0.75		76.8	81.1	81.7
1		77.0	83.5	82.5
1.5		84.0	86.5	83.8
2		85.5	86.5	N/A
3		85.5	86.9	N/A

a. Average full-load efficiencies shall be established in accordance with 10 CFR 431.

TABLE C405.8(4)
MINIMUM AVERAGE FULL-LOAD EFFICIENCY FOR CAPACITOR-START CAPACITOR-RUN AND CAPACITOR-START INDUCTION-RUN SMALL ELECTRIC MOTORS[a]

MOTOR HORSEPOWER	OPEN MOTORS			
	Number of Poles	2	4	6
	Synchronous Speed (RPM)	3600	1800	1200
0.25		66.6	68.5	62.2
0.33		70.5	72.4	66.6
0.50		72.4	76.2	76.2
0.75		76.2	81.8	80.2
1		80.4	82.6	81.1
1.5		81.5	83.8	N/A
2		82.9	84.5	N/A
3		84.1	N/A	N/A

a. Average full-load efficiencies shall be established in accordance with 10 CFR 431.

C405.9.2.1 Regenerative drive. An escalator designed either for one-way down operation only or for reversible operation shall have a variable frequency regenerative drive that supplies electrical energy to the building electrical system when the escalator is loaded with passengers whose combined weight exceeds 750 pounds (340 kg).

SECTION C406
ADDITIONAL EFFICIENCY PACKAGE OPTIONS

C406.1 Requirements. Buildings shall comply with at least one of the following:

1. More efficient HVAC performance in accordance with Section C406.2.
2. Reduced lighting power density system in accordance with Section C406.3.
3. Enhanced lighting controls in accordance with Section C406.4.
4. On-site supply of renewable energy in accordance with Section C406.5.
5. Provision of a dedicated outdoor air system for certain HVAC equipment in accordance with Section C406.6.
6. High-efficiency service water heating in accordance with Section C406.7.

C406.1.1 Tenant spaces. Tenant spaces shall comply with Section C406.2, C406.3, C406.4, C406.6 or C406.7. Alternatively, tenant spaces shall comply with Section C406.5 where the entire building is in compliance.

C406.2 More efficient HVAC equipment performance. Equipment shall exceed the minimum efficiency requirements listed in Tables C403.2.3(1) through C403.2.3(7) by 10 percent, in addition to the requirements of Section C403. Where multiple performance requirements are provided, the equipment shall exceed all requirements by 10 percent. *Variable refrigerant flow systems* shall exceed the energy efficiency provisions of ANSI/ASHRAE/IESNA 90.1 by 10 percent. Equipment not listed in Tables C403.2.3(1) through C403.2.3(7) shall be limited to 10 percent of the total building system capacity.

C406.3 Reduced lighting power density. The total interior lighting power (watts) of the building shall be determined by using 90 percent of the lighting power values specified in Table C405.4.2(1) times the floor area for the building types, or by using 90 percent of the interior lighting power allowance calculated by the Space-by-Space Method in Section C405.4.2.

C406.4 Enhanced digital lighting controls. Interior lighting in the building shall have the following enhanced lighting controls that shall be located, scheduled and operated in accordance with Section C405.2.2.

1. Luminaires shall be capable of continuous dimming.
2. Luminaires shall be capable of being addressed individually. Where individual addressability is not available for the luminaire class type, a controlled group of not more than four luminaries shall be allowed.
3. Not more than eight luminaires shall be controlled together in a *daylight zone.*
4. Fixtures shall be controlled through a digital control system that includes the following function:
   4.1. Control reconfiguration based on digital addressability.
   4.2. Load shedding.
   4.3. Individual user control of overhead general illumination in open offices.
   4.4. Occupancy sensors shall be capable of being reconfigured through the digital control system.
5. Construction documents shall include submittal of a Sequence of Operations, including a specification outlining each of the functions in Item 4 of this section.
6. Functional testing of lighting controls shall comply with Section C408.

C406.5 On-site renewable energy. Total minimum ratings of on-site renewable energy systems shall comply with one of the following:

1. Provide not less than 0.50 watts per square foot (5.4 W/m^2) of conditioned floor area.
2. Provide not less than 3 percent of the energy used within the building for building mechanical and service water heating equipment and lighting regulated in Chapter 4.

C406.6 Dedicated outdoor air system. Buildings covered by Section C403.4 shall be equipped with an independent ventilation system designed to provide not less than the minimum 100-percent outdoor air to each individual occupied space, as specified by the *Florida Building Code, Mechanical.* The ventilation system shall be capable of total energy recovery. The HVAC system shall include supply-air temperature controls that automatically reset the supply-air temperature in response to representative building loads, or to outdoor air temperatures. The controls shall reset the supply-air temperature at least 25 percent of the difference between the design supply-air temperature and the design room-air temperature.

C406.7 Reduced energy use in service water heating. Buildings shall be of the following types to use this compliance method:

1. Group R-1: Boarding houses, hotels or motels.
2. Group I-2: Hospitals, psychiatric hospitals and nursing homes.
3. Group A-2: Restaurants and banquet halls or buildings containing food preparation areas.
4. Group F: Laundries.
5. Group R-2: Buildings with residential occupancies.
6. Group A-3: Health clubs and spas.
7. Buildings showing a service hot water load of 10 percent or more of total building energy loads, as shown with an energy analysis as described in Section C407.

C406.7.1 Load fraction. The building service water-heating system shall have one or more of the following that are sized to provide not less than 60 percent of hot water requirements, or sized to provide 100 percent of hot water requirements if the building shall otherwise comply with Section C403.4.5.

1. Waste heat recovery from service hot water, heat-recovery chillers, building equipment, process equipment, or a combined heat and power system.
2. Solar water-heating systems.

SECTION C407 TOTAL BUILDING PERFORMANCE

C407.1 Scope. This section establishes criteria for compliance using total building performance. The following systems and loads shall be included in determining the total building performance: heating systems, cooling systems, service water heating, fan systems, lighting power, receptacle loads and process loads.

C407.2 Mandatory requirements. Compliance with this section requires that the criteria of Sections C402.5, C403.2, C404 and C405 be met.

C407.2.1 Roof/ceiling thermal envelope. The roof or ceiling that functions as the building's thermal envelope shall be insulated to an *R*-value of at least R-10. Multiple-family residential roofs/ceilings shall be insulated to an *R*-value of at least R-19, space permitting. Where cavities beneath a roof deck are ventilated, the ceiling shall be considered the envelope component utilized in the Commission approved compliance software tools.

C407.3 Performance-based compliance. Compliance based on total building performance requires that a proposed building (*proposed design*) be shown to have an annual energy cost that is less than or equal to the annual energy cost of the *standard reference design.* Energy prices used in the total building performance compliance calculation shall be those contained in software approved by the Florida Building Commission. Nondepletable energy collected off site shall be treated and priced the same as purchased energy. Energy from nondepletable energy sources collected on site shall be omitted from the annual energy cost of the *proposed design.*

C407.4 Documentation. Documentation verifying that the methods and accuracy of compliance software tools conform to the provisions of this section shall be provided to the Florida Building Commission. Computer software utilized for demonstration of code compliance shall have been approved by the Florida Building Commission in accordance with requirements of this code.

C407.4.1 Compliance report. Compliance software tools used to demonstrate code compliance by Section C407 shall generate a report that documents that the *proposed design* has annual energy costs less than or equal to the annual energy costs of the *standard reference design*. The compliance documentation shall include the following information:

1. Address of the building;
2. An inspection checklist documenting the building component characteristics of the *proposed design* as *listed* in Table C407.5.1(1). The inspection checklist shall show the estimated annual energy cost for both the *standard reference design* and the *proposed design*;
3. Name of individual completing the compliance report; and
4. Name and version of the compliance software tool.

C407.4.2 Additional documentation. The *code official* shall be permitted to require the following documents:

1. Thermal zoning diagrams consisting of floor plans showing the thermal zoning scheme for *standard reference design* and *proposed design*;
2. Input and output reports from the energy analysis simulation program containing the complete input and output files, as applicable. The output file shall include energy use totals and energy use by energy source and end-use served, total hours that space conditioning loads are not met and any errors or warning messages generated by the simulation tool as applicable;
3. An explanation of any error or warning messages appearing in the simulation tool output; and
4. A certification signed by the builder providing the building component characteristics of the *proposed design* as given in Table C407.5.1(1).

C407.5 Calculation procedure. Except as specified by this section, the *standard reference design* and *proposed design* shall be configured and analyzed using identical methods and techniques.

C407.5.1 Building specifications. The *standard reference design* and *proposed design* shall be configured and analyzed as specified by Table C407.5.1(1). Table C407.5.1(1) shall include by reference all notes contained in Table C402.1.4.

C407.5.2 Thermal blocks. The *standard reference design* and *proposed design* shall be analyzed using identical thermal blocks as specified in Section C407.5.2.1, C407.5.2.2 or C407.5.2.3.

C407.5.2.1 HVAC zones designed. Where HVAC *zones* are defined on HVAC design drawings, each HVAC *zone* shall be modeled as a separate thermal block.

Exception: Different HVAC *zones* shall be allowed to be combined to create a single thermal block or identical thermal blocks to which multipliers are applied provided:

1. The space use classification is the same throughout the thermal block.
2. All HVAC *zones* in the thermal block that are adjacent to glazed exterior walls face the same orientation or their orientations are within 45 degrees (0.79 rad) of each other.
3. All of the *zones* are served by the same HVAC system or by the same kind of HVAC system.

C407.5.2.2 HVAC zones not designed. Where HVAC *zones* have not yet been designed, thermal blocks shall be defined based on similar internal load densities, occupancy, lighting, thermal and temperature schedules, and in combination with the following guidelines:

1. Separate thermal blocks shall be assumed for interior and perimeter spaces. Interior spaces shall be those located more than 15 feet (4572 mm) from an exterior wall. Perimeter spaces shall be those located closer than 15 feet (4572 mm) from an *exterior wall*.
2. Separate thermal blocks shall be assumed for spaces adjacent to glazed exterior walls: a separate *zone* shall be provided for each orientation, except orientations that differ by not more than 45 degrees (0.79 rad) shall be permitted to be considered to be the same orientation. Each *zone* shall include floor area that is 15 feet (4572 mm) or less from a glazed perimeter wall, except that floor area within 15 feet (4572 mm) of glazed perimeter walls having more than one orientation shall be divided proportionately between *zones*.
3. Separate thermal blocks shall be assumed for spaces having floors that are in contact with the ground or exposed to ambient conditions from *zones* that do not share these features.
4. Separate thermal blocks shall be assumed for spaces having exterior ceiling or roof assemblies from *zones* that do not share these features.

C407.5.2.3 Multifamily residential buildings. Residential spaces shall be modeled using one thermal block per space except that those facing the same orientations are permitted to be combined into one thermal block. Corner units and units with roof or floor loads shall only be combined with units sharing these features.

C407.5.2.4 Requirements specific to credit options. Credit may be claimed in the compliance calculation for technologies that meet the criteria for various options specified below.

C407.5.2.4.1 Vegetative roofs. Credit may be claimed in whole building performance method calculations for the area of a proposed building's roof that is covered with a vegetative roof that is designed and installed in accordance with ANSI/SPRI VF-1, with a minimum growth media depth of 4 inches. The credit shall provide a 45 percent reduction in the heating and cooling roof heat flux rates for the roof area covered with the vegetative

TABLE C407.5.1(1)
SPECIFICATIONS FOR THE STANDARD REFERENCE AND PROPOSED DESIGNS

BUILDING COMPONENT CHARACTERISTICS	STANDARD REFERENCE DESIGN	PROPOSED DESIGN
Space use classification	Same as proposed	The space use classification shall be chosen in accordance with Table C405.5.2 for all areas of the building covered by this permit. Where the space use classification for a building is not known, the building shall be categorized as an office building.
Roofs	Type: Insulation entirely above deck	As proposed
	Gross area: same as proposed	As proposed
	U-factor: as specified in Table C402.1.4	As proposed
	Solar absorptance: 0.75	As proposed
	Emittance: 0.90	As proposed
Walls, above-grade	Type: Mass wall where proposed wall is mass; otherwise steel-framed wall	As proposed
	Gross area: same as proposed	As proposed
	U-factor: as specified in Table C402.1.4	As proposed
	Solar absorptance: 0.75	As proposed
	Emittance: 0.90	As proposed
Walls, below-grade	Type: Mass wall	As proposed
	Gross area: same as proposed	As proposed
	U-Factor: as specified in Table C402.1.4 with insulation layer on interior side of walls	As proposed
Floors, above-grade	Type: joist/framed floor	As proposed
	Gross area: same as proposed	As proposed
	U-factor: as specified in Table C402.1.4	As proposed
Floors, slab-on-grade	Type: Unheated	As proposed
	F-factor: as specified in Table C402.1.4	As proposed
Opaque doors	Type: Swinging	As proposed
	Area: Same as proposed	As proposed
	U-factor: as specified in Table C402.1.4	As proposed
Vertical fenestration other than opaque doors	Area 1. The proposed vertical fenestration area; where the proposed vertical fenestration area is less than 40 percent of above-grade wall area. 2. 40 percent of above-grade wall area; where the proposed vertical fenestration area is 40 percent or more of the above-grade wall area.	As proposed
	U-factor: as specified in Table C402.4	As proposed
	SHGC: as specified in Table C402.4 except that for climates with no requirement (NR) SHGC = 0.40 shall be used.	As proposed
	External shading and PF: None	As proposed
Skylights	Area 1. The proposed skylight area; where the proposed skylight area is less than that permitted by Section C402.1. 2. The area permitted by Section C402.1; where the proposed skylight area exceeds that permitted by Section C402.1.	As proposed
	U-factor: as specified in Table C402.4	As proposed
	SHGC: as specified in Table C402.4 except that for climates with no requirement (NR) SHGC = 0.40 shall be used.	As proposed
Lighting, interior	The interior lighting power shall be determined in accordance with Section C405.4.2. Where the occupancy of the building is not known, the lighting power density shall be 1.0 Watt per square foot (10.7 W/m^2) based on the categorization of buildings with unknown space classification as offices.	As proposed
Lighting, exterior	The lighting power shall be determined in accordance with Table C405.5.2(2). Areas and dimensions of tradable and nontradable surfaces shall be the same as proposed.	As proposed

(continued)

TABLE C407.5.1(1)—continued
SPECIFICATIONS FOR THE STANDARD REFERENCE AND PROPOSED DESIGNS

BUILDING COMPONENT CHARACTERISTICS	STANDARD REFERENCE DESIGN	PROPOSED DESIGN
Internal gains	Same as proposed	Receptacle, motor and process loads shall be modeled and estimated based on the space use classification. All end-use load components within and associated with the building shall be modeled to include, but not be limited to, the following: exhaust fans, parking garage ventilation fans, exterior building lighting, swimming pool heaters and pumps, elevators, escalators, refrigeration equipment and cooking equipment.
Schedules	Same as proposed	Operating schedules shall include hourly profiles for daily operation and shall account for variations between weekdays, weekends, holidays and any seasonal operation. Schedules shall model the time-dependent variations in occupancy, illumination, receptacle loads, thermostat settings, mechanical ventilation, HVAC equipment availability, service hot water usage and any process loads. The schedules shall be typical of the proposed building type as determined by the designer and approved by the jurisdiction.
Mechanical ventilation	Same as proposed	As proposed, in accordance with Section C403.2.6.
Heating systems	Fuel type: same as proposed design	As proposed
	Equipment type[a]: as specified in Tables C407.5.1(2) and C407.5.1(3)	As proposed
	Efficiency: as specified in Tables C403.2.3(4) and C403.2.3(5)	As proposed
	Capacity[b]: sized proportionally to the capacities in the proposed design based on sizing runs	As proposed
Cooling systems	Fuel type: same as proposed design	As proposed
	Equipment type[c]: as specified in Tables C407.5.1(2) and C407.5.1(3)	As proposed
	Efficiency: as specified in Tables C403.2.3(1), C403.2.3(2) and C403.2.3(3)	As proposed
	Capacity[b]: sized proportionally to the capacities in the proposed design based on sizing runs	As proposed
	Economizer[d]: same as proposed, in accordance with Section C403.3.	As proposed
Service water heating[e]	Fuel type: same as proposed	As proposed
	Efficiency: as specified in Table C404.2	For Group R, as proposed multiplied by SWHF. For other than Group R, as proposed multiplied by efficiency as provided by the manufacturer of the DWHR unit.
	Capacity: same as proposed	As proposed
	Where no service water hot water system exists or is specified in the proposed design, no service hot water heating shall be modeled.	

SWHF = Service water heat recovery factor, DWHR = Drain water heat recovery.

a. Where no heating system exists or has been specified, the heating system shall be modeled as fossil fuel. The system characteristics shall be identical in both the standard reference design and proposed design.

b. The ratio between the capacities used in the annual simulations and the capacities determined by sizing runs shall be the same for both the standard reference design and proposed design.

c. Where no cooling system exists or no cooling system has been specified, the cooling system shall be modeled as an air-cooled single-zone system, one unit per thermal zone. The system characteristics shall be identical in both the standard reference design and proposed design.

d. If an economizer is required in accordance with Table C403.3 and where no economizer exists or is specified in the proposed design, then a supply-air economizer shall be provided in the standard reference design in accordance with Section C403.3.

e. The SWHF shall be applied as follows:

1. Where potable water from the DWHR unit supplies not less than one shower and not greater than two showers, of which the drain water from the same showers flows through the DWHR unit then SWHF = [1 – (DWHR unit efficiency · 0.36)].
2. Where potable water from the DWHR unit supplies not less than three showers and not greater than four showers, of which the drain water from the same showers flows through the DWHR unit then SWHF = [1 – (DWHR unit efficiency · 0.33)].
3. Where potable water from the DWHR unit supplies not less than five showers and not greater than six showers, of which the drain water from the same showers flows through the DWHR unit, then SWHF = [1 – (DWHR unit efficiency · 0.26)].
4. Where Items 1 through 3 are not met, SWHF = 1.0.

TABLE C407.5.1(2)
HVAC SYSTEMS MAP

CONDENSER COOLING SOURCE[a]	HEATING SYSTEM CLASSIFICATION[b]	STANDARD REFERENCE DESIGN HVC SYSTEM TYPE[c]		
		Single-zone Residential System	Single-zone Nonresidential System	All Other
Water/ground	Electric resistance	System 5	System 5	System 1
	Heat pump	System 6	System 6	System 6
	Fossil fuel	System 7	System 7	System 2
Air/none	Electric resistance	System 8	System 9	System 3
	Heat pump	System 8	System 9	System 3
	Fossil fuel	System 10	System 11	System 4

a. Select "water/ground" where the proposed design system condenser is water or evaporatively cooled; select "air/none" where the condenser is air cooled. Closed-circuit dry coolers shall be considered air cooled. Systems utilizing district cooling shall be treated as if the condenser water type were "water." Where no mechanical cooling is specified or the mechanical cooling system in the proposed design does not require heat rejection, the system shall be treated as if the condenser water type were "Air." For proposed designs with ground-source or groundwater-source heat pumps, the standard reference design HVAC system shall be water-source heat pump (System 6).

b. Select the path that corresponds to the proposed design heat source: electric resistance, heat pump (including air source and water source), or fuel fired. Systems utilizing district heating (steam or hot water) and systems with no heating capability shall be treated as if the heating system type were "fossil fuel." For systems with mixed fuel heating sources, the system or systems that use the secondary heating source type (the one with the smallest total installed output capacity for the spaces served by the system) shall be modeled identically in the standard reference design and the primary heating source type shall be used to determine *standard* reference design HVAC system type.

c. Select the standard reference design HVAC system category: The system under "single-zone residential system" shall be selected where the HVAC system in the proposed design is a single-zone system and serves a residential space. The system under "single-zone nonresidential system" shall be selected where the HVAC system in the proposed design is a single-zone system and serves other than residential spaces. The system under "all other" shall be selected for all other cases.

TABLE C407.5.1(3)
SPECIFICATIONS FOR THE STANDARD REFERENCE DESIGN HVAC SYSTEM DESCRIPTIONS

SYSTEM NO.	SYSTEM TYPE	FAN CONTROL	COOLING TYPE	HEATING TYPE
1	Variable air volume with parallel fan-powered boxes[a]	VAV[d]	Chilled water[e]	Electric resistance
2	Variable air volume with reheat[b]	VAV[d]	Chilled water[e]	Hot water fossil fuel boiler[f]
3	Packaged variable air volume with parallel fan-powered boxes[a]	VAV[d]	Direct expansion[c]	Electric resistance
4	Packaged variable air volume with reheat[b]	VAV[d]	Direct expansion[c]	Hot water fossil fuel boiler[f]
5	Two-pipe fan coil	Constant volume[i]	Chilled water[e]	Electric resistance
6	Water-source heat pump	Constant volume[i]	Direct expansion[c]	Electric heat pump and boiler[g]
7	Four-pipe fan coil	Constant volume[i]	Chilled water[e]	Hot water fossil fuel boiler[f]
8	Packaged terminal heat pump	Constant volume[i]	Direct expansion[c]	Electric heat pump[h]
9	Packaged rooftop heat pump	Constant volume[i]	Direct expansion[c]	Electric heat pump[h]
10	Packaged terminal air conditioner	Constant volume[i]	Direct expansion	Hot water fossil fuel boiler[f]
11	Packaged rooftop air conditioner	Constant volume[i]	Direct expansion	Fossil fuel furnace

For SI: 1 foot = 304.8 mm, 1 cfm/ft^2 = 0.4719 L/s, 1 Btu/h = 0.293/W, °C = [(°F) - 32]/1.8.

a. **VAV with parallel boxes:** Fans in parallel VAV fan-powered boxes shall be sized for 50 percent of the peak design flow rate and shall be modeled with 0.35 W/cfm fan power. Minimum volume setpoints for fan-powered boxes shall be equal to the minimum rate for the space required for ventilation consistent with Section C403.4.4, Exception 4. Supply air temperature setpoint shall be constant at the design condition.

b. **VAV with reheat:** Minimum volume setpoints for VAV reheat boxes shall be 0.4 cfm/ft^2 of floor area. Supply air temperature shall be reset based on zone demand from the design temperature difference to a 10°F temperature difference under minimum load conditions. Design airflow rates shall be sized for the reset supply air temperature, i.e., a 10°F temperature difference.

c. **Direct expansion:** The fuel type for the cooling system shall match that of the cooling system in the proposed design.

d. VAV: Where the proposed design system has a supply, return or relief fan motor 25 hp or larger, the corresponding fan in the VAV system of the standard reference design shall be modeled assuming a variable-speed drive. For smaller fans, a forward-curved centrifugal fan with inlet vanes shall be modeled. Where the proposed design's system has a direct digital control system at the zone level, static pressure setpoint reset based on zone requirements in accordance with Section C403.4.1 shall be modeled.

e. **Chilled water:** For systems using purchased chilled water, the chillers are not explicitly modeled and chilled water costs shall be based as determined in Sections C407.3 and C407.5.2. Otherwise, the standard reference design's chiller plant shall be modeled with chillers having the number as indicated in Table C407.5.1(4) as a function of standard reference building chiller plant load and type as indicated in Table C407.5.1(5) as a function of individual chiller load. Where chiller fuel source is mixed, the system in the standard reference design shall have chillers with the same fuel types and with capacities having the same proportional capacity as the proposed design's chillers for each fuel type. Chilled water supply temperature shall be modeled at 44°F design supply temperature and 56°F return temperature. Piping losses shall not be modeled in either building model. Chilled water supply water temperature shall be reset in accordance with Section C403.4.3.3. Pump system power for each pumping system shall be the same as the proposed design; where the proposed design has no chilled water pumps, the standard reference design pump power shall be 22 W/gpm (equal to a pump operating against a 75-foot head, 65-percent combined impeller and motor efficiency). The chilled water system shall be modeled as primary-only variable flow with flow maintained at the design rate through each chiller using a bypass. Chilled water pumps shall be modeled as riding the pump curve or with variable-speed drives when required in Section C403.4.3.3. The heat rejection device shall be an axial fan cooling tower with two-speed fans where required in Section C403.4.3. Condenser water design supply temperature shall be 85°F or 10°F approach to design wet-bulb temperature, whichever is lower, with a design temperature rise of 10°F. The tower shall be controlled to maintain a 70°F leaving water temperature where weather permits, floating up to leaving water temperature at design conditions. Pump system power for each pumping system shall be the same as the proposed design; where the proposed design has no condenser water pumps, the standard reference design pump power shall be 19 W/gpm (equal to a pump operating against a 60-foot head, 60-percent combined impeller and motor efficiency). Each chiller shall be modeled with separate condenser water and chilled water pumps interlocked to operate with the associated chiller.

f. **Fossil fuel boiler:** For systems using purchased hot water or steam, the boilers are not explicitly modeled and hot water or steam costs shall be based on actual utility rates. Otherwise, the boiler plant shall use the same fuel as the proposed design and shall be natural draft. The standard reference design boiler plant shall be modeled with a single boiler where the standard reference design plant load is 600,000 Btu/h and less and with two equally sized boilers for plant capacities exceeding 600,000 Btu/h. Boilers shall be staged as required by the load. Hot water supply temperature shall be modeled at 180°F design supply temperature and 130°F return temperature. Piping losses shall not be modeled in either building model. Hot water supply water temperature shall be reset in accordance with Section C403.4.3.3. Pump system power for each pumping system shall be the same as the proposed design; where the proposed design has no hot water pumps, the standard reference design pump power shall be 19 W/gpm (equal to a pump operating against a 60-foot head, 60-percent combined impeller and motor efficiency). The hot water system shall be modeled as primary only with continuous variable flow. Hot water pumps shall be modeled as riding the pump curve or with variable speed drives when required by Section C403.4.3.3.

g. **Electric heat pump and boiler:** Water-source heat pumps shall be connected to a common heat pump water loop controlled to maintain temperatures between 60°F and 90°F. Heat rejection from the loop shall be provided by an axial fan closed-circuit evaporative fluid cooler with two-speed fans where required in Section C403.4.1. Heat addition to the loop shall be provided by a boiler that uses the same fuel as the proposed design and shall be natural draft. Where no boilers exist in the proposed design, the standard reference building boilers shall be fossil fuel. The standard reference design boiler plant shall be modeled with a single boiler where the standard reference design plant load is 600,000 Btu/h or less and with two equally sized boilers for plant capacities exceeding 600,000 Btu/h. Boilers shall be staged as required by the load. Piping losses shall not be modeled in either building model. Pump system power shall be the same as the proposed design; where the proposed design has no pumps, the standard reference design pump power shall be 22 W/gpm, which is equal to a pump operating against a 75-foot head, with a 65-percent combined impeller and motor efficiency. Loop flow shall be variable with flow shutoff at each heat pump when its compressor cycles off as required by Section C403.4.3.3. Loop pumps shall be modeled as riding the pump curve or with variable speed drives when required by Section C403.4.3.3.

h. **Electric heat pump:** Electric air-source heat pumps shall be modeled with electric auxiliary heat. The system shall be controlled with a multistage space thermostat and an outdoor air thermostat wired to energize auxiliary heat only on the last thermostat stage and when outdoor air temperature is less than 40°F.

i. **Constant volume:** Fans shall be controlled in the same manner as in the proposed design; i.e., fan operation whenever the space is occupied or fan operation cycled on calls for heating and cooling. Where the fan is modeled as cycling and the fan energy is included in the energy efficiency rating of the equipment, fan energy shall not be modeled explicitly.

TABLE C407.5.1(4)
NUMBER OF CHILLERS

TOTAL CHILLER PLANT CAPACITY	NUMBER OF CHILLERS
≤ 300 tons	1
> 300 tons, < 600 tons	2, sized equally
≥ 600 tons	2 minimum, with chillers added so that no chiller is larger than 800 tons, all sized equally

For SI: 1 ton = 3517 W.

TABLE C407.5.1(5)
WATER CHILLER TYPES

INDIVIDUAL CHILLER PLANT CAPACITY	ELECTRIC CHILLER TYPE	FOSSIL FUEL CHILLER TYPE
≤ 100 tons	Reciprocating	Single-effect absorption, direct fired
> 100 tons, < 300 tons	Screw	Double-effect absorption, direct fired
≥ 300 tons	Centrifugal	Double-effect absorption, direct fired

For SI: 1 ton = 3517 W.

roof. Minimum roof/ceiling insulation levels shall be code minimums as per Section C407.2.1.

C407.5.2.4.2 Enthalpy Recovery Ventilation systems (ERVs). Credit may be claimed in the whole building performance method calculations for Enthalpy Recovery Ventilation systems used in the proposed building. This credit is applicable for buildings in which every HVAC system has a design supply airflow of less than 5,000 cfm. The credit shall also be applicable to buildings where one or more HVAC systems in the building have a design supply flow equal to 5,000 cfm or greater but shall have minimum outdoor air supply less than 70 percent of the design supply airflow for that HVAC system.

The credit shall provide for a reduction of 6 percent of total HVAC annual energy use for buildings located in Climate Zone 1 and 4 percent of total HVAC annual energy use for buildings located in Climate Zone 2.

C407.6 Calculation software tools. Calculation procedures used to comply with this section shall be software tools capable of calculating the annual energy consumption of all building elements that differ between the *standard reference design* and the *proposed design* and shall include the following capabilities.

1. Building operation for a full calendar year (8,760 hours).
2. Climate data for a full calendar year (8,760 hours) and shall reflect *approved* coincident hourly data for temperature, solar radiation, humidity and wind speed for the building location.
3. Ten or more thermal zones.
4. Thermal mass effects.
5. Hourly variations in occupancy, illumination, receptacle loads, thermostat settings, mechanical ventilation, HVAC equipment availability, service hot water usage and any process loads.
6. Part-load performance curves for mechanical equipment.
7. Capacity and efficiency correction curves for mechanical heating and cooling equipment.
8. Printed *code official* inspection checklist listing each of the *proposed design* component characteristics from Table C407.5.1(1) determined by the analysis to provide compliance, along with their respective performance ratings including, but not limited to, *R*-value, *U*-factor, SHGC, HSPF, AFUE, SEER, EF.

C407.6.1 Specific approval. Performance analysis tools meeting the applicable subsections of Section C407 and tested according to ASHRAE Standard 140 shall be permitted to be *approved* by the Florida Building Commission. The *code official* shall be permitted to approve tools for a specified application or limited scope in accordance with Section C101.4.3.

C407.6.2 Input values. Where calculations require input values not specified by Sections C402, C403, C404 and C405, those input values shall be taken from an *approved* source.

C407.6.3 Exceptional calculation methods. Where the simulation program does not model a design, material or device of the *proposed design*, an exceptional calculation method shall be used where approved by the *code official.* Where there are multiple designs, materials or devices that the simulation program does not model, each shall be calculated separately and exceptional savings determined for each. The total exceptional savings shall not constitute more than half of the difference between the baseline building performance and the proposed building performance. Applications for approval of an exceptional method shall include all of the following:

1. Step-by-step documentation of the exceptional calculation method performed, detailed enough to reproduce the results.
2. Copies of all spreadsheets used to perform the calculations.

3. A sensitivity analysis of energy consumption where each of the input parameters is varied from half to double the value assumed.
4. The calculations shall be performed on a time step basis consistent with the simulation program used.
5. The performance rating calculated with and without the exceptional calculation method.

SECTION C408 SYSTEM COMMISSIONING

C408.1 General. This section covers the commissioning of the building mechanical systems in Section C403 and electrical power and lighting systems in Section C405.

C408.2 Mechanical systems and service water-heating systems commissioning and completion requirements. Prior to the final mechanical and plumbing inspections, the licensed design professional, electrical engineer, mechanical engineer or *approved agency* shall provide evidence of mechanical systems *commissioning* and completion in accordance with the provisions of this section.

Construction document notes shall clearly indicate provisions for *commissioning* and completion requirements in accordance with this section and are permitted to refer to specifications for further requirements. Copies of all documentation shall be given to the owner or owner's authorized agent and made available to the *code official* upon request in accordance with Sections C408.2.4 and C408.2.5.

Exceptions: The following systems are exempt:

1. Mechanical systems and service water heater systems in buildings where the total mechanical equipment capacity is less than 480,000 Btu/h (140.7 kW) cooling capacity and 600,000 Btu/h (175.8 kW) combined service water-heating and space-heating capacity.
2. Systems included in Section C403.3 that serve individual *dwelling units* and *sleeping units*.

C408.2.1 Commissioning plan. A *commissioning plan* shall be developed by a licensed design professional, electrical engineer, mechanical engineer or *approved agency* and shall include the following items:

1. A narrative description of the activities that will be accomplished during each phase of *commissioning,* including the personnel intended to accomplish each of the activities.
2. A listing of the specific equipment, appliances or systems to be tested and a description of the tests to be performed.
3. Functions to be tested including, but not limited to, calibrations and economizer controls.
4. Conditions under which the test will be performed. Testing shall affirm winter and summer design conditions and full outside air conditions.
5. Measurable criteria for performance.

C408.2.2 Air distribution system testing, adjusting and balancing. Construction documents shall require that a written balance report be provided to the owner or the designated representative of the building owner for HVAC systems serving zones with a total conditioned area exceeding 5000 square feet (465 m^2). Air distribution systems shall be tested, adjusted and balanced by a licensed engineer or a company or individual holding a current certification from a recognized testing and balancing agency organization in accordance with generally accepted engineering standards.

Exceptions:

1. Buildings with cooling or heating system capacities of 15 tons or less per system may be tested and balanced by a mechanical contractor licensed to design and install such system(s).
2. Buildings with cooling or heating system capacities of 65,000 Btu/h or less per system are exempt from the requirements of this section.

C408.2.2.1 Air systems balancing. Air system balancing shall be accomplished in a manner to first minimize throttling losses; then for fans with fan system power greater than 1 hp, fan speeds shall be adjusted to meet design flow conditions. Balancing procedures shall be in accordance with the National Environmental Balancing Bureau (NEBB) Procedural Standards, the Associated Air Balance Council (AABC) National Standards, or equivalent procedures.

Exception: Damper throttling may be used for air system balancing with fan motors of 1 hp or less, or if throttling results in no greater than $^1/_3$ hp fan horsepower draw above that required if the fan speed were adjusted.

Notes:

1. Building envelope pressurization should be either neutral or positive to prevent infiltration of excess latent load.
2. Commercial kitchen hood exhaust cfm should be sized to prevent depressurization. Discharge dampers are prohibited on constant volume fans and variable volume fans with motors 10 hp (7.5 kW) and larger.

C408.2.2.2 Hydronic systems balancing. Individual hydronic heating and cooling coils shall be equipped with means for balancing and measuring flow. Hydronic systems shall be proportionately balanced in a manner to first minimize throttling losses, then the pump impeller shall be trimmed or pump speed shall be adjusted to meet design flow conditions. Each hydronic system shall have either the capability to measure pressure across the pump, or test ports at each side of each pump.

Exceptions: The following equipment is not required to be equipped with a means for balancing or measuring flow:

1. Pumps with pump motors of 5 hp (3.7 kW) or less.
2. Where throttling results in no greater than 5 percent of the nameplate horsepower draw

above that required if the impeller were trimmed.

C408.2.3 Functional performance testing. Functional performance testing specified in Sections C408.2.3.1 through C408.2.3.3 shall be conducted.

C408.2.3.1 Equipment. Equipment functional performance testing shall demonstrate the installation and operation of components, systems, and system-to-system interfacing relationships in accordance with approved plans and specifications such that operation, function, and maintenance serviceability for each of the commissioned systems is confirmed. Testing shall include all modes and *sequence of operation*, including under full-load, part-load and the following emergency conditions:

1. All modes as described in the *sequence* of *operation*.
2. Redundant or *automatic* back-up mode.
3. Performance of alarms.
4. Mode of operation upon a loss of power and restoration of power.

Exception: Unitary or packaged HVAC equipment listed in Tables C403.2.3(1) through C403.2.3(3) that do not require supply air economizers.

C408.2.3.2 Controls. HVAC and service water-heating control systems shall be tested to document that control devices, components, equipment and systems are calibrated and adjusted and operate in accordance with approved plans and specifications. Sequences of operation shall be functionally tested to document they operate in accordance with *approved* plans and specifications.

C408.2.3.3 Economizers. Air economizers shall undergo a functional test to determine that they operate in accordance with manufacturer's specifications.

C408.2.4 Preliminary commissioning report. A preliminary report of *commissioning* test procedures and results shall be completed and certified by the licensed design professional, electrical engineer, mechanical engineer or *approved agency* and provided to the building owner or owner's authorized agent. The report shall be organized with mechanical and service hot water findings in separate sections to allow independent review. The report shall be identified as "Preliminary Commissioning Report" and shall identify:

1. Itemization of deficiencies found during testing required by this section that have not been corrected at the time of report preparation.
2. Deferred tests that cannot be performed at the time of report preparation because of climatic conditions.
3. Climatic conditions required for performance of the deferred tests.

C408.2.4.1 Acceptance of report. Buildings, or portions thereof, shall not be considered acceptable for a final inspection pursuant to Section C104.3 until the *code official* has received a letter of transmittal from the building owner acknowledging that the building owner or owner's authorized agent has received the Preliminary Commissioning Report.

C408.2.4.2 Copy of report. The *code official* shall be permitted to require that a copy of the Preliminary Commissioning Report be made available for review by the *code official*.

C408.2.5 Documentation requirements. The *construction documents* shall specify that the documents described in this section be provided to the building owner or owner's authorized agent within 90 days of the date of receipt of the *certificate of occupancy*.

C408.2.5.1 Drawings. *Construction documents* shall include the location and performance data on each piece of equipment.

C408.2.5.2 Manuals. An operating and maintenance manual shall be provided and include all of the following:

1. Submittal data stating equipment size and selected options for each piece of equipment requiring maintenance.
2. Manufacturer's operation manuals and maintenance manuals for each piece of equipment requiring maintenance, except equipment not furnished as part of the project. Required routine maintenance actions shall be clearly identified.
3. Name and address of at least one service agency.
4. HVAC and service hot water controls system maintenance and calibration information, including wiring diagrams, schematics and control sequence descriptions. Desired or field-determined set points shall be permanently recorded on control drawings at control devices or, for digital control systems, in system programming instructions.
5. Submittal data indicating all selected options for each piece of lighting equipment and lighting controls.
6. Operation and maintenance manuals for each piece of lighting equipment. Required routine maintenance actions, cleaning and recommended relamping shall be clearly identified.
7. A schedule for inspecting and recalibrating all lighting controls.
8. A narrative of how each system is intended to operate, including recommended set points.

C408.2.5.3 System balancing report. A written report describing the activities and measurements completed in accordance with Section C408.2.2.

C408.2.5.4 Final commissioning report. A report of test procedures and results identified as "Final Commissioning Report" shall be delivered to the building owner or owner's authorized agent. The report shall be organized with mechanical system and service hot water system findings in separate sections to allow independent review. The report shall include the following:

1. Results of functional performance tests.
2. Disposition of deficiencies found during testing, including details of corrective measures used or proposed.
3. Functional performance test procedures used during the commissioning process including measurable criteria for test acceptance, provided herein for repeatability.

Exception: Deferred tests that cannot be performed at the time of report preparation due to climatic conditions.

C408.3 Lighting system functional testing. Controls for automatic lighting systems shall comply with this section.

C408.3.1 Functional testing. Prior to passing final inspection, the *registered design professional* shall provide evidence that the lighting control systems have been tested to ensure that control hardware and software are calibrated, adjusted, programmed and in proper working condition in accordance with the *construction documents* and manufacturer's instructions. Functional testing shall be in accordance with Sections C408.3.1.1 and C408.3.1.2 for the applicable control type.

C408.3.1.1 Occupant sensor controls. Where *occupant sensor controls* are provided, the following procedures shall be performed:

1. Certify that the *occupant sensor* has been located and aimed in accordance with manufacturer recommendations.
2. For projects with seven or fewer *occupant sensors*, each sensor shall be tested.
3. For projects with more than seven *occupant sensors,* testing shall be done for each unique combination of sensor type and space geometry. Where multiples of each unique combination of sensor type and space geometry are provided, not less than 10 percent, but in no case less than one, of each combination shall be tested unless the *code official* or design professional requires a higher percentage to be tested. Where 30 percent or more of the tested controls fail, all remaining identical combinations shall be tested.

   For *occupant sensor controls* to be tested, verify the following:

   3.1. Where *occupant sensor controls* include status indicators, verify correct operation.

   3.2. The controlled lights turn off or down to the permitted level within the required time.

   3.3. For auto-on *occupant sensor controls*, the lights turn on to the permitted level when an occupant enters the space.

   3.4. For manual-on *occupant sensor controls*, the lights turn on only when manually activated.

   3.5. The lights are not incorrectly turned on by movement in adjacent areas or by HVAC operation.

C408.3.1.2 Time-switch controls. Where *time-switch controls* are provided, the following procedures shall be performed:

1. Confirm that the *time-switch control* is programmed with accurate weekday, weekend and holiday schedules.
2. Provide documentation to the owner of *time-switch controls* programming including weekday, weekend, holiday schedules, and set-up and preference program settings.
3. Verify the correct time and date in the time switch.
4. Verify that any battery back-up is installed and energized.
5. Verify that the override time limit is set to not more than 2 hours.
6. Simulate occupied condition. Verify and document the following:

   6.1. All lights can be turned on and off by their respective area control switch.

   6.2. The switch only operates lighting in the enclosed space in which the switch is located.

7. Simulate unoccupied condition. Verify and document the following:

   7.1. Nonexempt lighting turns off.

   7.2. Manual override switch allows only the lights in the enclosed space where the override switch is located to turn on or remain on until the next scheduled shutoff occurs.

8. Additional testing as specified by the *registered design professional.*

C408.3.1.3 Daylight responsive controls. Where *daylight responsive controls* are provided, the following shall be verified:

1. Control devices have been properly located, field calibrated and set for accurate setpoints and threshold light levels.
2. Daylight controlled lighting loads adjust to light level set points in response to available daylight.
3. The locations of calibration adjustment equipment are readily accessible only to authorized personnel.

C408.3.2 Documentation requirements. The *construction documents* shall specify that documents certifying that the installed lighting controls meet documented performance criteria of Section C405 are to be provided to the building owner within 90 days from the date of receipt of the *certificate of occupancy.*

CHAPTER 5 [CE]
EXISTING BUILDINGS

**

SECTION C501
GENERAL

C501.1 Scope. The provisions of this chapter shall control the *alteration*, *repair*, *addition* and change of occupancy of existing buildings and structures.

C501.2 Existing buildings. Except as specified in this chapter, this code shall not be used to require the removal, *alteration* or abandonment of, nor prevent the continued use and maintenance of, an existing building or building system lawfully in existence at the time of adoption of this code.

C501.3 Maintenance. Buildings and structures, and parts thereof, shall be maintained in a safe and sanitary condition. Devices and systems that are required by this code shall be maintained in conformance to the code edition under which installed. The owner or the owner's authorized agent shall be responsible for the maintenance of buildings and structures. The requirements of this chapter shall not provide the basis for removal or abrogation of energy conservation, fire protection and safety systems and devices in existing structures.

C501.4 Compliance. *Alterations*, *repairs*, *additions* and changes of occupancy to, or relocation of, existing buildings and structures shall comply with the provisions for *alterations*, *repairs*, *additions* and changes of occupancy or relocation, respectively, in the *Florida Building Code, Building*; *Florida Fire Prevention Code*; *Florida Building Code, Fuel Gas*; *Florida Building Code, Mechanical*; *Florida Building Code, Plumbing*; and NFPA 70.

C501.5 New and replacement materials. Except as otherwise required or permitted by this code, materials permitted by the applicable code for new construction shall be used. Like materials shall be permitted for *repairs*, provided hazards to life, health or property are not created. Hazardous materials shall not be used where the code for new construction would not permit use of these materials in buildings of similar occupancy, purpose and location.

** **C501.6 Historic buildings.** No provisions of this code relating to the construction, *repair, alteration*, restoration and movement of structures, and *change of occupancy* shall be mandatory for *historic buildings* provided a report has been submitted to the *code official* and signed by a *registered design professional*, or a representative of the State Historic Preservation Office or the historic preservation authority having jurisdiction, demonstrating that compliance with that provision would threaten, degrade or destroy the historic form, fabric or function of the building.

C501.7 Building systems and components. Thermal efficiency standards are set for the following building systems and components where new products are installed or replaced in existing buildings, and for which a permit must be obtained. New products shall meet the minimum efficiencies allowed by this code for the following systems and components:

Heating, ventilating or air-conditioning systems;
Service water or pool heating systems;
Lighting systems; and
Replacement fenestration.

Exceptions:

1. Where part of a functional unit is repaired or replaced. For example, replacement of an entire HVAC system is not required because a new compressor or other part does not meet code when installed with an older system.
2. If the unit being replaced is itself a functional unit, such as a condenser, it does not constitute a repair. Outdoor and indoor units that are not designed to be operated together must meet the U.S. Department of Energy certification requirements contained in Section R303.1.2. Matched systems are required; this match may be verified by any one of the following means:
   a. AHRI data
   b. Accredited laboratory
   c. Manufacturer's letter
   d. Letter from registered P.E. State of Florida
3. Where existing components are utilized with a replacement system, such as air distribution system ducts or electrical wiring for lights, such components or controls need not meet code if meeting code would require that component's replacement.
4. Replacement equipment that would require extensive revisions to other systems, equipment or elements of a building where such replacement is a like-for-like replacement, such as through-the-wall condensing units and PTACs, chillers and cooling towers in confined spaces.

C501.7.1 Existing equipment efficiencies. Existing cooling and heating equipment in residential applications need not meet the minimum equipment efficiencies, including system sizing and duct sealing.

SECTION C502
ADDITIONS

**

C502.1 General. *Additions* to an existing building, building system or portion thereof shall conform to the provisions of this code as those provisions relate to new construction without requiring the unaltered portion of the existing building or building system to comply with this code. *Additions* shall not create an unsafe or hazardous condition or overload existing building systems. An *addition* shall be deemed to comply with this code if the *addition* alone complies or if the existing building and *addition* comply with this code as a single building. *Additions* shall comply with Section C502.2.

Additions complying with ANSI/ASHRAE/IESNA 90.1. need not comply with Sections C402, C403, C404 and C405.

C502.2 Prescriptive compliance. *Additions* shall comply with Sections C502.2.1 through C502.2.6.2.

C502.2.1 Vertical fenestration. New *vertical fenestration* area that results in a total building *fenestration* area less than or equal to that specified in Section C402.4.1 shall comply with Section C402.4. *Additions* with *vertical fenestration* that result in a total building *fenestration* area greater than Section C402.4.1 or *additions* that exceed the fenestration area greater than Section C402.4.1 shall comply with Section C402.4.1.1 for the *addition* only. *Additions* that result in a total building vertical glass area exceeding that specified in Section C402.4.1.1 shall comply with Section C407.

C502.2.2 Skylight area. New *skylight* area that results in a total building *fenestration* area less than or equal to that specified in Section C402.4.1 shall comply with Section C402.4. *Additions* with *skylight* area that result in a total building *skylight* area greater than C402.4.1 or additions that exceed the *skylight* area shall comply with Section C402.4.1.2 for the *addition* only. *Additions* that result in a total building *skylight* area exceeding that specified in Section C402.4.1.2 shall comply with Section C407.

C502.2.3 Building mechanical systems. New mechanical systems and equipment that are part of the *addition* and serve the building heating, cooling and ventilation needs shall comply with Section C403.

C502.2.4 Service water-heating systems. New service water-heating equipment, controls and service water heating piping shall comply with Section C404.

C502.2.5 Pools and inground permanently installed spas. New pools and inground permanently installed spas shall comply with Section C404.9.

C502.2.6 Lighting power and systems. New lighting systems that are installed as part of the addition shall comply with Section C405.

C502.2.6.1 Interior lighting power. The total interior lighting power for the *addition* shall comply with Section C405.4.2 for the *addition* alone, or the existing building and the *addition* shall comply as a single building.

C502.2.6.2 Exterior lighting power. The total exterior lighting power for the *addition* shall comply with Section C405.5.1 for the *addition* alone, or the existing building and the *addition* shall comply as a single building.

SECTION C503 ALTERATIONS

C503.1 General. *Alterations* to any building or structure shall comply with the requirements of the code for new construction. *Alterations* shall be such that the existing building or structure is no less conforming to the provisions of this code than the existing building or structure was prior to the *alteration*. *Alterations* to an existing building, building system or portion thereof shall conform to the provisions of this code as those provisions relate to new construction without requiring the unaltered portions of the existing building or building system to comply with this code. *Alterations* shall not create an unsafe or hazardous condition or overload existing building systems.

Alterations complying with ANSI/ASHRAE/IESNA 90.1. need not comply with Sections C402, C403, C404 and C405.

Exception: The following *alterations* need not comply with the requirements for new construction, provided the energy use of the building is not increased:

1. Storm windows installed over existing *fenestration*.
2. Surface-applied window film installed on existing single-pane *fenestration* assemblies reducing solar heat gain, provided the code does not require the glazing or *fenestration* to be replaced.
3. Existing ceiling, wall or floor cavities exposed during construction, provided that these cavities are filled with insulation.
4. Construction where the existing roof, wall or floor cavity is not exposed.
5. *Roof recover*.
6. *Air barriers* shall not be required for *roof recover* and roof replacement where the *alterations* or renovations to the building do not include *alterations*, renovations or *repairs* to the remainder of the building envelope.
7. *Alterations* that replace less than 50 percent of the luminaires in a space, provided that such *alterations* do not increase the installed interior lighting power.

C503.2 Change in space conditioning. Any nonconditioned or low-energy space that is altered to become conditioned space shall be required to be brought into full compliance with this code. **

C503.3 Building envelope. New building envelope assemblies that are part of the *alteration* shall comply with Sections C402.1 through C402.5.

C503.3.1 Roof replacement. *Roof replacements* shall comply with Table C402.1.3 or C402.1.4 where the existing roof assembly is part of the *building thermal envelope* and contains insulation entirely above the roof deck.

C503.3.2 Vertical fenestration. The addition of *vertical fenestration* that results in a total building *fenestration* area less than or equal to that specified in Section

C402.4.1 shall comply with Section C402.4. The addition of *vertical fenestration* that results in a total building *fenestration* area greater than Section C402.4.1 shall comply with Section C402.4.1.1 for the space adjacent to the new fenestration only. *Alterations* that result in a total building vertical glass area exceeding that specified in Section C402.4.1.1 shall comply with Section C407.

C503.3.3 Skylight area. The addition of *skylight* area that results in a total building *skylight* area less than or equal to that specified in Section C402.4.1 shall comply with Section C402.4. The addition of *skylight* area that results in a total building skylight area greater than Section C402.4.1 shall comply with Section C402.4.1.2 for the space adjacent to the new skylights. *Alterations* that result in a total building skylight area exceeding that specified in Section C402.4.1.2 shall comply with Section C407.

C503.4 Heating and cooling systems. New heating, cooling and duct systems that are part of the *alteration* shall comply with Sections C403.

C503.4.1 Economizers. New cooling systems that are part of *alteration* shall comply with Section C403.3.

C503.5 Service hot water systems. New service hot water systems that are part of the *alteration* shall comply with Section C404.

C503.6 Lighting systems. New lighting systems that are part of the *alteration* shall comply with Section C405.

Exception. *Alterations* that replace less than 10 percent of the luminaires in a space, provided that such *alterations* do not increase the installed interior lighting power.

**

SECTION C504 REPAIRS

C504.1 General. Buildings and structures, and parts thereof, shall be repaired in compliance with Section C501.3 and this section. Work on nondamaged components that is necessary for the required *repair* of damaged components shall be considered part of the *repair* and shall not be subject to the requirements for *alterations* in this chapter. Routine maintenance required by Section C501.3, ordinary *repairs* exempt from *permit* and abatement of wear due to normal service conditions shall not be subject to the requirements for *repairs* in this section.

Where a building was constructed to comply with ANSI/ASHRAE/IESNA 90.1, repairs shall comply with the standard and need not comply with Sections C402, C403, C404 and C405.

C504.2 Application. For the purposes of this code, the following shall be considered repairs:

1. Glass-only replacements in an existing sash and frame.
2. *Roof repairs.*
3. Air barriers shall not be required for *roof repair* where the repairs to the building do not include *alterations*, renovations or *repairs* to the remainder of the building envelope.
4. Replacement of existing doors that separate conditioned space from the exterior shall not require the installation of a vestibule or revolving door, provided that an existing vestibule that separates a conditioned space from the exterior shall not be removed.
5. *Repairs* where only the bulb, the ballast or both within the existing luminaires in a space are replaced, provided that the replacement does not increase the installed interior lighting power.

**

SECTION C505 CHANGE OF OCCUPANCY OR USE

C505.1 General. Spaces undergoing a change in occupancy that would result in an increase in demand for either fossil fuel or electrical energy shall comply with this code. Where the use in a space changes from one use in Table C405.4.2(1) or C405.4.2(2) to another use in Table C405.4.2(1) or C405.4.2(2), the installed lighting wattage shall comply with Section C405.4.

CHAPTER 6 [CE]
REFERENCED STANDARDS

This chapter lists the standards that are referenced in various sections of this document. The standards are listed herein by the promulgating agency of the standard, the standard identification, the effective date and title, and the section or sections of this document that reference the standard. The application of the referenced standards shall be as specified in Section 106.

AABC

Associated Air Balance Council
1518 K Street, Suite 503
Washington, DC 20005

Standard reference number	Title	Referenced in code section number
AABC, 1989	Associated Air Balance Council National Standards	C408.2.2.1

AAMA

American Architectural Manufacturers Association
1827 Walden Office Square
Suite 550
Schaumburg, IL 60173-4268

Standard reference number	Title	Referenced in code section number
AAMA/WDMA/CSA 101/I.S.2/A C440—11	North American Fenestration Standard/ Specifications for Windows, Doors and Unit Skylights	Table C402.5.2

ACCA

Air Conditioning Contractors of America
2800 Shirlington Road, Suite 300
Arlington, VA 22206

Standard reference number	Title	Referenced in code section number
ACCA Manual D-1995	Residential Duct Systems	C403.2.9.5
ACCA Manual N-2005	Commercial Load Calculation	C403.2.1
ANSI/ASHRAE/ ACCA 183-2007	Peak Cooling and Heating Load Calculations in Buildings Except Low-rise Residential Buildings	C403.2.1

ADC

Air Duct Council
1901 N. RoselleRd., Suite 800
Schaumburg, IL 60195

Standard reference number	Title	Referenced in code section number
ADC 2003	Flexible Duct Performance & Installation Standards, Fourth Edition	Table C403.2.9.2

AHAM

Association of Home Appliance Manufacturers
1111 19th Street, NW, Suite 402
Washington, DC 20036

Standard reference number	Title	Referenced in code section number
ANSI/ AHAM RAC-1—2008	Room Air Conditioners	Table C403.2.3(3)
AHAM HRF-1—2007	Energy, Performance and Capacity of Household Refrigerators, Refrigerator-Freezers and Freezers	Table C403.2.14.1

AHRI

Air-Conditioning, Heating, & Refrigeration Institute
2111 Wilson Blvd, Suite 500
Arlington, VA 22201

Standard reference number	Title	Referenced in code section number
ISO/AHRI/ASHRAE 13256-1 (2011)	Water-to-Air and Brine-to-Air Heat Pumps— Testing and Rating for Performance	Table C403.2.3(2)
ISO/AHRI/ASHRAE 13256-2 (2011)	Water-to-Water and Brine-to-Water Heat Pumps — Testing and Rating for Performance	Table C403.2.3(2)
210/240—08 with Addenda 1 and 2	Performance Rating of Unitary Air-Conditioning and Air-Source Heat Pump Equipment	Table C403.2.3(1), Table C403.2.3(2)
310/380—04 (CSA-C744-04)	Standard for Packaged Terminal Air Conditioners and Heat Pumps	Table C403.2.3(3)
340/360—2007 with Addendum 2	Performance Rating of Commercial and Industrial Unitary Air-Conditioning and Heat Pump Equipment	Table C403.2.3(1), Table C403.2.3(2)
365(I-P)—09	Commercial and Industrial Unitary Air-Conditioning Condensing Units	Table C403.2.3(1), Table C403.2.3(6)
390—03	Performance Rating of Single Package Vertical Air-Conditioners and Heat Pumps	Table C403.2.3(3)
400—2001	Liquid to Liquid Heat Exchangers with Addendum 1 and 2	Table C403.2.3(10)
440—2008	Performance Rating of Room Fan Coils	C403.2.10
460—2005	Performance Rating of Remote Mechanical-Draft Air-Cooled Refrigerant Condensers	Table C403.2.3(8)
550/590—2011 With Addendum 1	Performance Rating of Water-Chilling and Heat Pump Water-Heating Packages Using the Vapor Compression Cycle	C403.2.3.1, Table C403.2.3(7)
560—00	Absorption Water Chilling and Water Heating Packages	Table C403.2.3(7)
1160 (I-P) —09	Performance Rating of Heat Pump Pool Heaters	Table C404.2
1200-2010	Performance Rating of Commercial Refrigerated Display Merchandisers and Storage Cabinets	C403.2.14, Table C403.2.14(1), Table C403.2.14(2)
1230-2010	Performance Rating of Variable Refrigerant Flow (VRF) Multi-split Air-conditioning and Heat Pump Equipment with Addendum 1	Table C403.2.3(11)

AMCA

Air Movement and Control Association International
30 West University Drive
Arlington Heights, IL 60004-1806

Standard reference number	Title	Referenced in code section number
205—12	Energy Efficiency Classification for Fans	C403.2.12.3
220—08 (R2012)	Laboratory Methods of Testing Air Curtain Units for Aerodynamic Performance Rating	C402.5.7
500D—12	Laboratory Methods for Testing Dampers for Rating	C403.2.4.3

ANSI

American National Standards Institute
25 West 43rd Street
4th Floor
New York, NY 10036

Standard reference number	Title	Referenced in code section number
A 112.18.1M—1999	Finished and Rough Brass Plumbing Fixture Fittings	C404.12.1
Z21.10.3/CSA 4.3—11	Gas Water Heaters, Volume III—Storage Water Heaters with Input Ratings Above 75,000 Btu per Hour, Circulating Tank and Instantaneous	Table C404.2
Z21.47/CSA 2.3—12	Gas-fired Central Furnaces	Table C403.2.3(4)
Z83.8/CSA 2.6—09	Gas Unit Heaters, Gas Packaged Heaters, Gas Utility Heaters and Gas-fired Duct Furnaces	Table C403.2.3(4)

APSP

The Association of Pool & Spa Professionals
2111 Eisenhower Avenue, Suite 500
Alexandria, VA 22314

Standard reference number	Title	Referenced in code section number
ANSI/APSP/ICC 14-14	American National Standard for Portable Electric Spa Energy Efficiency	C404.10

ASHRAE

ASHRAE
1791 Tullie Circle NE
Atlanta, GA 30329-2305

Standard reference number	Title	Referenced in code section number
ASHRAE 127-2007	Method of Testing for Rating Computer	Table C403.2.3(9)
ANSI/ASHRAE Standard 55—1992	Thermal Environmental Conditions for Human Occupancy	C403.5.3
ANSI/ASHRAE/ACCA Standard 183—2007 (RA2011)	Peak Cooling and Heating Load Calculations in Buildings, Except Low-rise Residential Buildings	C403.2.1
ASHRAE—2008	HVAC Systems and Equipment Handbook	C403.2.1
ASHRAE—2012	ASHRAE HVAC Systems and Equipment Handbook	C403.2.1
ISO/AHRI/ASHRAE 13256-1 (2011)	Water-to-Air and Brine-to-Air Heat Pumps—Testing and Rating for Performance	Table C403.2.3(2)
ISO/AHRI/ASHRAE 13256-2 (2011)	Water-to-Water and Brine-to-Water Heat Pumps—Testing and Rating for Performance	Table C403.2.3(2)
ANSI/ASHRAE/IESNA 90.1—2013	Energy Standard for Buildings Except Low-rise Residential Buildings, excluding section 9.4.1.1(g)	C304.1,1, C304.3.1.4, C304.3.2.1, C304.3.2.2, C401.2, C405.6.1, C406.2, C502.1, C504.1
140—2011	Standard Method of Test for the Evaluation of Building Energy Analysis Computer Programs	C407.6.1
146—2011	Testing and Rating Pool Heaters	Table C404.2

ASME

American Society of Mechanical Engineers
Two Park Avenue
New York, NY 10016-5990

Standard reference number	Title	Referenced in code section number
ASME A17.1/ CSA B44—2013	Safety Code for Elevators and Escalators	C405.9.2

ASTM

ASTM International
100 Barr Harbor Drive, P.O. Box C700
West Conshohocken, PA 19428-2959

Standard reference number	Title	Referenced in code section number
C36/C36M—03	Standard Specification for Gypsum Wallboard	202
C90—13	Specification for Load-bearing Concrete Masonry Units	Table C401.3, C304.1.1
C177—04	Test Method for Steady-state Heat Flux Measurements and Thermal Transmission Properties by Means of the Guarded-hot-plate Apparatus	C304.2.1
C236—89 (1993el)	Test Method for Steady-state Thermal Performance of Building Assemblies by Means of a Guarded Hot Box	C304.2.1
C 518—04	Test Method for Steady-state Thermal Transmission Properties by Means of the Heat Flow Meter Apparatus	C304.2.1
C1363—05	Standard Test Method for Thermal Performance of Building Materials and Envelope Assemblies by Means of a Hot Box Apparatus	C304.2.2
C1363—11	Standard Test Method for Thermal Performance of Building Materials and Envelope Assemblies by Means of a Hot Box Apparatus	C303.1.4.1, Table C402.1.4
C1371—04a(2010)e1	Standard Test Method for Determination of Emittance of Materials Near Room Temperature Using Portable Emissometers	Table C402.3
C1549—09	Standard Test Method for Determination of Solar Reflectance Near Ambient Temperature Using A Portable Solar Reflectometer	Table C402.3
D1003—11e1	Standard Test Method for Haze and Luminous Transmittance of Transparent Plastics	C402.4.2.2
D2412—02(2008)	Test Method for Determination of External Loading Characteristics of Plastic Pipe by Parallel Pipe Loading	Table C403.2.9.2
E84—09	Test Method for Surface Burning Characteristics of Building Materials	202, C403.2.9.3.7
E283—04	Test Method for Determining the Rate of Air Leakage Through Exterior Windows, Curtain Walls and Doors Under Specified Pressure Differences Across the Specimen	C402.5.1.2.2, Table C402.5.2, C402.5.8
E408—71(2008)	Test Methods for Total Normal Emittance of Surfaces Using Inspection-meter Techniques	Table C402.3
E779—10	Standard Test Method for Determining Air Leakage Rate by Fan Pressurization	C402.5
E903—96	Standard Test Method Solar Absorptance, Reflectance and Transmittance of Materials Using Integrating Spheres (Withdrawn 2005)	Table C402.3
E1677—11	Standard Specification for an Air-retarder (AR) Material or System for Low-rise Framed Building Walls	C402.5.1.2.2
E1918—06	Standard Test Method for Measuring Solar Reflectance of Horizontal or Low-sloped Surfaces in the Field	Table C402.3
E1980—11	Standard Practice for Calculating Solar Reflectance Index of Horizontal and Low-sloped Opaque Surfaces	Table C402.3, C402.3.2
E2178—13	Standard Test Method for Air Permanence of Building Materials	C402.5.1.2.1
E2357—11	Standard Test Method for Determining Air Leakage of Air Barriers Assemblies	C402.5.1.2.2

CRRC

Cool Roof Rating Council
449 15th Street, Suite 400
Oakland, CA 94612

Standard reference number	Title	Referenced in code section number
ANSI/CRRC-1—2012	CRRC-1 Standard	Table C402.3, C402.3.2, C402.3.2.1, Table C407.5.1(1)

CSA

CSA Group
8501 East Pleasant Valley Road
Cleveland, OH 44131-5516

Standard reference number	Title	Referenced in code section number
AAMA/WDMA/CSA 101/I.S.2/A440—11	North American Fenestration Standard/Specification for Windows, Doors and Unit Skylights	Table C402.5.2
CSA B55.1—2012	Test Method for Measuring Efficiency and Pressure Loss of Drain Water Heat Recovery Units	C404.8
CSA B55.2—2012	Drain Water Heat Recover Units	C404.8

CTI

Cooling Technology Institute
P. O. Box 681807
Houston, TX 77268

Standard reference number	Title	Referenced in code section number
ATC 105 (00)	Acceptance Test Code for Water Cooling Tower	Table C403.2.3(8)
ATC 105S—11	Acceptance Test Code for Closed Circuit Cooling Towers	Table C403.2.3(8)
ATC 106—11	Acceptance Test For Mechanical Draft Evaporative Vapor Condensers	Table C403.2.3(8)
STD 201—11	Standard for Certification of Water Cooling Towers Thermal Performances	Table C403.2.3(8)

DASMA

Door & Access Systems Manufacturers Association
1300 Sumner Avenue
Cleveland, OH 44115-2851

Standard reference number	Title	Referenced in code section number
105—92 (R2004)—13	Test Method for Thermal Transmittance and Air Infiltration of Garage Doors	C303.1.3, Table C402.5.2

DOE

U.S. Department of Energy
c/o Superintendent of Documents
1000 Independence Avenue SW
Washington, DC 20585

Standard reference number	Title	Referenced in code section number
10 CFR, Part 430—1998	Energy Conservation Program for Consumer Products: Test Procedures and Certification and Enforcement Requirement for Plumbing Products; and Certification and Enforcement Requirements for Residential Appliances; Final Rule	Table C403.2.3(4), Table C403.2.3(5), Table C404.2
10 CFR, Part 430, Subpart B, Appendix N—1998	Uniform Test Method for Measuring the Energy Consumption of Furnaces and Boilers	C202
10 CFR, Part 431—2004	Energy Efficiency Program for Certain Commercial and Industrial Equipment: Test Procedures and Efficiency Standards; Final Rules	Table C403.2.3(5), C405.7, C405.8, Table C405.8
10 CFR 431 Subpart B App B	Uniform Test Method for Measuring Nominal Full Load Efficiency of Electric Motors	C403.4.4.4, Table C405.8(1), Table C405.8(2), Table C405.8(3), C405.8(4)
NAECA 87—(88)	National Appliance Energy Conservation Act 1987 [(Public Law 100-12 (with Amendments of 1988-P.L. 100-357)]	Tables C403.2.3(1), C403.2.3(2), C403.2.3(4)

Florida Codes

Building Codes and Standards Office
Florida Department of Business and Professional Regulation
1940 N Monroe Street, Suite 90A
Tallahassee, FL 32399-0772

Standard reference number	Title	Referenced in code section number
FBC-M—Sixth Edition (2017)	Florida Building Code, Mechanical	C201.3, C403.2.6, C403.2.7, Table C403.2.9.2, C403.4.4.6
FBC-FG—Sixth Edition (2017)	Florida Building Code, Fuel Gas	C201.3
FBC-P—Sixth Edition (2017)	Florida Building Code, Plumbing	C201.3
FBC-R—Sixth Edition (2017)	Florida Building Code, Residential	C201.3, C202
FFPC—Sixth Edition (2017)	Florida Fire Prevention Code	C201.3
FS	Florida Statutes	C103.1.1.1.2, C103.1.1.2

IEEE

Institute of Electrical and Electronic Engineers Inc.
3 Park Avenue, 17th Floor
New York, NY 10016

Standard reference number	Title	Referenced in code section number
IEEE 515.1—2012	IEE Standard for the Testing, Design, Installation, and Maintenance of Electrical Resistance Trace Heating for Commercial Applications	C404.6.2

IES

Illuminating Engineering Society
120 Wall Street, 17th Floor
New York, NY 10005-4001

Standard reference number	Title	Referenced in code section number
ANSI/ASHRAE/IESNA 90.1—2013	Energy Standard for Buildings Except Low-rise Residential Buildings, excluding section 9.4.1.1(g)	C401.2, Table C402.1.3, Table C402.1.4, C406.2, C502.1, C503.1, C504.1

ISO

International Organization for Standardization
Chemin de Blandonnet 8
CP 401
1214 Vernier
Geneva, Switzerland

Standard reference number	Title	Referenced in code section number
ISO/AHRI/ASHRAE 13256-1 (2011)	Water-to-Air and Brine-to-air Heat Pumps -Testing and Rating for Performance	Table C403.2.3(2)
ISO/AHRI/ASHRAE 13256-2(2011)	Water-to-Water and Brine-to-Water Heat Pumps -Testing and Rating for Performance	C403.2.3(2)

NAIMA

North American Insulation Manufacturers Association
11 Canal Center Plaza, Suite 103
Alexandria, VA 22314

Standard reference number	Title	Referenced in code section number
NAIMA 2002	Fibrous Glass Duct Construction Standards, Fifth Edition	Table C403.2.9.2

NEBB

National Environmental Balancing Bureau
8575 Grovemont Circle
Gaithersburg, MD 20877-4121

Standard reference number	Title	Referenced in code section number
NEBB, 2005	Procedural Standards for Testing Adjusting Balancing of Environmental Systems, Seventh Edition	C408.2.2.1

NEMA

National Electrical Manufacturers Association
1300 North 17th Street, Suite 900
Arlington, VA 22209

Standard reference number	Title	Referenced in code section number
MG1—1993	Motors and Generators	C202

NFPA

National Fire Protection Association
1 Batterymarch Park
Quincy, MA 02169-7471

Standard reference number	Title	Referenced in code section number
70—14	National Electrical Code	C501.4

NFRC

National Fenestration Rating Council, Inc.
6305 Ivy Lane, Suite 140
Greenbelt, MD 20770

Standard reference number	Title	Referenced in code section number
100—2009	Procedure for Determining Fenestration Products *U*-factors—Second Edition	C303.1.3, C402.2.2
200—2009	Procedure for Determining Fenestration Product Solar Heat Gain Coefficients and Visible Transmittance at Normal Incidence—Second Edition	C303.1.3, C402.4.1.1
400—2009	Procedure for Determining Fenestration Product Air Leakage—Second Edition	Table C402.5.2

SMACNA

Sheet Metal and Air Conditioning Contractors' National Association, Inc.
4021 Lafayette Center Drive
Chantilly, VA 20151-1219

Standard reference number	Title	Referenced in code section number
SMACNA—2012	HVAC Air Duct Leakage Test Manual 2nd Edition	Table C403.2.9.2, C403.2.9.3.7

SPRI

Single Ply Roofing Industry
465 Waverly Oaks Road, Suite 421
Waltham, MA 02452

Standard reference number	Title	Referenced in code section number
ANSI/SPRI VF-1 2010	External Fire Design Standard for Vegetative Roofs	C407.5.2.4.1

UL

UL LLC
333 Pfingsten Road
Northbrook, IL 60062-2096

Standard reference number	Title	Referenced in code section number
181—05	Standard for Factory-made Air Ducts and Air Connectors—with Revisions through December 1998	Table C403.2.9.2
181A—05	Closure Systems for Use with Rigid Air Ducts and Air Connectors—with Revisions through December 1998	Table C403.2.9.2, C403.2.9.3.7
181B—05	Closure Systems for Use with Flexible Air Ducts and Air Connectors—with Revisions through May 2000	Table C403.2.9.2, C403.2.9.3.7
710—12	Exhaust Hoods for Commercial Cooking Equipment	C403.2.8
723—03	Standard for Test for Surface Burning Characteristics of Building Materials	C403.2.9.3.7
727—06	Oil-fired Central Furnaces—with Revisions through April 2010	Table C403.2.3(4)
731—95	Oil-fired Unit Heaters—with Revisions through August 2012	Table C403.2.3(4)
1784—01	Air Leakage Tests of Door Assemblies—with Revisions through July 2009	C402.5.3

US-FTC

United States-Federal Trade Commission
600 Pennsylvania Avenue NW
Washington, DC 20580

Standard reference number	Title	Referenced in code section number
CFR Title 16 (May 31, 2005)	*R*-value Rule	C303.1.4

WDMA

Window and Door Manufacturers Association
2025 M Street NW, Suite 800
Washington, DC 20036-3309

Standard reference number	Title	Referenced in code section number
AAMA/WDMA/CSA 101/I.S.2/A440—11	North American Fenestration Standard/Specification for Windows, Doors and Unit Skylights	Table C402.5.2

APPENDIX CA

FORMS

FLORIDA BUILDING CODE, ENERGY CONSERVATION **CHAPTER C4—COMMERCIAL ENERGY EFFICIENCY**					
Form C402-2017 ALTERATIONS, RENOVATIONS and BUILDING SYSTEMS					
			Climate Zone:		
Project Name:			*Occupancy type:*		
Address:			Alteration ☐ Renovation ☐ Building System ☐		
City, Zip Code:			*Building Permit No.:*		
Builder:			*Permitting Office:*		
Owner:					

BUILDING ENVELOPE INFORMATION (Where changed)

Envelope Component	Description	Requirement		Efficiency	
		Location	Unit	Required	Installed
Roof type		*Table C402.1.4 or Table C402.1.3*	*≤ U-factor or ≥ R-value*		
Roof reflectance/Emittance (low slope roofs)		*Table C402.3*	*≥ Solar reflectance, ≥ Thermal emittance*		
Wall type, above grade		*Table C402.1.4 or Table C402.1.3*	*≤ U-factor or ≥ R-value*		
Wall, below grade					
Floor type					
Vertical fenestrations		*Table C402.4*	*≤ U-factor*		
			≤ SHGC		
Skylights			*≤ U-factor*		
			≤ SHGC		

BUILDING SYSTEMS INFORMATION [for HVAC, service hot water or pool heating, lighting systems and replacement fenestration (C501.7)]

System	Type (describe system)	Requirement		Efficiency	
		Location	Unit	Required	Installed
Air-conditioning system		*Tables C403.2.3 (1-3, 6-8, 9-11)*	*SEER or EER, IEER*		
Heating system		*Tables C403.2.3 (2-6)*	*HSPF or COP AFUE, E_t or E_c*		
Ventilation/air handling system		*Tables C403.2.12.1(1-2)*	*Fan power (cfm)*		
Ducts	*Location:*	*Table C403.2.9.1*	*R-value*		
Piping	*Fluid design operating temp:*	*Table C403.2.10*	*Inches*		
Hot water		*Table C404.2*	*EF, E_t, COP*		
Lighting	*Space types: (append list)*	*Table C405.4.2 (1 or 2)*	*Lighting power density*		
Fenestrations: Enter information in BUILDING ENVELOPE INFORMATION box above.					
Other:					

COMPLIANCE IS BY ANSI/ASHRAE/IESNA 90.1 ☐
(Submit alternate form or append documents as needed)

I hereby certify that the plans and specifications covered by the calculation are in compliance with the Florida Building Code, Energy Conservation. *PREPARED BY:* ____________ *DATE:* ______ *I hereby certify that this building is in compliance with the Florida Building Code, Energy Conservation:* *OWNER/AGENT:* ____________ *DATE:* ______	*Review of plans and specifications covered by this calculation indicates compliance with the Florida Building Code, Energy Conservation. Before construction is completed, this building will be inspected for compliance in accordance with Section 553.908, F.S.* *BUILDING OFFICIAL:* ____________ *DATE:* ______

INDEX

C

D

E

F

S

T

U

V

W

Z

RESIDENTIAL PROVISIONS

TABLE OF CONTENTS

CHAPTER 1 [RE]

SCOPE AND ADMINISTRATION

PART 1—SCOPE AND APPLICATION

SECTION R101
SCOPE AND GENERAL REQUIREMENTS

R101.1 Title. This code shall be known as the *Florida Building Code, Energy Conservation* and shall be cited as such. It is referred to herein as "this code."

R101.2 Scope. This code applies to *residential buildings* and the building sites and associated systems and equipment.

R101.3 Intent. This code shall regulate the design and construction of buildings for the effective use and conservation of energy over the useful life of each building. This code is intended to provide flexibility to permit the use of innovative approaches and techniques to achieve this objective. This code is not intended to abridge safety, health or environmental requirements contained in other applicable codes or ordinances.

R101.4 Applicability. Where, in any specific case, different sections of this code specify different materials, methods of construction or other requirements, the most restrictive shall govern. Where there is a conflict between a general requirement and a specific requirement, the specific requirement shall govern.

*

R101.4.1 Mixed occupancy. Where a building includes both *residential* and *commercial* occupancies, each occupancy shall be separately considered and meet the applicable provisions of the *Florida Building Code, Energy Conservation*—Commercial Provisions or *Florida Building Code, Energy Conservation*—Residential Provisions.

*

R101.4.2 Exempt buildings. Buildings exempt from the provisions of the *Florida Building Code, Energy Conservation*, include existing buildings except those considered renovated buildings, changes of occupancy type or previously unconditioned buildings to which comfort conditioning is added. Exempt buildings include those specified in Sections R101.4.2.1 through R101.4.2.4.

R101.4.2.1 Federal standards. Any building for which federal mandatory standards preempt state energy codes.

R101.4.2.2 Hunting or recreational buildings < 1,000 square feet. Any building of less than 1,000 square feet (93 m^2) whose primary use is not as a principal residence and which is constructed and owned by a natural person for hunting or similar recreational purposes is exempt from this code; however, no such person may build more than one exempt building in any 12-month period.

R101.4.2.3 Historic buildings. Any building meeting the criteria for historic buildings as defined in Chapter 2 of this Code.

R101.4.2.4 Low-energy buildings as described in Section R402.1. Such buildings shall not contain electrical, plumbing or mechanical systems that have been designed to accommodate the future installation of heating or cooling equipment.

R101.5 Compliance. *Residential buildings* shall meet the provisions of *Florida Building Code, Energy Conservation*—Residential Provisions. *Commercial buildings* shall meet the provisions of *Florida Building Code, Energy Conservation*—Commercial Provisions.

R101.5.1 Compliance materials. The Florida Building Commission shall approve specific computer software, worksheets, compliance manuals and other similar materials that meet the intent of this code. Commission approved code compliance demonstration forms can be found in Table R101.5.1.

TABLE R101.5.1
INDEX TO CODE COMPLIANCE FORMS

FORM	WHERE FOUND
Form R402	Appendix RD
Florida REScheck	Computer printout
Form R405	Commission approved software printout

R101.5.1.1 Residential ≤ 3 stories.

R101.5.1.1.1 Building thermal envelope alternative. An accurately completed Residential Building Form R402 shall be submitted to the code official to demonstrate code compliance by this method. Alternatively, a Florida REScheck computer printout may be submitted to demonstrate compliance by Sections R402, R403 and R404.

R101.5.1.1.2 Simulated performance alternative. An accurately completed Residential Building Form R405 (generated by Commission approved software) demonstrating that code compliance has been achieved shall be submitted to the building official for compliance by Section R405.

R101.5.1.2 Commercial and residential > 3 stories. See *Florida Building Code, Energy Conservation*—Commercial Provisions.

SECTION R102
ALTERNATIVE MATERIALS, DESIGN AND METHODS OF CONSTRUCTION AND EQUIPMENT

R102.1 General. The provisions of this Code are not intended to prevent the installation of any material or to prohibit any design or method of construction not specifically prescribed by this code, provided that any such alternative has been approved. The *code official* shall be permitted to approve an alternative material, design or method of construction where the *code official* finds that the proposed design is satisfactory and complies with the intent of the provisions of this code, and that the material, method or work offered is, for the purpose intended, at least the equivalent of that prescribed in this code.

R102.1.1 Above code programs. The *code official* or other authority having jurisdiction shall be permitted to deem a national, state or local energy-efficiency program to exceed the energy efficiency required by this code. Buildings *approved* in writing by such an energy-efficiency program shall be considered in compliance with this code. The requirements identified as "mandatory" in Chapter 4 shall be met.

PART 2—ADMINISTRATION AND ENFORCEMENT

SECTION R103 CONSTRUCTION DOCUMENTS

R103.1 General. Construction documents, technical reports and other supporting data shall be submitted in one or more sets with each application for a permit. The construction documents and technical reports shall be prepared by a registered design professional where required by the statutes of the jurisdiction in which the project is to be constructed. Where special conditions exist, the *code official* is authorized to require necessary construction documents to be prepared by a registered design professional.

Exception: The *code official* is authorized to waive the requirements for construction documents or other supporting data if the *code official* determines they are not necessary to confirm compliance with this code.

R103.1.1 Compliance certification.

R103.1.1.1 Code compliance demonstration.

R103.1.1.1.1 Residential. No license or registration is required to prepare the code compliance form for single-family residential dwellings, duplexes and townhouses.

R103.1.1.1.2 Commercial and multiple-family residential. Completion of procedures demonstrating compliance with this code for multiple-family residential buildings shall be in accordance with the provisions of Section 481.229, *Florida Statutes*, or Section 471.003, *Florida Statutes*.

Exception: Where HVAC systems are nominal 15 tons per system or smaller, commercial building energy raters certified in accordance with Section 553.99, *Florida Statutes*, or as authorized by *Florida Statutes,* may prepare the code compliance form.

R103.1.1.2 Code compliance certification. The building's owner, the owner's architect or other authorized agent legally designated by the owner shall certify that the building is in compliance with the code, as per Section 553.907, *Florida Statutes,* prior to receiving the permit to begin construction or renovation.

R103.1.1.2.1 Reporting to entity representing the Florida Building Commission. A reporting form shall be submitted to the local building department by the owner or owner's agent with the submittal certifying compliance with this code. Reporting forms shall be a copy of the front page of the form applicable for the code chapter under which compliance is demonstrated.

R103.1.1.2.1.1 Reporting schedule. It shall be the responsibility of the local building official to forward the reporting section of the proper form to the entity representing the Florida Building Commission on a quarterly basis.

R103.2 Information on construction documents. Construction documents shall be drawn to scale upon suitable material. Electronic media documents are permitted to be submitted where *approved* by the *code official.* Construction documents shall be of sufficient clarity to indicate the location, nature and extent of the work proposed, and show in sufficient detail pertinent data and features of the *building*, systems and equipment as herein governed. Details shall include, but are not limited to, the following as applicable:

1. Insulation materials and their *R*-values.
2. Fenestration *U*-factors and solar heat gain coefficients (SHGC).
3. Area-weighted *U*-factor and solar heat gain coefficients (SHGC) calculations.
4. Mechanical system design criteria.
5. Mechanical and service water-heating system and equipment types, sizes and efficiencies.
6. Equipment and system controls.
7. Duct sealing, duct and pipe insulation and location.
8. Air sealing details.

R103.2.1 Building thermal envelope depiction. The *building's thermal envelope* shall be represented on the construction documents.

R103.3 Examination of documents. The *code official* shall examine or cause to be examined the accompanying construction documents and shall ascertain whether the construction indicated and described is in accordance with the requirements of this code and other pertinent laws or ordinances. The *code official* is authorized to utilize a registered design professional, or other *approved* entity not affiliated with the building design or construction, in conducting the review of the plans and specifications for compliance with the code.

R103.3.1 Approval of construction documents. When the *code official* issues a permit where construction documents are required, the construction documents shall be endorsed in writing and stamped "Reviewed for Code Compliance." Such *approved* construction documents shall not be changed, modified or altered without authorization from the *code official*. Work shall be done in accordance with the *approved* construction documents.

One set of construction documents so reviewed shall be retained by the *code official*. The other set shall be returned to the applicant, kept at the site of work and shall be open to inspection by the *code official* or a duly authorized representative.

R103.3.2 Previous approvals. This code shall not require changes in the construction documents, construction or designated occupancy of a structure for which a lawful permit has been heretofore issued or otherwise lawfully authorized, and the construction of which has been pursued in good faith within 180 days after the effective date of this code and has not been abandoned.

R103.3.3 Phased approval. The *code official* shall have the authority to issue a permit for the construction of part of an energy conservation system before the construction documents for the entire system have been submitted or *approved*, provided adequate information and detailed statements have been filed complying with all pertinent requirements of this code. The holders of such permit shall proceed at their own risk without assurance that the permit for the entire energy conservation system will be granted.

R103.4 Amended construction documents. Work shall be installed in accordance with the approved construction documents, and any changes made during construction that are not in compliance with the *approved* construction documents shall be resubmitted for approval as an amended set of construction documents.

R103.5 Retention of construction documents. One set of *approved* construction documents shall be retained by the *code official* for a period of not less than 180 days from date of completion of the permitted work, or as required by state or local laws.

SECTION R104 INSPECTIONS

R104.1 General. Construction or work for which a permit is required shall be subject to inspection by the *code official* or his or her designated agent, and such construction or work shall remain accessible and exposed for inspection purposes until *approved*. It shall be the duty of the permit applicant to cause the work to remain accessible and exposed for inspection purposes. Neither the *code official* nor the jurisdiction shall be liable for expense entailed in the removal or replacement of any material, product, system or building component required to allow inspection to validate compliance with this code.

R104.2 Required inspections. The *code official* or his or her designated agent, upon notification, shall make the inspections set forth in Sections R104.2.1 through R104.2.5.

R104.2.1 Footing and foundation inspection. Inspections associated with footings and foundations shall verify compliance with the code as to *R*-value, location, thickness, depth of burial and protection of insulation as required by the code and *approved* plans and specifications.

R104.2.2 Framing and rough-in inspection. Inspections at framing and rough-in shall be made before application of interior finish and shall verify compliance with the code as to types of insulation and corresponding *R*-values and their correct location and proper installation; fenestration properties (*U*-factor and SHGC) and proper installation; and air leakage controls as required by the code and approved plans and specifications.

R104.2.3 Plumbing rough-in inspection. Inspections at plumbing rough-in shall verify compliance as required by the code and *approved* plans and specifications as to types of insulation and corresponding *R*-values and protection, and required control.

R104.2.4 Mechanical rough-in inspection. Inspections at mechanical rough-in shall verify compliance as required by the code and *approved* plans and specifications as to installed HVAC equipment type and size, required controls, system insulation and corresponding *R*-value, system air leakage control, programmable thermostats, dampers, whole-house ventilation, and minimum fan efficiency.

Exception: Systems serving multiple dwelling units shall be inspected in accordance with Section C104.2.4.

R104.2.5 Final inspection. The *building* shall have a final inspection and shall not be occupied until *approved*. The final inspection shall include verification of the installation of all required *building* systems, equipment and controls and their proper operation and the required number of high-efficacy lamps and fixtures.

R104.3 Reinspection. A *building* shall be reinspected when determined necessary by the *code official*.

R104.4 Approved inspection agencies. The *code official* is authorized to accept inspection reports in whole or in part from either individuals as defined in Section 553.993(5) or (7), *Florida Statutes* or *third-party inspection agencies not affiliated with the building design or construction,* provided such agencies are *approved* as to qualifications and reliability relevant to the building components and systems they are inspecting.

R104.5 Inspection requests. It shall be the duty of the holder of the permit or their duly authorized agent to notify the *code official* when work is ready for inspection. It shall be the duty of the permit holder to provide access to and means for inspections of such work that are required by this code.

R104.6 Reinspection and testing. Where any work or installation does not pass an initial test or inspection, the necessary corrections shall be made to achieve compliance with this code. The work or installation shall then be resubmitted to the *code official* for inspection and testing.

R104.7 Approval. After the prescribed tests and inspections indicate that the work complies in all respects with this code, a notice of approval shall be issued by the *code official*.

R104.7.1 Revocation. The *code official* is authorized to, in writing, suspend or revoke a notice of approval issued under the provisions of this code wherever the certificate is issued in error, or on the basis of incorrect information supplied, or where it is determined that the *building* or structure, premise, or portion thereof is in violation of any ordinance or regulation or any of the provisions of this code.

SECTION R105
VALIDITY

R105.1 General. If a portion of this code is held to be illegal or void, such a decision shall not affect the validity of the remainder of this code.

SECTION R106
REFERENCED STANDARDS

R106.1 Referenced codes and standards. The codes and standards referenced in this code shall be those listed in Chapter 5, and such codes and standards shall be considered as part of the requirements of this code to the prescribed extent of each such reference and as further regulated in Sections R106.1.1 and R106.1.2.

R106.1.1 Conflicts. Where conflicts occur between provisions of this code and referenced codes and standards, the provisions of this code shall apply.

R106.1.2 Provisions in referenced codes and standards. Where the extent of the reference to a referenced code or standard includes subject matter that is within the scope of this code, the provisions of this code, as applicable, shall take precedence over the provisions in the referenced code or standard.

R106.2 Application of references. References to chapter or section numbers, or to provisions not specifically identified by number, shall be construed to refer to such chapter, section or provision of this code.

R106.3 Other laws. The provisions of this code shall not be deemed to nullify any provisions of local, state or federal law.

SECTION R107
FEES
RESERVED

SECTION R108
STOP WORK ORDER

R108.1 Authority. Where the *code official* finds any work regulated by this code being performed in a manner either contrary to the provisions of this code or dangerous or unsafe, the *code official* is authorized to issue a stop work order.

R108.2 Issuance. The stop work order shall be in writing and shall be given to the owner of the property involved, to the owner's authorized agent, or to the person doing the work. Upon issuance of a stop work order, the cited work shall immediately cease. The stop work order shall state the reason for the order and the conditions under which the cited work will be permitted to resume.

R108.3 Emergencies. Reserved.

R108.4 Failure to comply. Any person who shall continue any work after having been served with a stop work order, except such work as that person is directed to perform to remove a violation or unsafe condition, shall be subject to penalties as prescribed by law.

SECTION R109
BOARD OF APPEALS
RESERVED

CHAPTER 2 [RE]
DEFINITIONS

SECTION R201
GENERAL

R201.1 Scope. Unless stated otherwise, the following words and terms in this code shall have the meanings indicated in this chapter.

R201.2 Interchangeability. Words used in the present tense include the future; words in the masculine gender include the feminine and neuter; the singular number includes the plural and the plural includes the singular.

R201.3 Terms defined in other codes. Terms that are not defined in this code but are defined in the *Florida Building Code, Building*; *Florida Fire Prevention Code*; *Florida Building Code, Fuel Gas*; *Florida Building Code, Mechanical*; *Florida Building Code, Plumbing* or the *Florida Building Code, Residential* shall have the meanings ascribed to them in those codes.

R201.4 Terms not defined. Terms not defined by this chapter shall have ordinarily accepted meanings such as the context implies.

SECTION R202
GENERAL DEFINITIONS

ABOVE-GRADE WALL. A wall more than 50 percent above grade and enclosing *conditioned space*. This includes between-floor spandrels, peripheral edges of floors, roof and basement knee walls, dormer walls, gable end walls, walls enclosing a mansard roof and skylight shafts.

ACCESSIBLE. Admitting close approach as a result of not being guarded by locked doors, elevation or other effective means (see "Readily *accessible*").

ADDITION. An extension or increase in the *conditioned space* floor area or height of a building or structure.

ADJACENT WALL, CEILING or FLOOR. A wall, ceiling or floor of a structure that separates conditioned space from enclosed but unconditioned space, such as an unconditioned attached garage, storage or utility room.

AIR BARRIER. Relating to air distribution systems, a material object(s) that impedes or restricts the free movement of air under specified conditions. For fibrous glass duct, the air barrier is its foil cladding; for flexible nonmetal duct, the air barrier is the nonporous core; and for sheet metal duct and air handling units, the air barrier is the metal in contact with the air stream. For mechanical closets, the air barrier may be a uniform panelized material such as gypsum wallboard that meets ASTM C36, or it may be a membrane that alone acts as an air barrier which is attached to a panel, such as the foil cladding of fibrous glass duct board.

Relating to the building envelope, air barriers comprise the planes of primary resistance to airflow between the interior spaces of a building and the outdoors and the planes of primary airflow resistance between adjacent air zones of a building, including planes between adjacent conditioned and unconditioned air spaces of a building. To be classed as an air barrier, a building plane must be substantially leak free; that is, it shall have an air leakage rate not greater than 0.5 cfm/ft^2 when subjected to an air pressure gradient of 25 pascal. In general, air barriers are made of durable, nonporous materials and are sealed to adjoining wall, ceiling or floor surfaces with a suitable long-life mastic. House wraps and taped and sealed drywall may constitute an air barrier, but dropped acoustical tile ceilings (T-bar ceilings) may not. Batt insulation facings and asphalt-impregnated fiberboard and felt paper are not considered air barriers.

AIR CONDITIONING. The treatment of air so as to control simultaneously the temperature, humidity, cleanness and distribution of the air to meet the requirements of a conditioned space.

AIR DISTRIBUTION SYSTEM. Any system of ducts, plenums and air-handling equipment that circulates air within a space or spaces and includes systems made up of one or more air-handling units.

AIR-HANDLING UNIT. The fan unit of a furnace and the fan-coil unit of a split-system, packaged air conditioner or heat pump.

ALTERATION. Any construction, retrofit or renovation to an existing structure other than repair or addition that requires a permit. Also, a change in a building, electrical, gas, mechanical or plumbing system that involves an extension, addition or change to the arrangement, type or purpose of the original installation that requires a permit.

APPROVED. Approval by the *code official* as a result of investigation and tests conducted by him or her, or by reason of accepted principles or tests by nationally recognized organizations.

APPROVED AGENCY. An established and recognized agency regularly engaged in conducting tests or furnishing inspection services, when such agency has been approved by the *code official*.

ATTIC. An enclosed unconditioned space located immediately below an uninsulated roof and immediately above the ceiling of a building. For the roof to be considered insulated, roof insulation shall be at least the *R*-value required to meet Section R405.2.1.

AUTOMATIC. Self-acting, operating by its own mechanism when actuated by some impersonal influence, as, for example, a change in current strength, pressure, temperature or mechanical configuration (see "*Manual*").

BASEMENT WALL. A wall 50 percent or more below grade and enclosing *conditioned space*.

BUILDING. Any structure used or intended for supporting or sheltering any use or occupancy. For each purpose of this

Code, each portion of a building separated from other portions by a firewall shall be considered as a separate building. The term "building" shall be construed as if followed by the words "or part thereof."

BUILDING SITE. A continguous area of land that is under the ownership or control of one entity.

BUILDING THERMAL ENVELOPE. The basement walls, exterior walls, floor, roof and any other building elements that enclose conditioned space or provide a boundary between conditioned space and exempt or unconditioned space. See *"Adjacent wall, ceiling or floor."*

***C*-FACTOR (THERMAL CONDUCTANCE).** The coefficient of heat transmission (surface to surface) through a building component or assembly, equal to the time rate of heat flow per unit area and the unit temperature difference between the warm side and cold side surfaces (Btu/h $\cdot$ ft^2 $\cdot$ °F) [W/(m^2 $\cdot$ K)].

CIRCULATING HOT WATER SYSTEM. A specifically designed water distribution system where one or more pumps are operated in the service hot water piping to circulate heated water from the water-heating equipment to fixtures and back to the water-heating equipment.

CLIMATE ZONE. A geographical region based on climatic criteria as specified in this code.

CODE OFFICIAL. The officer or other designated authority charged with the administration and enforcement of this code, or a duly authorized representative.

COMMERCIAL BUILDING. For this code, all buildings that are not included in the definition of "Residential building."

CONDITIONED FLOOR AREA. The horizontal projection of that portion of space that is conditioned directly or indirectly by an energy-using system.

CONDITIONED SPACE. An area, room or space that is enclosed within the building thermal envelope and that is directly or indirectly heated or cooled. Spaces are indirectly heated or cooled where they communicate through openings with conditioned spaces; where they are separated from conditioned spaces by uninsulated walls, floors or ceilings; or where they contain uninsulated ducts, piping or other sources of heating or cooling. See *"Space."*

CONTINUOUS AIR BARRIER. A combination of materials and assemblies that restrict or prevent the passage of air through the building thermal envelope.

CONTINUOUS INSULATION (ci). Insulating material that is continuous across all structural members without thermal bridges other than fasteners and service openings. It is installed on the interior or exterior, or is integral to any opaque surface, of the building envelope.

CRAWL SPACE WALL. The opaque portion of a wall that encloses a crawl space and is partially or totally below grade.

CURTAIN WALL. Fenestration products used to create an external nonload-bearing wall that is designed to separate the exterior and interior environments.

DEMAND RECIRCULATION WATER SYSTEM. A water distribution system where pump(s) prime the service hot water piping with heated water upon demand for hot water.

DRAWBAND. A fastener that surrounds and fastens a duct fitting with either the inner lining or the outer jacket of flexible ducts. Tension ties, clinch bands, draw ties, and straps are considered drawbands.

DUCT. A tube or conduit utilized for conveying air. The air passages of self-contained systems are not to be construed as air ducts.

DUCT SYSTEM. A continuous passageway for the transmission of air that, in addition to ducts, includes duct fittings, dampers, plenums, fans and accessory air-handling equipment and appliances.

DWELLING UNIT. A single unit providing complete independent living facilities for one or more persons, including permanent provisions for living, sleeping, eating, cooking and sanitation.

EFFICIENCY. Performance at specified rating conditions.

ENERGY. The capacity for doing work. It takes a number of forms that may be transformed from one into another such as thermal (heat), mechanical (work), electrical and chemical. Customary measurement units are British thermal units (Btu).

ENERGY ANALYSIS. A method for estimating the annual energy use of the *proposed design* and *standard reference design* based on estimates of energy use.

ENERGY COST. The total estimated annual cost for purchased energy for the building functions regulated by this code, including applicable demand charges.

ENERGY SIMULATION TOOL. An *approved* software program or calculation-based methodology that projects the annual energy use of a building.

EQUIPMENT. Devices for comfort conditioning, electric power, lighting, transportation or service water heating including, but not limited to, furnaces, boilers, air conditioners, heat pumps, chillers, water heaters, lamps, luminaires, ballasts, elevators, escalators or other devices or installations.

ERI REFERENCE DESIGN. A version of the rated design that meets the minimum requirements of the 2006 *International Energy Conservation Code.*

EXISTING BUILDING. A building or portion thereof that was previously occupied or approved for occupancy by the authority having jurisdiction.

EXTERIOR WALL. Walls including both above-grade walls and basement walls that form a boundary between a conditioned and an outdoor space.

FENESTRATION. Products classified as either *vertical fenestration* or *skylights.*

FENESTRATION AREA. Total area of the fenestration measured using the rough opening and including the glazing, sash and frame. For doors where the glazed vision area is less than 50 percent of the door area, the fenestration area is the glazed vision area. For all other doors, the fenestration area is the door area.

FENESTRATION PRODUCT, SITE-BUILT. A fenestration designed to be made up of field-glazed or field-assembled units using specific factory cut or otherwise factory-formed framing and glazing units. Examples of site-built fenestration include storefront systems, curtain walls and atrium roof systems.

***F*-FACTOR.** The perimeter heat loss factor for slab-on-grade floors (Btu/h·ft·°F) [W/(m·K)].

HEAT. The form of energy that is transferred by virtue of a temperature difference or a change in the state of a material.

HEATED SLAB. Slab-on-grade construction in which the heating elements, hydronic tubing, or hot air distribution system is in contact with, or placed within or under, the slab.

HIGH-EFFICACY LAMPS. Compact fluorescent lamps, T-8 or smaller diameter linear fluorescent lamps, or lamps with a minimum efficacy of:

1. 60 lumens per watt for lamps over 40 watts;
2. 50 lumens per watt for lamps over 15 watts to 40 watts; and
3. 40 lumens per watt for lamps 15 watts or less.

HISTORIC BUILDING. Any building or structure that is one or more of the following:

1. Listed, or certified as eligible for listing by the State Historic Preservation Officer or the Keeper of the National Register of Historic Places, in the National Register of Historic Places.
2. Designated as historic under an applicable state or local law.
3. Certified as a contributing resource within a National Register-listed, state-designated or locally designated historic district.

HVAC. Heating, ventilating and air conditioning.

HVAC SYSTEM. The equipment, distribution systems and terminals that provide, either collectively or individually, the processes of heating, ventilating, or air conditioning to a building or portion of a building.

INDOOR. Within the conditioned building envelope.

INFILTRATION. The uncontrolled inward air leakage through cracks and crevices in any building element and around windows and doors of a building caused by pressure differences across these elements due to factors such as wind, inside and outside temperature differences (stack effect), and imbalance between supply and exhaust air systems.

INSULATED SIDING. A type of continuous insulation with manufacturer-installed insulating material as an integral part of the cladding product having a minimum *R*-value of R-2.

INSULATING SHEATHING. An insulating board with a core material having a minimum *R*-value of R-2.

INSULATION. Material mainly used to retard the flow of heat. See Section R303.1.1.

LABELED. Equipment, materials or products to which have been affixed a label, seal, symbol or other identifying mark of a nationally recognized testing laboratory, inspection agency or other organization concerned with product evaluation that maintains periodic inspection of the production of the above-labeled items and where labeling indicates either that the equipment, material or product meets identified standards or has been tested and found suitable for a specified purpose.

LISTED. Equipment, materials, products or services included in a list published by an organization acceptable to the *code official* and concerned with evaluation of products or services that maintains periodic inspection of production of *listed* equipment or materials or periodic evaluation of services and where the listing states either that the equipment, material, product or service meets identified standards or has been tested and found suitable for a specified purpose.

LOW-VOLTAGE LIGHTING. Lighting equipment powered through a transformer such as a cable conductor, a rail conductor and track lighting.

MANUAL. Capable of being operated by personal intervention (see "*Automatic*").

MANUFACTURER. The company engaged in the original production and assembly of products or equipment or a company that purchases such products and equipment manufactured in accordance with company specifications.

MECHANICAL CLOSET. For the purposes of this code, a closet used as an air plenum that contains the blower unit or air handler of a central air-conditioning or heating unit.

OUTDOOR. The environment exterior to the building structure.

OUTDOOR (OUTSIDE) AIR. Air that is outside the building envelope or is taken from outside the building that has not been previously circulated through the building.

OUTSIDE. The environment exterior to the conditioned space of the building and may include attics, garages, crawlspaces, etc., but not return air plenums.

PLENUM. A compartment or chamber to which one or more ducts are connected, that forms a part of the air distribution system, and that is not used for occupancy or storage. A plenum often is formed in part or in total by portions of the building.

POSITIVE INDOOR PRESSURE. A positive pressure condition within a conditioned space caused by bringing in more outside air than the amount of air that is exhausted and/or lost through air leakage.

PROPOSED DESIGN. A description or computer representation of the proposed *building* used to estimate annual energy use for determining compliance based on total building performance or design energy cost.

RATED DESIGN. A description of the proposed *building* used to determine the energy rating index.

READILY ACCESSIBLE. Capable of being reached quickly for operation, renewal or inspection without requiring those to whom ready access is requisite to climb over or remove obstacles or to resort to portable ladders or access equipment (see "*Accessible*").

RENOVATED BUILDING. A residential or nonresidential building undergoing alteration that varies or changes insulation, HVAC systems, water heating systems or exterior envelope conditions, provided the estimated cost of renovation exceeds 30 percent of the assessed value of the structure.

REPAIR. The reconstruction or renewal of any part of an existing building for the purpose of its maintenance or to correct damage.

REPLACEMENT. The installation of part or all of an existing mechanical or electrical system in an existing building.

REROOFING. The process of recovering or replacing an existing *roof covering*. See "*Roof recover*" and "*Roof replacement*."

RESIDENTIAL BUILDING. For this code, includes detached one- and two-family dwellings and multiple single-family dwellings (townhouses) as well as Group R-2, R-3 and R-4 buildings three stories or less in height above grade plane.

ROOF ASSEMBLY. A system designed to provide weather protection and resistance to design loads. The system consists of a roof covering and roof deck or a single component serving as both the roof covering and the roof deck. A roof assembly includes the roof covering, underlayment, roof deck, insulation, vapor retarder and interior finish.

ROOF RECOVER. The process of installing an additional *roof covering* over a prepared existing *roof covering* without removing the existing *roof covering*.

ROOF REPAIR. Reconstruction or renewal of any part of an existing roof for the purposes of its maintenance.

ROOF REPLACEMENT. The process of removing the existing *roof covering*, repairing any damaged substrate and installing a new *roof covering*.

***R*-VALUE (THERMAL RESISTANCE).** The inverse of the time rate of heat flow through a body from one of its bounding surfaces to the other surface for a unit temperature difference between the two surfaces, under steady state conditions, per unit area ($h \cdot ft^2 \cdot °F/Btu$) [$(m^2 \cdot K)/W$].

SEAL or SEALING – AIR DUCT. The use of closure products, either welds, mastic, mastic plus embedded fabric, adhesives, caulking, gaskets, pressure-sensitive tapes, heat-activated tapes or combinations thereof as allowed by specific sections of this code, to close cracks, joints, seams and other openings in the air barriers of air ducts, air handling units and plenum chambers for the purpose of preventing air leakage. No joining of opening from which a closure product is absent shall be considered sealed unless considered otherwise in specific cases identified by this code. Closeness of fit between mated parts alone shall not be considered a seal.

SERVICE WATER HEATING. Supply of hot water for purposes other than comfort heating.

SKYLIGHT. Glass or other transparent or translucent glazing material installed at a slope of less than 60 degrees (1.05 rad) from horizontal. Glazing materials in skylights, including unit skylights, tubular daylighting devices, solariums, sunrooms, roofs and sloped walls, are included in this definition.

SOLAR HEAT GAIN COEFFICIENT (SHGC). The ratio of the solar heat gain entering the space through the fenestration assembly to the incident solar radiation. Solar heat gain includes directly transmitted solar heat and absorbed solar radiation that is then reradiated, conducted or convected into the space. (See "Fenestration area.")

SPACE. An enclosed space within a building. The classifications of spaces are as follows for the purpose of determining building envelope requirements.

1. Conditioned space: a cooled space, heated space or indirectly conditioned space or unvented attic assembly defined as follows:
   a. Cooled space: an enclosed space within a building that is cooled by a cooling system whose sensible output capacity exceeds 5 $Btu/h \cdot ft^2$ of floor area.
   b. Heated space: an enclosed space within a building that is heated by a heating system whose output capacity relative to the floor area is greater than or equal to 5 $Btu/h \cdot ft^2$.
   c. Indirectly conditioned space: an enclosed space within a building that is not a heated space or a cooled space, which is heated or cooled indirectly by being connected to adjacent space(s) provided (a) the product of the *U*-factor(s) and surface area(s) of the space adjacent to connected space(s) exceeds the combined sum of the product of the *U*-factor(s) and surface area(s) of the space adjoining the outdoors, unconditioned spaces, and to or from semiheated spaces (e.g., corridors) or (b) that air from heated or cooled spaces is intentionally transferred (naturally or mechanically) into the space at a rate exceeding 3 air changes per hour (ACH) (e.g., atria).
   d. Unvented attic assembly: as defined in Section R806.5 of the *Florida Building Code, Residential*. These spaces shall not require supply or return outlets.
2. Semiheated space: an enclosed space within a building that is heated by a heating system whose output capacity is greater than or equal to 3.4 $Btu/h \cdot ft^2$ of floor area but is not a conditioned space.
3. Unconditioned space: an enclosed space within a building that is not a conditioned space or a semiheated space. Crawl spaces, attics, and parking garages with natural or mechanical ventilation are not considered enclosed spaces.

STANDARD REFERENCE DESIGN. A version of the *proposed design* that meets the minimum requirements of this code and is used to determine the maximum annual energy use requirement for compliance based on total building performance.

STRUCTURE. That which is built or constructed.

SUNROOM. For the purposes of this code, the term "sunroom" as used herein shall be as follows and shall include conservatories, sunspaces, solariums, and porch or patio covers or enclosures.

1. A room with roof panels that includes sloped glazing that is a one-story structure added to an existing dwelling with an open or glazed area in excess of 40 percent

of the gross area of the sunroom structure's exterior walls and roof.

2. A one-story structure added to a dwelling with structural roof panels without sloped glazing. The sunroom walls may have any configuration, provided the open area of the longer wall and one additional wall is equal to at least 65 percent of the area below 6 feet 8 inches of each wall, measured from the floor.

SYSTEM. A combination of equipment and auxiliary devices (e.g., controls, accessories, interconnecting means and terminal elements) by which energy is transformed so it performs a specific function such as HVAC, service water heating or lighting.

THERMAL ENVELOPE. The primary insulation layer of a building; that part of the envelope that provides the greatest resistance to heat flow to or from the building.

THERMAL ISOLATION. Physical and space conditioning separation from *conditioned space(s)*. The *conditioned space*(s) shall be controlled as separate zones for heating and cooling or conditioned by separate equipment.

THERMOSTAT. An automatic control device used to maintain temperature at a fixed or adjustable set point.

***U*-FACTOR (THERMAL TRANSMITTANCE).** The coefficient of heat transmission (air to air) through a building component or assembly, equal to the time rate of heat flow per unit area and unit temperature difference between the warm side and cold side air films (Btu/h · ft^2 · °F) [W/(m^2 · K)].

UNCONDITIONED SPACE. See "*Space*."

VENTILATION. The natural or mechanical process of supplying conditioned or unconditioned air to, or removing such air from, any space.

VENTILATION AIR. That portion of supply air that comes from outside (outdoors) plus any recirculated air that has been treated to maintain the desired quality of air within a designated space.

VERTICAL FENESTRATION. Windows (fixed or moveable), opaque doors, glazed doors, glazed block and combination opaque/glazed doors composed of glass or other transparent or translucent glazing materials and installed at a slope of a least 60 degrees (1.05 rad) from horizontal.

VISIBLE TRANSMITTANCE [VT]. The ratio of visible light entering the space through the fenestration product assembly to the incident visible light, Visible Transmittance, includes the effects of glazing material and frame and is expressed as a number between 0 and 1.

WALL. That portion of the building envelope, including opaque area and fenestration, that is vertical or tilted at an angle of 60 degrees from horizontal or greater. This includes above- and below-grade walls, between floor spandrels, peripheral edges of floors and foundation walls. For the purposes of determining building envelope requirements, the classifications are defined as follows:

1. Above-grade wall: a wall that is not a below-grade wall.
2. Below-grade wall: that portion of a wall in the building envelope that is entirely below the finish grade and in contact with the ground.
3. Mass wall: a wall with a heat capacity exceeding (1) 7 Btu/ft^2 · °F or (2) 5 Btu/ft^2 · °F, provided that the wall has a material unit weight not greater than 120 lb/ft^3.
4. Metal building wall: a wall whose structure consists of metal spanning members supported by steel structural members (i.e., does not include spandrel glass or metal panels in curtain wall systems).
5. Steel-framed wall: a wall with a cavity (insulated or otherwise) whose exterior surfaces are separated by steel framing members (i.e., typical steel stud walls and curtain wall systems).
6. Wood-framed and other walls: all other wall types, including wood stud walls.

WHOLE HOUSE MECHANICAL VENTILATION SYSTEM. An exhaust system, supply system, or combination thereof that is designed to mechanically exchange indoor air with outdoor air when operating continuously or through a programmed intermittent schedule to satisfy the whole house ventilation rates.

ZONE. A space or group of spaces within a building with heating or cooling requirements that are sufficiently similar so that desired conditions can be maintained throughout using a single controlling device.

CHAPTER 3 [RE]

GENERAL REQUIREMENTS

SECTION R301
CLIMATE ZONES

R301.1 General. Table R301.1 shall be used in determining the applicable requirements from Chapter 4. Locations are assigned a *climate zone* based on Section R301.3.

Figure R301.1 Climate Zones. Reserved.

R301.2 Warm humid counties. Warm humid counties are identified in Table R301.1 by an asterisk.

R301.3 International climate zones. The *climate zone* for any location outside the United States shall be determined by applying Table R301.3(1) and then Table R301.3(2).

R301.4 Tropical climate zone. The tropical *climate zone* shall be defined as:

1. Hawaii, Puerto Rico, Guam, American Samoa, U.S. Virgin Islands, Commonwealth of Northern Mariana Islands; and
2. Islands in the area between the Tropic of Cancer and the Tropic of Capricorn.

SECTION R302
DESIGN CONDITIONS

R302.1 Interior design conditions. The interior design temperatures used for heating and cooling load calculations shall be a maximum of 72°F (22°C) for heating and minimum of 75°F (24°C) for cooling.

SECTION R303
MATERIALS, SYSTEMS AND EQUIPMENT

R303.1 Identification. Materials, systems and equipment shall be identified in a manner that will allow a determination of compliance with the applicable provisions of this code.

R303.1.1 Building thermal envelope insulation.

R303.1.1.1 Insulation product rating. The thermal resistance (*R*-value) of insulation shall be determined in accordance with the U.S. Federal Trade Commission *R*-value rule (CFR Title 16, Part 460) in units of h · ft^2 · °F/Btu at a mean temperature of 75°F (24°C).

R303.1.1.1.1 *R*-values referenced in Chapter 4 of this code refer to the *R*-values of the added insulation only. The *R*-values of structural building materials such as framing members, concrete blocks or gypsum board shall not be included.

Exception: R402.1.5 Total UA Alternative.

R303.1.1.1.2 When installing two layers of bulk or board insulation, the *R*-values of each material may be added together for a total *R*-value. When installing two separate reflective insulation products in layers, the total *R*-value of the system shall have been achieved by testing under FTC regulations, 16 CFR Part 460.

TABLE R301.1
CLIMATE ZONES, MOISTURE REGIMES AND WARM-HUMID DESIGNATIONS BY COUNTY

Key: A – Moist
Asterisk (*) indicates a warm-humid location.

FLORIDA

2A Alachua*	2A Duval*	2A Indian River*	2A Nassau*	2A Sumter*
2A Baker*	2A Escambia*	2A Jackson*	2A Okaloosa*	2A Suwannee*
2A Bay*	2A Flagler*	2A Jefferson*	2A Okeechobee*	2A Taylor*
2A Bradford*	2A Franklin*	2A Lafayette*	2A Orange*	2A Union*
2A Brevard*	2A Gadsden*	2A Lake*	2A Osceola*	2A Volusia*
1A Broward*	2A Gilchrist*	1A Lee*	1A Palm Beach*	2A Wakulla*
2A Calhoun*	2A Glades*	2A Leon*	2A Pasco*	2A Walton*
2A Charlotte*	2A Gulf*	2A Levy*	2A Pinellas*	2A Washington*
2A Citrus*	2A Hamilton*	2A Liberty*	2A Polk*	
2A Clay*	2A Hardee*	2A Madison*	2A Putnam*	
1A Collier*	1A Hendry*	2A Manatee*	2A Santa Rosa*	
2A Columbia*	2A Hernando*	2A Marion*	2A Sarasota*	
2A DeSoto*	2A Highlands*	2A Martin*	2A Seminole*	
2A Dixie*	2A Hillsborough*	1A Miami-Dade*	2A St. Johns*	
	2A Holmes*	1A Monroe*	2A St. Lucie*	

TABLE R301.3(1)
INTERNATIONAL CLIMATE ZONE DEFINITIONS

MAJOR CLIMATE TYPE DEFINITIONS
Marine (C) Definition—Locations meeting all four criteria: 1. Mean temperature of coldest month between -3°C (27°F) and 18°C (65°F). 2. Warmest month mean < 22°C (72°F). 3. At least four months with mean temperatures over 10°C (50°F). 4. Dry season in summer. The month with the heaviest precipitation in the cold season has at least three times as much precipitation as the month with the least precipitation in the rest of the year. The cold season is October through March in the Northern Hemisphere and April through September in the Southern Hemisphere.
Dry (B) Definition—Locations meeting the following criteria: Not marine and $P_{in} < 0.44 \times (TF - 19.5)$ [$P_{cm} < 2.0 \times (TC + 7)$ in SI units] where: P_{in} = Annual precipitation in inches (cm) T = Annual mean temperature in °F (°C)
Moist (A) Definition—Locations that are not marine and not dry.
Warm-humid Definition—Moist (A) locations where either of the following wet-bulb temperature conditions shall occur during the warmest six consecutive months of the year: 1. 67°F (19.4°C) or higher for 3,000 or more hours; or 2. 73°F (22.8°C) or higher for 1,500 or more hours.

For SI: °C = [(°F) - 32]/1.8, 1 inch = 2.54 cm.

TABLE R301.3(2)
INTERNATIONAL CLIMATE ZONE DEFINITIONS

ZONE NUMBER	THERMAL CRITERIA	
	IP Units	SI Units
1	9000 < CDD50°F	5000 < CDD10°C
2	6300 < CDD50°F ≤ 9000	3500 < CDD10°C ≤ 5000
3A and 3B	4500 < CDD50°F ≤ 6300 AND HDD65°F ≤ 5400	2500 < CDD10°C ≤ 3500 AND HDD18°C ≤ 3000
4A and 4B	CDD50°F ≤ 4500 AND HDD65°F ≤ 5400	CDD10°C ≤ 2500 AND HDD18°C ≤ 3000
3C	HDD65°F ≤ 3600	HDD18°C ≤ 2000
4C	3600 < HDD65°F ≤ 5400	2000 < HDD18°C ≤ 3000
5	5400 < HDD65°F ≤ 7200	3000 < HDD18°C ≤ 4000
6	7200 < HDD65°F ≤ 9000	4000 < HDD18°C ≤ 5000
7	9000 < HDD65°F ≤ 12600	5000 < HDD18°C ≤ 7000
8	12600 < HDD65°F	7000 < HDD18°C

For SI: °C = [(°F) - 32]/1.8.

R303.1.1.1.3 Insulated siding. The thermal resistance (*R*-value) of insulated siding shall be determined in accordance with ASTM C1363. Installation for testing shall be in accordance with the manufacturer's instructions.

R303.1.1.2 Building thermal envelope insulation markers. An *R*-value identification mark shall be applied by the manufacturer to each piece of *building thermal envelope* insulation 12 inches (305 mm) or greater in width. Alternately, the insulation installers shall provide a certification listing the type, manufacturer and *R*-value of insulation installed in each element of the *building thermal envelope*. For blown or sprayed insulation (fiberglass and cellulose), the initial installed thickness, settled thickness, settled *R*-value, installed density, coverage area and number of bags installed shall be *listed* on the certification. For sprayed polyurethane foam (SPF) insulation, the installed thickness of the areas covered and *R*-value of installed thickness shall be *listed* on the certification. For insulated siding, the *R*-value shall be labeled on the product's package and shall be *listed* on the certification. The insulation installer shall sign, date and post the certification in a conspicuous location on the job site.

R303.1.1.2.1 Blown or sprayed roof/ceiling insulation. The thickness of blown-in or sprayed roof/ceiling insulation (fiberglass or cellulose) shall be written in inches (mm) on markers that are installed at least one for every 300 square feet (28 m^2) throughout the attic space. The markers shall be affixed to the trusses or joists and marked with the minimum initial installed thickness with numbers not less than 1 inch (25 mm) in height. Each marker shall face the attic access opening. Spray polyurethane foam thickness and installed *R*-value shall be *listed* on certification provided by the insulation installer.

R303.1.1.2.2 Insulation mark installation. Insulating materials shall be installed such that the manufacturer's *R*-value mark is readily observable upon inspection.

R303.1.2 Equipment efficiency ratings. Minimum equipment efficiency rating identification for heating, cooling, hot water, swimming pool heating and filtration, and lighting shall be in accordance with industry standards and as described in Chapter 4 of the Commercial Provisions of this code, as applicable, for such equipment.

R303.1.3 Fenestration product rating. *U*-factors of fenestration products (windows, doors and skylights) shall be determined in accordance with NFRC 100.

Exception: Where required, garage door *U*-factors shall be determined in accordance with either NFRC 100 or ANSI/DASMA 105.

U-factors shall be determined by an accredited, independent laboratory, and *labeled* and certified by the manufacturer.

Products lacking such a *labeled* *U*-factor shall be assigned a default *U*-factor from Table R303.1.3(1) or R303.1.3(2). The solar heat gain coefficient (SHGC) and *visible transmittance* (VT) of glazed fenestration products (windows, glazed doors and skylights) shall be determined in accordance with NFRC 200 by an accredited, independent laboratory, and *labeled* and certified by the manufacturer. Products lacking such a *labeled* SHGC or VT shall be assigned a default SHGC or VT from Table R303.1.3(3).

TABLE R303.1.3(1)
DEFAULT GLAZED FENESTRATION *U*-FACTORS

FRAME TYPE	SINGLE PANE	DOUBLE PANE	SKYLIGHT	
			Single	Double
Metal	1.20	0.80	2.00	1.30
Metal with Thermal Break	1.10	0.65	1.90	1.10
Nonmetal or Metal Clad	0.95	0.55	1.75	1.05
Glazed Block	0.60			

TABLE R303.1.3(2)
DEFAULT DOOR *U*-FACTORS

DOOR TYPE	*U*-FACTOR
Uninsulated Metal	1.20
Insulated Metal	0.60
Wood	0.50
Insulated, nonmetal edge, max 45% glazing, any glazing double pane	0.35

TABLE R303.1.3(3)
DEFAULT GLAZED FENESTRATION SHGC AND VT

	SINGLE GLAZED		DOUBLE GLAZED		GLAZED BLOCK
	Clear	Tinted	Clear	Tinted	
SHGC	0.8	0.7	0.7	0.6	0.6
VT	0.6	0.3	0.6	0.3	0.6

R303.2 Installation. Materials, systems and equipment shall be installed in accordance with the manufacturer's instructions and the *Florida Building Code, Building* or *Florida Building Code, Residential*, as applicable.

R303.2.1 Insulation installation. Insulation materials shall comply with the requirements of their respective ASTM standard specification and shall be installed in accordance with their respective ASTM installation practice in Table R303.2.1 in such a manner as to achieve *rated R-value of insulation.* Open-blown or poured loose-fill insulation shall not be used in *attic roof* spaces when the slope of the ceiling is more than 3 in 12. When eave vents are installed, baffling of the vent openings shall be provided to deflect the incoming air above the surface of the insulation.

Exception: Where *metal building roof* and *metal building wall* insulation is compressed between the *roof* or *wall* skin and the structure.

R303.2.1.1 Compressed insulation. Insulation that has been compressed to 85 percent or less of the manufacturer's rated thickness for the product shall use the *R*-values given in Table 303.2.1.1. These values are to be used except where data developed by an independent testing laboratory are provided.

R303.2.1.2 Substantial contact. Insulation shall be installed in a permanent manner in *substantial contact* with the inside surface in accordance with manufacturer's recommendations for the framing system used. Flexible batt insulation installed in floor cavities shall be supported in a permanent manner by supports no greater than 24 inches (610 mm) on center (o.c.).

Exception: Insulation materials that rely on air-spaces adjacent to reflective surfaces for their rated performance.

TABLE R303.2.1
INSULATION INSTALLATION STANDARDS

INSULATION MATERIAL	STANDARD SPECIFICATION	INSTALLATION PRACTICE
Mineral Fiber Batt/Blanket	ASTM C665	ASTM C1320
Mineral Fiber Loose Fill	ASTM C764	ASTM C1015
Cellulose Loose Fill	ASTM C739	ASTM C1015
Polystyrene Foam	ASTM C578	—
Polyisocyanurate Foam	ASTM C1289	—
Reflective	ASTM C1224	ASTM C727
Radiant Barrier	ASTM C1313	ASTM C1158
Vermiculite	ASTM C516	—
Perlite	ASTM C549	
Spray-applied Rigid Cellular Polyurethane Foam	ASTM C1029	—
Interior Radiation Control Coating Systems	—	ASTM C1321

TABLE R303.2.1.1
***R*-VALUES OF COMPRESSED INSULATION**

% OF ORIGINAL THICKNESS	R-5	R-7	R-11	R-14	R-19	R-30	R-38
90	5	6	10	13	18	28	36
80	4	6	10	12	17	26	33
70	4	5	9	11	15	24	30
60	3	5	8	10	14	22	27
50	3	4	7	9	12	18	24
40	2	4	6	8	10	15	20
30	2	3	4	6	8	12	16
20	2	2	2	3	4	10	10

R303.2.1.3 Insulation protection. Exterior insulation shall be covered with a protective material to prevent damage from sunlight, moisture, landscaping operations, equipment maintenance and wind. In *attics* and mechanical rooms, a way to access equipment that prevents damaging or compressing the insulation shall be provided. Foundation vents shall not interfere with the insulation. Insulation materials in ground contact shall have a water absorption rate no greater than .3 percent when tested in accordance with ASTM C272, shall cover the exposed exterior insulation and shall extend a minimum of 6 inches (153 mm) below grade.

R303.3 Maintenance information. Maintenance instructions shall be furnished for equipment and systems that require preventive maintenance. Required regular maintenance actions shall be clearly stated and incorporated on a readily accessible label. The label shall include the title or publication number for the operation and maintenance manual for that particular model and type of product.

CHAPTER 4 [RE]

RESIDENTIAL ENERGY EFFICIENCY

SECTION R401
GENERAL

R401.1 Scope. This chapter applies to residential buildings.

R401.2 Compliance. Projects shall comply with one of the following:

1. Sections R401 through R404.
2. Section R405 and the provisions of Sections R401 through R404 labeled "Mandatory."
3. An energy rating index (ERI) approach in Section R406.

R401.2.1 Tropical zone. *Residential buildings* in the tropical zone at elevations below 2,400 feet (731.5 m) above sea level shall be deemed to comply with this chapter where the following conditions are met:

1. Not more than one-half of the *occupied* space is air conditioned.
2. The *occupied* space is not heated.
3. Solar, wind or other renewable energy source supplies not less than 80 percent of the energy for service water heating.
4. Glazing in *conditioned* space has a *solar heat gain coefficient* of less than or equal to 0.40, or has an overhang with a projection factor equal to or greater than 0.30.
5. Permanently installed lighting is in accordance with Section R404.
6. The exterior roof surface complies with one of the options in Table C402.3 or the roof/ceiling has insulation with an *R-value* of R-15 or greater. If present, attics above the insulation are vented and attics below the insulation are unvented.
7. Roof surfaces have a minimum slope of $^1/_4$ inch per foot of run. The finished roof does not have water accumulation areas.
8. Operable fenestration provides ventilation area equal to not less than 14 percent of the floor area in each room. Alternatively, equivalent ventilation is provided by a ventilation fan.
9. Bedrooms with exterior walls facing two different directions have operable fenestration.
10. Interior doors to bedrooms are capable of being secured in the open position.
11. A ceiling fan or ceiling fan rough-in is provided for bedrooms and the largest space that is not used as a bedroom.

R401.3 Energy performance level (EPL) display card (Mandatory). The building official shall require that an energy performance level (EPL) display card be completed and certified by the builder to be accurate and correct before final approval of the building for occupancy. Florida law (Section 553.9085, *Florida Statutes*) requires the EPL display card to be included as an addendum to each sales contract for both presold and nonpresold residential buildings. The EPL display card contains information indicating the energy performance level and efficiencies of components installed in a dwelling unit. The building official shall verify that the EPL display card completed and signed by the builder accurately reflects the plans and specifications submitted to demonstrate code compliance for the building. A copy of the EPL display card can be found in Appendix RD.

SECTION R402
BUILDING THERMAL ENVELOPE

R402.1 General (Prescriptive). The *building thermal envelope* shall meet the requirements of Sections R402.1.1 through R402.1.5.

Exception: The following low-energy buildings, or portions thereof, separated from the remainder of the building by *building thermal envelope* assemblies complying with this section shall be exempt from the *building thermal envelope* provisions of Section R402.

1. Those with a peak design rate of energy usage less than 3.4 Btu/h · ft^2 (10.7 W/m^2) or 1.0 watt/ft^2 of floor area for space-conditioning purposes.
2. Those that do not contain *conditioned space*.

R402.1.1 Vapor retarder. Wall assemblies in the *building thermal envelope* shall comply with the vapor retarder requirements of Section R702.7 of the *Florida Building Code, Residential* or Section 1405.3 of the *Florida Building Code, Building,* as applicable.

R402.1.2 Insulation and fenestration criteria. The *building thermal envelope* shall meet the requirements of Table R402.1.2, based on the climate zone specified in Chapter 3.

R402.1.3 *R*-value computation. Insulation material used in layers, such as framing cavity insulation, or continuous insulation shall be summed to compute the corresponding component *R*-value. The manufacturer's settled *R*-value shall be used for blown insulation. Computed *R*-values shall not include an *R*-value for other building materials or air films. Where insulated siding is used for the purpose of complying with the continuous insulation requirements of Table R402.1.2, the manufacturer's labeled *R*-value for insulated siding shall be reduced by R-0.6.

R402.1.4 *U*-factor alternative. An assembly with a *U*-factor equal to or less than that specified in Table R402.1.4 shall be permitted as an alternative to the *R*-value in Table R402.1.2.

R402.1.5 Total UA alternative. If the total *building thermal envelope* UA (sum of *U*-factor times assembly area) is less than or equal to the total UA resulting from using the *U*-factors in Table R402.1.4 (multiplied by the same assembly area as in the proposed building), the building shall be considered in compliance with Table R402.1.2. The UA calculation shall be done using a method consistent with the ASHRAE *Handbook of Fundamentals* and shall include the thermal bridging effects of framing materials. The SHGC requirements shall be met in addition to UA compliance.

R402.2 Specific insulation requirements (Prescriptive). In addition to the requirements of Section R402.1, insulation shall meet the specific requirements of Sections R402.2.1 through R402.2.13.

R402.2.1 Ceilings with attic spaces. Where Section R402.1.2 would require R-38 insulation in the ceiling, installing R-30 over 100 percent of the ceiling area requiring insulation shall be deemed to satisfy the requirement for R-38 wherever the full height of uncompressed R-30 insulation extends over the wall top plate at

TABLE R402.1.2
INSULATION AND FENESTRATION REQUIREMENTS BY COMPONENT[a]

CLIMATE ZONE	FENESTRATION *U*-FACTOR[b, j]	SKYLIGHT[b] *U*-FACTOR	GLAZED FENESTRATION SHGC[b, e]	CEILING *R*-VALUE	WOOD FRAME WALL *R*-VALUE	MASS WALL *R*-VALUE[i]	FLOOR *R*-VALUE	BASEMENT[c] WALL *R*-VALUE	SLAB[d] *R*-VALUE & DEPTH	CRAWL SPACE[c] WALL *R*-VALUE
1	NR	0.75	0.25	30	13	3/4	13	0	0	0
2	0.40	0.65	0.25	38	13	4/6	13	0	0	0
3	0.35	0.55	0.25	38	20 or 13+5[h]	8/13	19	5/13[f]	0	5/13
4 except Marine	0.35	0.55	0.40	49	20 or 13+5[h]	8/13	19	10 /13	10, 2 ft	10/13
5 and Marine 4	0.32	0.55	NR	49	20 or 13+5[h]	13/17	30[g]	15/19	10, 2 ft	15/19
6	0.32	0.55	NR	49	20+5 or 13+10[h]	15/20	30[g]	15/19	10, 4 ft	15/19
7 and 8	0.32	0.55	NR	49	20+5 or 13+10[h]	19/21	38[g]	15/19	10, 4 ft	15/19

For SI: 1 foot = 304.8 mm.

a. *R*-values are minimums. *U*-factors and SHGC are maximums. When insulation is installed in a cavity which is less than the label or design thickness of the insulation, the installed *R*-value of the insulation shall not be less than the *R*-value specified in the table.

b. The fenestration *U*-factor column excludes skylights. The SHGC column applies to all glazed fenestration. Exception: Skylights may be excluded from glazed fenestration SHGC requirements in climate zones 1 through 3 where the SHGC for such skylights does not exceed 0.30.

c. "15/19" means R-15 continuous insulation on the interior or exterior of the home or R-19 cavity insulation at the interior of the basement wall. "15/19" shall be permitted to be met with R-13 cavity insulation on the interior of the basement wall plus R-5 continuous insulation on the interior or exterior of the home. "10/13" means R-10 continuous insulation on the interior or exterior of the home or R-13 cavity insulation at the interior of the basement wall.

d. R-5 shall be added to the required slab edge *R*-values for heated slabs. Insulation depth shall be the depth of the footing or 2 feet, whichever is less in Climate Zones 1 through 3 for heated slabs.

e. There are no SHGC requirements in the Marine Zone.

f. Basement wall insulation is not required in warm-humid locations as defined by Figure R301.1 and Table R301.1.

g. Or insulation sufficient to fill the framing cavity, R-19 minimum.

h. The first value is cavity insulation, the second value is continuous insulation, so "13+5" means R-13 cavity insulation plus R-5 continuous insulation.

i. The second *R*-value applies when more than half the insulation is on the interior of the mass wall.

j. For impact rated fenestration complying with Section R301.2.1.2 of the *Florida Building Code, Residential* or Section 1609.1.2 of the *Florida Building Code, Building,* the maximum *U*-factor shall be 0.65 in Climate Zone 2.

TABLE R402.1.4
EQUIVALENT *U*-FACTORS[a]

CLIMATE ZONE	FENESTRATION *U*-FACTOR	SKYLIGHT *U*-FACTOR	CEILING *U*-FACTOR	FRAME WALL *U*-FACTOR	MASS WALL *U*-FACTOR[b]	FLOOR *U*-FACTOR	BASEMENT WALL *U*-FACTOR	CRAWL SPACE WALL *U*-FACTOR
1	0.50	0.75	0.035	0.084	0.197	0.064	0.360	0.477
2	0.40	0.65	0.030	0.084	0.165	0.064	0.360	0.477
3	0.35	0.55	0.030	0.060	0.098	0.047	0.091[c]	0.136
4 except Marine	0.35	0.55	0.026	0.060	0.098	0.047	0.059	0.065
5 and Marine 4	0.32	0.55	0.026	0.060	0.082	0.033	0.050	0.055
6	0.32	0.55	0.026	0.045	0.060	0.033	0.050	0.055
7 and 8	0.32	0.55	0.026	0.045	0.057	0.028	0.050	0.055

a. Nonfenestration *U*-factors shall be obtained from measurement, calculation or an approved source.

b. When more than half the insulation is on the interior, the mass wall U-factors shall be a maximum of 0.17 in Climate Zone 1, 0.14 in Climate Zone 2, 0.12 in Climate Zone 3, 0.087 in Climate Zone 4 except Marine, 0.065 in Climate Zone 5 and Marine 4, and 0.057 in Climate Zones 6 through 8.

c. Basement wall *U*-factor of 0.360 in warm-humid locations as defined by Table R301.1.

the eaves. Similarly, where Section R402.1.2 would require R-49 insulation in the ceiling, installing R-38 over 100 percent of the ceiling area requiring insulation shall be deemed to satisfy the requirement for R-49 insulation wherever the full height of uncompressed R-38 insulation extends over the wall top plate at the eaves. This reduction shall not apply to the *U*-factor alternative approach in Section R402.1.4 and the total UA alternative in Section R402.1.5.

R402.2.2 Ceilings without attic spaces. Where Section R402.1.2 would require insulation levels above R-30 and the design of the roof/ceiling assembly does not allow sufficient space for the required insulation, the minimum required insulation for such roof/ceiling assemblies shall be R-30. This reduction of insulation from the requirements of Section R402.1.2 shall be limited to 500 square feet (46 m^2) or 20 percent of the total insulated ceiling area, whichever is less. This reduction shall not apply to the *U*-factor alternative approach in Section R402.1.4 and the total UA alternative in Section R402.1.5.

R402.2.3 Eave baffle. For air-permeable insulations in vented attics, a baffle shall be installed adjacent to soffit and eave vents. Baffles shall maintain an opening equal or greater than the size of the vent. The baffle shall extend over the top of the attic insulation. The baffle shall be permitted to be any solid material.

R402.2.4 Access hatches and doors. Access doors from conditioned spaces to unconditioned spaces such as attics and crawl spaces shall be weatherstripped and insulated to a level equivalent to the insulation on the surrounding surfaces. Access shall be provided to all equipment that prevents damaging or compressing the insulation. A wood-framed or equivalent baffle or retainer is required to be provided when loose-fill insulation is installed, the purpose of which is to prevent the loose-fill insulation from spilling into the living space when the attic access is opened, and to provide a permanent means of maintaining the installed *R*-value of the loose-fill insulation.

Exception: Vertical doors that provide access from conditioned to unconditioned spaces shall be permitted to meet the fenestration requirements of Table R402.1.2 based on the applicable climate zone specified in Chapter 3.

R402.2.5 Mass walls. Mass walls for the purposes of this chapter shall be considered above-grade walls of concrete block, concrete, insulated concrete form (ICF), masonry cavity, brick (other than brick veneer), earth (adobe, compressed earth block, rammed earth) and solid timber/logs, or any other walls having a heat capacity greater than or equal to 6 Btu/ft^2 • °F (123 kJ/m^2 • K).

R402.2.6 Steel-frame ceilings, walls and floors. Steel-frame ceilings, walls, and floors shall meet the insulation requirements of Table R402.2.6 or shall meet the *U*-factor requirements of Table R402.1.4. The calculation of the *U*-factor for a steel-frame envelope assembly shall use a series-parallel path calculation method.

R402.2.7 Walls with partial structural sheathing. Where Section R402.1.2 would require continuous insulation on exterior walls and structural sheathing covers 40 percent or less of the gross area of all exterior walls, the continuous insulation *R*-value shall be permitted to be reduced by an amount necessary to result in a consistent total sheathing thickness, but not more than R-3, on areas of the walls covered by structural sheathing. This reduction shall not apply to the *U*-factor alternative approach in Section R402.1.4 and the total UA alternative in Section R402.1.5.

TABLE R402.2.6
STEEL-FRAME CEILING, WALL AND FLOOR INSULATION (*R*-VALUE)

WOOD FRAME *R*-VALUE REQUIREMENT	COLD-FORMED STEEL EQUIVALENT *R*-VALUE[a]
Steel Truss Ceilings[b]	
R-30	R-38 or R-30 + 3 or R-26 + 5
R-38	R-49 or R-38 + 3
R-49	R-38 + 5
Steel Joist Ceilings[b]	
R-30	R-38 in 2 × 4 or 2 × 6 or 2 × 8 R-49 in any framing
R-38	R-49 in 2 × 4 or 2 × 6 or 2 × 8 or 2 × 10
Steel-Framed Wall, 16″ on center	
R-13	R-13 + 4.2 or R-19 + 2.1 or R-21 + 2.8 or R-0 + 9.3 or R-15 + 3.8 or R-21 + 3.1
R-13 + 3	R-0 + 11.2 or R-13 + 6.1 or R-15 + 5.7 or R-19 + 5.0 or R-21 + 4.7
R-20	R-0 + 14.0 or R-13 + 8.9 or R-15 + 8.5 or R-19 + 7.8 or R-19 + 6.2 or R-21 + 7.5
R-20 + 5	R-13 + 12.7 or R-15 + 12.3 or R-19 + 11.6 or R-21 + 11.3 or R-25 + 10.9
R-21	R-0 + 14.6 or R-13 + 9.5 or R-15 + 9.1 or R-19 + 8.4 or R-21 + 8.1 or R-25 + 7.7
Steel Framed Wall, 24″ on center	
R-13	R-0 + 9.3 or R-13 + 3.0 or R-15 + 2.4
R-13 + 3	R-0 + 11.2 or R-13 + 4.9 or R-15 + 4.3 or R-19 + 3.5 or R-21 + 3.1
R-20	R-0 + 14.0 or R-13 + 7.7 or R-15 + 7.1 or R-19 + 6.3 or R-21 + 5.9
R-20 + 5	R-13 + 11.5 or R-15 + 10.9 or R-19 + 10.1 or R-21 + 9.7 or R-25 + 9.1
R-21	R-0 + 14.6 or R-13 + 8.3 or R-15 + 7.7 or R-19 + 6.9 or R-21 + 6.5 or R-25 + 5.9
Steel Joist Floor	
R-13	R-19 in 2 × 6, or R-19 + 6 in 2 × 8 or 2 × 10
R-19	R-19 + 6 in 2 × 6, or R-19 + 12 in 2 × 8 or 2 × 10

a Cavity insulation *R*-value is listed first, followed by continuous insulation *R*-value.

b. Insulation exceeding the height of the framing shall cover the framing.

R402.2.8 Floors. Floor framing-cavity insulation shall be installed to maintain permanent contact with the underside of the subfloor decking.

Exception: The floor framing-cavity insulation shall be permitted to be in contact with the topside of sheathing or continuous insulation installed on the bottom side of floor framing where combined with insulation that meets or exceeds the minimum wood frame wall *R*-value in Table 402.1.2 and that extends from the bottom to the top of all perimeter floor framing members.

R402.2.9 Basement walls. Walls associated with conditioned basements shall be insulated from the top of the *basement wall* down to 10 feet (3048 mm) below grade or to the basement floor, whichever is less. Walls associated with unconditioned basements shall meet this requirement unless the floor overhead is insulated in accordance with Sections R402.1.2 and R402.2.8.

R402.2.10 Slab-on-grade floors. Slab-on-grade floors with a floor surface less than 12 inches (305 mm) below grade shall be insulated in accordance with Table R402.1.2. The insulation shall extend downward from the top of the slab on the outside or inside of the foundation wall. Insulation located below grade shall be extended the distance provided in Table R402.1.2 by any combination of vertical insulation, insulation extending under the slab or insulation extending out from the building. Insulation extending away from the building shall be protected by pavement or by not less than 10 inches (254 mm) of soil. The top edge of the insulation installed between the *exterior wall* and the edge of the interior slab shall be permitted to be cut at a 45-degree (0.79 rad) angle away from the *exterior wall.* Slab-edge insulation is not required in jurisdictions designated by the *code official* as having a very heavy termite infestation.

R402.2.11 Crawl space walls. As an alternative to insulating floors over crawl spaces, crawl space walls shall be permitted to be insulated when the crawl space is not vented to the outside. Crawl space wall insulation shall be permanently fastened to the wall and extend downward from the floor to the finished grade level and then vertically and/or horizontally for at least an additional 24 inches (610 mm). Exposed earth in unvented crawl space foundations shall be covered with a continuous Class I vapor retarder in accordance with the *Florida Building Code, Building,* or *Florida Building Code, Residential*, as applicable. All joints of the vapor retarder shall overlap by 6 inches (153 mm) and be sealed or taped. The edges of the vapor retarder shall extend not less than 6 inches (153 mm) up the stem wall and shall be attached to the stem wall.

R402.2.12 Masonry veneer. Insulation shall not be required on the horizontal portion of the foundation that supports a masonry veneer.

R402.2.13 Sunroom insulation. *Sunrooms* enclosing conditioned space shall meet the insulation requirements of this code.

Exception: For *sunrooms* with *thermal isolation*, and enclosing conditioned space, the following exceptions to the insulation requirements of this code shall apply:

1. The minimum ceiling insulation *R*-values shall be R-19 in *Climate Zones* 1 through 4 and R-24 in *Climate Zones* 5 through 8.
2. The minimum wall *R*-value shall be R-13 in all *climate zones*. Walls separating a *sunroom* with a *thermal isolation* from *conditioned space* shall meet the *building thermal envelope* requirements of this code.

R402.2.14 Common walls/ceilings/floors. Walls, ceilings or floors common to separate conditioned tenancies shall be insulated to a minimum R-11, space permitting.

Exception: Mass common walls shall be insulated to a minimum of R-6.

R402.3 Fenestration (Prescriptive). In addition to the requirements of Section R402, fenestration shall comply with Sections R402.3.1 through R402.3.5.

R402.3.1 *U*-factor. An area-weighted average of fenestration products shall be permitted to satisfy the *U*-factor requirements.

R402.3.2 Glazed fenestration SHGC. An area-weighted average of fenestration products more than 50-percent glazed shall be permitted to satisfy the SHGC requirements.

Dynamic glazing shall be permitted to satisfy the SHGC requirements of Table R402.1.2 provided the ratio of the higher to lower labeled SHGC is greater than or equal to 2.4, and the *dynamic glazing* is automatically controlled to modulate the amount of solar gain into the space in multiple steps. *Dynamic glazing* shall be considered separately from other fenestration, and area-weighted averaging with other fenestration that is not dynamic glazing shall not be permitted.

Exception: *Dynamic glazing* is not required to comply with this section when both the lower and higher labeled SHGC already comply with the requirements of Table R402.1.2.

R402.3.3 Glazed fenestration exemption. Up to 15 square feet (1.4 m^2) of glazed fenestration per dwelling unit shall be permitted to be exempt from *U*-factor and SHGC requirements in Section R402.1.2. This exemption shall not apply to the *U*-factor alternative approach in Section R402.1.4 and the Total UA alternative in Section R402.1.5.

R402.3.4 Opaque door exemption. One side-hinged opaque door assembly up to 24 square feet (2.22 m^2) in area is exempted from the *U*-factor requirement in Section R402.1.4. This exemption shall not apply to the *U*-factor alternative approach in Section R402.1.4 and the total UA alternative in Section R402.1.5.

R402.3.5 Sunroom fenestration. *Sunrooms* enclosing *conditioned space* shall meet the fenestration requirements of this code.

Exception: For *sunrooms* with *thermal isolation* and enclosing *conditioned space* in *Climate Zones* 2 through 8, the maximum fenestration *U*-factor shall be 0.45 and the maximum skylight *U*-factor shall be 0.70.

New fenestration separating the *sunroom* with *thermal isolation* from *conditioned space* shall meet the *building thermal envelope* requirements of this code.

R402.4 Air leakage (Mandatory). The *building thermal envelope* shall be constructed to limit air leakage in accordance with the requirements of Sections R402.4.1 through R402.4.5.

Exception: Dwelling units of R-2 Occupancies and multiple attached single family dwellings shall be permitted to comply with Section C402.5.

R402.4.1 Building thermal envelope. The *building thermal envelope* shall comply with Sections R402.4.1.1 and R402.4.1.2. The sealing methods between dissimilar materials shall allow for differential expansion and contraction.

R402.4.1.1 Installation. The components of the *building thermal envelope* as listed in Table R402.4.1.1 shall be installed in accordance with the manufacturer's instructions and the criteria listed in Table R402.4.1.1, as applicable to the method of construction. Where required by the *code official*, an *approved* third party shall inspect all components and verify compliance.

R402.4.1.2 Testing. The building or dwelling unit shall be tested and verified as having an air leakage rate not exceeding seven air changes per hour in Climate Zones 1 and 2, and three air changes per hour in Climate Zones 3 through 8. Testing shall be conducted in accordance with ANSI/RESNET/ICC 380 and reported at a pressure of 0.2 inch w.g. (50 pascals). Testing shall be conducted by either individuals as defined in Section 553.993(5) or (7), *Florida Statutes,* or individuals licensed as set forth in Section 489.105(3)(f), (g) or (i) or an *approved* third party. A written report of the results of the test shall be signed by the party conducting the test and provided to the *code official*. Testing shall be performed at any time after creation of all penetrations of the *building thermal envelope*.

Exception: Testing is not required for additions, alterations, renovations or repairs of the building thermal envelope of existing buildings in which the new construction is less than 85 percent of the building thermal envelope.

During testing:

1. Exterior windows and doors, fireplace and stove doors shall be closed, but not sealed, beyond the intended weatherstripping or other infiltration control measures.
2. Dampers including exhaust, intake, makeup air, backdraft and flue dampers shall be closed, but not sealed beyond intended infiltration control measures.
3. Interior doors, if installed at the time of the test, shall be open.
4. Exterior doors for continuous ventilation systems and heat recovery ventilators shall be closed and sealed.
5. Heating and cooling systems, if installed at the time of the test, shall be turned off.
6. Supply and return registers, if installed at the time of the test, shall be fully open.

R402.4.2 Fireplaces. New wood-burning fireplaces shall have tight-fitting flue dampers or doors, and outdoor combustion air. Where using tight-fitting doors on factory-built fireplaces listed and labeled in accordance with UL 127, the doors shall be tested and listed for the fireplace. Where using tight-fitting doors on masonry fireplaces, the doors shall be listed and labeled in accordance with UL 907.

R402.4.3 Fenestration air leakage. Windows, skylights and sliding glass doors shall have an air infiltration rate of no more than 0.3 cfm per square foot (1.5 L/s/m^2), and swinging doors no more than 0.5 cfm per square foot (2.6 L/s/m^2), when tested according to NFRC 400 or AAMA/WDMA/CSA 101/I.S.2/A440 by an accredited, independent laboratory and *listed* and *labeled* by the manufacturer.

Exception: Site-built windows, skylights and doors.

R402.4.4 Rooms containing fuel-burning appliances. In Climate Zones 3 through 8, where open combustion air ducts provide combustion air to open combustion fuel burning appliances, the appliances and combustion air opening shall be located outside the building thermal envelope or enclosed in a room, isolated from inside the thermal envelope. Such rooms shall be sealed and insulated in accordance with the envelope requirements of Table R402.1.2, where the walls, floors and ceilings shall meet not less than the basement wall *R*-value requirement. The door into the room shall be fully gasketed and any water lines and ducts in the room insulated in accordance with Section R403. The combustion air duct shall be insulated where it passes through conditioned space to a minimum of R-8.

Exceptions:

1. Direct vent appliances with both intake and exhaust pipes installed continuous to the outside.
2. Fireplaces and stoves complying with Section R402.4.2 and Section R1006 of the *Florida Building Code, Residential.*

R402.4.5 Recessed lighting. Recessed luminaires installed in the *building thermal envelope* shall be sealed to limit air leakage between conditioned and unconditioned spaces. All recessed luminaires shall be IC-rated and *labeled* as having an air leakage rate not more than 2.0 cfm (0.944 L/s) when tested in accordance with ASTM E283 at a 1.57 psf (75 Pa) pressure differential. All recessed luminaires shall be sealed with a gasket or caulk between the housing and the interior wall or ceiling covering.

TABLE R402.4.1.1
AIR BARRIER AND INSULATION INSTALLATION

COMPONENT	AIR BARRIER CRITERIA	INSULATION INSTALLATION CRITERIA
General requirements	A continuous air barrier shall be installed in the building envelope. The exterior thermal envelope contains a continuous air barrier. Breaks or joints in the air barrier shall be sealed.	Air-permeable insulation shall not be used as a sealing material.
Ceiling/attic	The air barrier in any dropped ceiling/soffit shall be aligned with the insulation and any gaps in the air barrier shall be sealed. Access openings, drop down stairs or knee wall doors to unconditioned attic spaces shall be sealed.	The insulation in any dropped ceiling/soffit shall be aligned with the air barrier.
Walls	The junction of the foundation and sill plate shall be sealed. The junction of the top plate and the top of exterior walls shall be sealed. Knee walls shall be sealed.	Cavities within corners and headers of frame walls shall be insulated by completely filling the cavity with a material having a thermal resistance of R-3 per inch minimum. Exterior thermal envelope insulation for framed walls shall be installed in substantial contact and continuous alignment with the air barrier.
Windows, skylights and doors	The space between window/door jambs and framing, and skylights and framing shall be sealed.	
Rim joists	Rim joists shall include the air barrier.	Rim joists shall be insulated.
Floors (including above garage and cantilevered floors)	The air barrier shall be installed at any exposed edge of insulation.	Floor framing cavity insulation shall be installed to maintain permanent contact with the underside of subfloor decking, or floor framing cavity insulation shall be permitted to be in contact with the top side of sheathing, or continuous insulation installed on the underside of floor framing and extends from the bottom to the top of all perimeter floor framing members.
Crawl space walls	Exposed earth in unvented crawl spaces shall be covered with a Class I vapor retarder with overlapping joints taped.	Where provided instead of floor insulation, insulation shall be permanently attached to the crawlspace walls.
Shafts, penetrations	Duct shafts, utility penetrations, and flue shafts opening to exterior or unconditioned space shall be sealed.	
Narrow cavities		Batts in narrow cavities shall be cut to fit, or narrow cavities shall be filled by insulation that on installation readily conforms to the available cavity space.
Garage separation	Air sealing shall be provided between the garage and conditioned spaces.	
Recessed lighting	Recessed light fixtures installed in the building thermal envelope shall be sealed to the drywall.	Recessed light fixtures installed in the building thermal envelope shall be air tight and IC rated.
Plumbing and wiring		Batt insulation shall be cut neatly to fit around wiring and plumbing in exterior walls, or insulation that on installation readily conforms to available space shall extend behind piping and wiring.
Shower/tub on exterior wall	The air barrier installed at exterior walls adjacent to showers and tubs shall separate them from the showers and tubs.	Exterior walls adjacent to showers and tubs shall be insulated.
Electrical/phone box on exterior walls	The air barrier shall be installed behind electrical or communication boxes or air-sealed boxes shall be installed.	
HVAC register boots	HVAC register boots that penetrate building thermal envelope shall be sealed to the subfloor or drywall.	
Concealed sprinklers	When required to be sealed, concealed fire sprinklers shall only be sealed in a manner that is recommended by the manufacturer. Caulking or other adhesive sealants shall not be used to fill voids between fire sprinkler cover plates and walls or ceilings.	

a. In addition, inspection of log walls shall be in accordance with the provisions of ICC-400.

SECTION R403
SYSTEMS

R403.1 Controls.

R403.1.1 Thermostat provision (Mandatory). At least one thermostat shall be provided for each separate heating and cooling system.

R403.1.2 Programmable thermostat (Prescriptive). The thermostat controlling the primary heating or cooling system of the dwelling unit shall be capable of controlling the heating and cooling system on a daily schedule to maintain different temperature set points at different times of the day. This thermostat shall include the capability to set back or temporarily operate the system to maintain *zone* temperatures down to 55°F (13°C) or up to 85°F (29°C). The thermostat shall initially be programmed by the manufacturer with a heating temperature set point no higher than 70°F (21°C) and a cooling temperature set point no lower than 78°F (26°C).

R403.1.3 Heat pump supplementary heat (Mandatory). Heat pumps having supplementary electric-resistance heat shall have controls that, except during defrost, prevent supplemental heat operation when the heat pump compressor can meet the heating load.

R403.2 Hot water boiler outdoor temperature setback. Hot water boilers that supply heat to the building through one- or two-pipe heating systems shall have an outdoor setback control that lowers the boiler water temperature based on the outdoor temperature.

R403.3 Ducts. Ducts and air handlers shall be in accordance with Sections R403.3.1 through R403.3.5.

R403.3.1 Insulation (Prescriptive). Supply and return ducts in attics shall be insulated to a minimum of R-8 where 3 inches (76 mm) in diameter and greater and R-6 where less than 3 inches (76 mm) in diameter. Supply and return ducts in other portions of the building shall be insulated to a minimum of R-6 where 3 inches (76 mm) in diameter or greater and R-4.2 where less than 3 inches (76 mm) in diameter.

Exception: Ducts or portions thereof located completely inside the *building thermal envelope*.

R403.3.2 Sealing (Mandatory). All ducts, air handlers, filter boxes and building cavities that form the primary air containment passageways for air distribution systems shall be considered ducts or plenum chambers, shall be constructed and sealed in accordance with Section C403.2.9.2 of the Commercial Provisions of this code and shall be shown to meet duct tightness criteria below.

Duct tightness shall be verified by testing in accordance with ANSI/RESNET/ICC 380 by either individuals as defined in Section 553.993(5) or (7), *Florida Statutes*, or individuals licensed as set forth in Section 489.105(3)(f), (g) or (i), *Florida Statutes*, to be "substantially leak free" in accordance with Section R403.3.3.

R403.3.2.1 Sealed air handler. Air handlers shall have a manufacturer's designation for an air leakage of no more than 2 percent of the design airflow rate when tested in accordance with ASHRAE 193.

R403.3.3 Duct testing (Mandatory). Ducts shall be pressure tested to determine air leakage by one of the following methods:

1. Rough-in test: Total leakage shall be measured with a pressure differential of 0.1 inch w.g. (25 Pa) across the system, including the manufacturer's air handler enclosure if installed at the time of the test. All registers shall be taped or otherwise sealed during the test.
2. Postconstruction test: Total leakage shall be measured with a pressure differential of 0.1 inch w.g. (25 Pa) across the entire system, including the manufacturer's air handler enclosure. Registers shall be taped or otherwise sealed during the test.

Exceptions:

1. A duct air leakage test shall not be required where the ducts and air handlers are located entirely within the building thermal envelope.
2. Duct testing is not mandatory for buildings complying by Section 405 of this code.

A written report of the results of the test shall be signed by the party conducting the test and provided to the *code official*.

R403.3.4 Duct leakage (Prescriptive). The total leakage of the ducts, where measured in accordance with Section R403.3.3, shall be as follows:

1. Rough-in test: The total leakage shall be less than or equal to 4 cubic feet per minute (113.3 L/min) per 100 square feet (9.29 m^2) of conditioned floor area where the air handler is installed at the time of the test. Where the air handler is not installed at the time of the test, the total leakage shall be less than or equal to 3 cubic feet per minute (85 L/min) per 100 square feet (9.29 m^2) of conditioned floor area.
2. Postconstruction test: Total leakage shall be less than or equal to 4 cubic feet per minute (113.3 L/min) per 100 square feet (9.29 m^2) of conditioned floor area.

R403.3.5 Building cavities (Mandatory). Building framing cavities shall not be used as ducts or plenums.

R403.3.6 Air-handling units. Air-handling units shall not be installed in the attic when a home is brought into code compliance by Section R402. Air-handling units shall be allowed in attics for compliance by Section R405 only if the following conditions are met:

1. The service panel of the equipment is located within 6 feet (1829 mm) of an attic access.
2. A device is installed to alert the owner or shut down the unit when the condensation drain is not working properly.
3. The attic access opening is of sufficient size to replace the air handler.

4. A notice is posted on the electric service panel indicating to the homeowner that the air handler is located in the attic. Said notice shall be in all capitals, in 16-point type, with the title and first paragraph in bold:

NOTICE TO HOMEOWNER

A PART OF YOUR AIR-CONDITIONING SYSTEM, THE AIR HANDLER, IS LOCATED IN THE ATTIC. FOR PROPER, EFFICIENT AND ECONOMIC OPERATION OF THE AIR-CONDITIONING SYSTEM, YOU MUST ENSURE THAT REGULAR MAINTENANCE IS PERFORMED. YOUR AIR-CONDITIONING SYSTEM IS EQUIPPED WITH ONE OR BOTH OF THE FOLLOWING: (1) A DEVICE THAT WILL ALERT YOU WHEN THE CONDENSATION DRAIN IS NOT WORKING PROPERLY OR (2) A DEVICE THAT WILL SHUT DOWN THE SYSTEM WHEN THE CONDENSATION DRAIN IS NOT WORKING. TO LIMIT POTENTIAL DAMAGE TO YOUR HOME, AND TO AVOID DISRUPTION OF SERVICE, IT IS RECOMMENDED THAT YOU ENSURE PROPER WORKING ORDER OF THESE DEVICES BEFORE EACH SEASON OF PEAK OPERATION.

R403.4 Mechanical system piping insulation (Mandatory). Mechanical system piping capable of carrying fluids above 105°F (41°C) or below 55°F (13°C) shall be insulated to a minimum of R-3.

R403.4.1 Protection of piping insulation. Piping insulation exposed to weather shall be protected from damage, including that caused by sunlight, moisture, equipment maintenance and wind, and shall provide shielding from solar radiation that can cause degradation of the material. Adhesive tape shall not be permitted.

R403.5 Service hot water systems. Energy conservation measures for service hot water systems shall be in accordance with Sections R403.5.1 through R403.5.6.

R403.5.1 Heated water circulation and temperature maintenance systems (Mandatory). Heated water circulation systems shall be in accordance with Section R403.5.1.1. Heat trace temperature maintenance systems shall be in accordance with Section R403.5.1.2. Automatic controls, temperature sensors and pumps shall be accessible. Manual controls shall be readily accessible.

R403.5.1.1 Circulation systems. Heated water circulation systems shall be provided with a circulation pump. The system return pipe shall be a dedicated return pipe or a cold water supply pipe. Gravity and thermosyphon circulation systems shall be prohibited. Controls for circulating hot water system pumps shall start the pump based on the identification of a demand for hot water within the occupancy. The controls shall automatically turn off the pump when the water in the circulation loop is at the desired temperature and when there is no demand for hot water.

R403.5.1.2 Heat trace systems. Electric heat trace systems shall comply with IEEE 515.1 or UL 515. Controls for such systems shall automatically adjust the energy input to the heat tracing to maintain the desired water temperature in the piping in accordance with the times when heated water is used in the occupancy.

R403.5.2 Demand recirculation systems. A water distribution system having one or more recirculation pumps that pump water from a heated water supply pipe back to the heated water source through a cold water supply pipe shall be a *demand recirculation water system.* Pumps shall have controls that comply with both of the following:

1. The control shall start the pump upon receiving a signal from the action of a user of a fixture or appliance, sensing the presence of a user of a fixture or sensing the flow of hot or tempered water to a fixture fitting or appliance.
2. The control shall limit the temperature of the water entering the cold water piping to 104°F (40°C).

R403.5.3 Hot water pipe insulation (Prescriptive). Insulation for hot water pipe with a minimum thermal resistance (*R*-value) of R-3 shall be applied to the following:

1. Piping $^{3}/_{4}$ inch (19.1 mm) and larger in nominal diameter.
2. Piping serving more than one dwelling unit.
3. Piping located outside the conditioned space.
4. Piping from the water heater to a distribution manifold.
5. Piping located under a floor slab.
6. Buried in piping.
7. Supply and return piping in recirculation systems other than demand recirculation systems.

R403.5.4 Drain water heat recovery units. Drain water heat recovery units shall comply with CSA B55.2. Drain water heat recovery units shall be tested in accordance with CSA B55.1. Potable water-side pressure loss of drain water heat recovery units shall be less than 3 psi (20.7 kPa) for individual units connected to one or two showers. Potable water-side pressure loss of drain water heat recovery units shall be less than 2 psi (13.8 kPa) for individual units connected to three or more showers.

R403.5.5 Heat traps (Mandatory). Storage water heaters not equipped with integral heat traps and having vertical pipe risers shall have heat traps installed on both the inlets and outlets. External heat traps shall consist of either a commercially available heat trap or a downward and upward bend of at least $3^{1}/_{2}$ inches (89 mm) in the hot water distribution line and cold water line located as close as possible to the storage tank.

R403.5.6 Water heater efficiencies (Mandatory).

R403.5.6.1 Storage water heater temperature controls.

403.5.6.1.1 Automatic controls. Service water-heating systems shall be equipped with automatic temperature controls capable of adjustment from the lowest to the highest acceptable temperature settings for the intended use. The minimum temperature setting range shall be from 100°F to 140°F (38°C to 60°C).

R403.5.6.1.2 Shut down. A separate switch or a clearly marked circuit breaker shall be provided to permit the power supplied to electric service systems to be turned off. A separate valve shall be provided to permit the energy supplied to the main burner(s) of combustion types of service water-heating systems to be turned off.

R403.5.6.2 Water-heating equipment. Water-heating equipment installed in residential units shall meet the minimum efficiencies of Table C404.2 in Chapter 4 of the *Florida Building Code, Energy Conservation,* Commercial Provisions, for the type of equipment installed. Equipment used to provide heating functions as part of a combination system shall satisfy all stated requirements for the appropriate water-heating category. Solar water heaters shall meet the criteria of Section R403.5.6.2.1.

R403.5.6.2.1 Solar water-heating systems. Solar systems for domestic hot water production are rated by the annual solar energy factor of the system. The solar energy factor of a system shall be determined from the Florida Solar Energy Center Directory of Certified Solar Systems. Solar collectors shall be tested in accordance with ISO Standard 9806, *Test Methods for Solar Collectors,* and SRCC Standard TM-1, *Solar Domestic Hot Water System and Component Test Protocol.* Collectors in installed solar water-heating systems should meet the following criteria:

1. Be installed with a tilt angle between 10 degrees and 40 degrees of the horizontal; and
2. Be installed at an orientation within 45 degrees of true south.

R403.6 Mechanical ventilation (Mandatory). The building shall be provided with ventilation that meets the requirements of the *Florida Building Code, Residential,* or *Florida Building Code, Mechanical*, as applicable, or with other approved means of ventilation including: Natural, Infiltration or Mechanical means. Outdoor air intakes and exhausts shall have automatic or gravity dampers that close when the ventilation system is not operating.

R403.6.1 Whole-house mechanical ventilation system fan efficacy. When installed to function as a whole-house mechanical ventilation system, fans shall meet the efficacy requirements of Table R403.6.1.

Exception: Where whole-house mechanical ventilation fans are integral to tested and listed HVAC equipment, they shall be powered by an electronically commutated motor.

R403.6.2 Ventilation air. Residential buildings designed to be operated at a positive indoor pressure or for mechanical ventilation shall meet the following criteria:

1. The design air change per hour minimums for residential buildings in ASHRAE 62.2, *Ventilation for Acceptable Indoor Air Quality*, shall be the maximum rates allowed for residential applications.
2. No ventilation or air-conditioning system make-up air shall be provided to conditioned space from attics, crawlspaces, attached enclosed garages or outdoor spaces adjacent to swimming pools or spas.
3. If ventilation air is drawn from enclosed space(s), then the walls of the space(s) from which air is drawn shall be insulated to a minimum of R-11 and the ceiling shall be insulated to a minimum of R-19, space permitting, or R-10 otherwise.

R403.7 Heating and cooling equipment (Mandatory).

R403.7.1 Equipment sizing. Heating and cooling equipment shall be sized in accordance with ACCA Manual S based on the equipment loads calculated in accordance with ACCA Manual J or other *approved* heating and cooling calculation methodologies, based on building loads for the directional orientation of the building. The manufacturer and model number of the outdoor and indoor units (if split system) shall be submitted along with the sensible and total cooling capacities at the design conditions described in Section R302.1. This Code does not allow designer safety factors, provisions for future expansion or other factors that affect equipment sizing. System sizing calculations shall not include loads created by local intermittent mechanical ventilation such as standard kitchen and bathroom exhaust systems. New or replacement heating and cooling equipment shall have an efficiency rating equal to or greater than the minimum required by federal

TABLE R403.6.1
WHOLE-HOUSE MECHANICAL VENTILATION SYSTEM FAN EFFICACY

FAN LOCATION	AIRFLOW RATE MINIMUM (CFM)	MINIMUM EFFICACY[a] (CFM/WATT)	AIRFLOW RATE MAXIMUM (CFM)
Range hoods	Any	2.8 cfm/watt	Any
In-line fan	Any	2.8 cfm/watt	Any
Bathroom, utility room	10	1.4 cfm/watt	< 90
Bathroom, utility room	90	2.8 cfm/watt	Any

For SI: 1 cfm = 28.3 L/min.

a. When tested in accordance with HVI Standard 916

law for the geographic location where the equipment is installed.

R403.7.1.1 Cooling equipment capacity. Cooling only equipment shall be selected so that its total capacity is not less than the calculated total load but not more than 1.15 times greater than the total load calculated according to the procedure selected in Section 403.7, or the closest available size provided by the manufacturer's product lines. The corresponding latent capacity of the equipment shall not be less than the calculated latent load.

The published value for AHRI total capacity is a nominal, rating-test value and shall not be used for equipment sizing. Manufacturer's expanded performance data shall be used to select cooling-only equipment. This selection shall be based on the outdoor design dry-bulb temperature for the load calculation (or entering water temperature for water-source equipment), the blower CFM provided by the expanded performance data, the design value for entering wet-bulb temperature and the design value for entering dry-bulb temperature.

Design values for entering wet-bulb and dry-bulb temperatures shall be for the indoor dry bulb and relative humidity used for the load calculation and shall be adjusted for return side gains if the return duct(s) is installed in an unconditioned space.

Exceptions:

1. Attached single- and multiple-family residential equipment sizing may be selected so that its cooling capacity is less than the calculated total sensible load but not less than 80 percent of that load.
2. When signed and sealed by a Florida-registered engineer, in attached single- and multiple-family units, the capacity of equipment may be sized in accordance with good design practice.

R403.7.1.2 Heating equipment capacity.

R403.7.1.2.1 Heat pumps. Heat pump sizing shall be based on the cooling requirements as calculated according to Section R403.7.1.1, and the heat pump total cooling capacity shall not be more than 1.15 times greater than the design cooling load even if the design heating load is 1.15 times greater than the design cooling load.

R403.7.1.2.2 Electric resistance furnaces. Electric resistance furnaces shall be sized within 4 kW of the design requirements calculated according to the procedure selected in Section R403.7.1.

R403.7.1.2.3 Fossil fuel heating equipment. The capacity of fossil fuel heating equipment with natural draft atmospheric burners shall not be less than the design load calculated in accordance with Section R403.7.1.

R403.7.1.3 Extra capacity required for special occasions. Residences requiring excess cooling or heating equipment capacity on an intermittent basis, such as anticipated additional loads caused by major entertainment events, shall have equipment sized or controlled to prevent continuous space cooling or heating within that space by one or more of the following options:

1. A separate cooling or heating system is utilized to provide cooling or heating to the major entertainment areas.
2. A variable capacity system sized for optimum performance during base load periods is utilized.

R403.8 Systems serving multiple dwelling units (Mandatory). Systems serving multiple dwelling units shall comply with Sections C403 and C404 of the IECC—Commercial Provisions in lieu of Section R403.

R403.9 Snow melt and ice system controls (Mandatory). Snow- and ice-melting systems, supplied through energy service to the building, shall include automatic controls capable of shutting off the system when the pavement temperature is above 50°F (10°C), and no precipitation is falling and an automatic or manual control that will allow shutoff when the outdoor temperature is above 40°F (4.8°C).

R403.10 Pools and permanent spa energy consumption (Mandatory). The energy consumption of pools and permanent spas shall be in accordance with Sections R403.10.1 through R403.10.5.

R403.10.1 Heaters. The electric power to heaters shall be controlled by a readily *accessible* on-off switch that is an integral part of the heater mounted on the exterior of the heater, or external to and within 3 feet (914 mm) of the heater. Operation of such switch shall not change the setting of the heater thermostat. Such switches shall be in addition to a circuit breaker for the power to the heater. Gas-fired heaters shall not be equipped with continuously burning ignition pilots.

R403.10.2 Time switches. Time switches or other control methods that can automatically turn off and on according to a preset schedule shall be installed for heaters and pump motors. Heaters and pump motors that have built-in time switches shall be in compliance with this section.

Exceptions:

1. Where public health standards require 24-hour pump operation.
2. Pumps that operate solar- and waste-heat-recovery pool heating systems.
3. Where pumps are powered exclusively from on-site renewable generation.

R403.10.3 Covers. Outdoor heated swimming pools and outdoor permanent spas shall be equipped with a vapor-retardant cover on or at the water surface or a liquid cover or other means proven to reduce heat loss.

Exception: Where more than 70 percent of the energy for heating, computed over an operation season, is from site-recovered energy, such as from a heat pump or solar energy source, covers or other vapor-retardant means shall not be required.

R403.10.4 Gas- and oil-fired pool and spa heaters. All gas- and oil-fired pool and spa heaters shall have a minimum thermal efficiency of 82 percent for heaters manufactured on or after April 16, 2013, when tested in accordance with ANSI Z 21.56. Pool heaters fired by natural or LP gas shall not have continuously burning pilot lights.

R403.10.5 Heat pump pool heaters. Heat pump pool heaters shall have a minimum COP of 4.0 when tested in accordance with AHRI 1160, Table 2, Standard Rating Conditions-Low Air Temperature. A test report from an independent laboratory is required to verify procedure compliance. Geothermal swimming pool heat pumps are not required to meet this standard.

R403.11 Portable spas (Mandatory). The energy consumption of electric-powered portable spas shall be controlled by the requirements of APSP-14.

R403.12 Residential pools and permanent residential spas. Residential swimming pools and permanent residential spas that are accessory to detached one- and two-family dwellings and townhouses three stories or less in height above grade plane and that are available only to the household and its guests shall be in accordance with APSP-15.

SECTION R404
ELECTRICAL POWER AND LIGHTING SYSTEMS

R404.1 Lighting equipment (Mandatory). Not less than 75 percent of the lamps in permanently installed lighting fixtures shall be high-efficacy lamps or not less than 75 percent of the permanently installed lighting fixtures shall contain only high-efficacy lamps.

Exception: Low-voltage lighting.

R404.1.1 Lighting equipment (Mandatory). Fuel gas lighting systems shall not have continuously burning pilot lights.

SECTION R405
SIMULATED PERFORMANCE ALTERNATIVE (PERFORMANCE)

R405.1 Scope. This section establishes criteria for compliance using simulated energy performance analysis. Such analysis shall include heating, cooling and service water heating energy only.

R405.2 Mandatory requirements. Compliance with this section requires that the mandatory provisions identified in Section R401.2 be met. All supply and return ducts not completely inside the *building thermal envelope* shall be insulated to a minimum of R-6.

R405.2.1 Ceiling insulation. Ceilings shall have an insulation level of at least R-19, space permitting. For the purposes of this code, types of ceiling construction that are considered to have inadequate space to install R-19 include single assembly ceilings of the exposed deck and beam type and concrete deck roofs. Such ceiling assemblies shall be insulated to at least a level of R-10.

R405.3 Performance-based compliance. Compliance based on simulated energy performance requires that a proposed residence (*proposed design)* be shown to have annual total normalized Modified Loads that are less than or equal to the annual total loads of the *standard reference design* as calculated in accordance with Appendix RC of this standard.

R405.4 Documentation. Documentation of the software used for the performance design and the parameters for the building shall be in accordance with Sections R405.4.1 through R405.4.3.

R405.4.1 Compliance software tools. Computer software utilized for demonstration of code compliance shall have been approved by the Florida Building Commission in accordance with requirements of this code.

R405.4.2 Compliance report. Compliance software tools shall generate a report that documents that the *proposed design* complies with Section R405.3. A compliance report on the *proposed design* shall be submitted with the application for the building permit. Upon completion of the building, a compliance report based on the as-built condition of the building shall be submitted to the *code official* before a certificate of occupancy is issued. Batch sampling of buildings to determine energy code compliance for all buildings in the batch shall be prohibited.

Compliance reports shall include information in accordance with Sections R405.4.2.1 and R405.4.2.2. Where the *proposed design* of a building could be built on different sites where the cardinal orientation of the building on each site is different, compliance of the *proposed design* for the purposes of the application for the building permit shall be based on the worst-case orientation, worst-case configuration, worst-case building air leakage and worst- case duct leakage. Such worst-case parameters shall be used as inputs to the compliance software for energy analysis.

R405.4.2.1 Compliance report for permit application. A compliance report submitted with the application for building permit shall include the following:

1. Building street address, or other building site identification.
2. A statement indicating that the *proposed design* complies with Section R405.3.
3. An inspection checklist documenting the building component characteristics of the *proposed design* as indicated in Table R405.5.2(1). The inspection checklist shall show results for the *proposed design* with user inputs to the compliance software to generate the results.
4. A site-specific energy analysis report that is in compliance with Section R405.3.

5. The name of the individual performing the analysis and generating the report.
6. The name and version of the compliance software tool.

Exception: Multiple orientations. When an otherwise identical building model is offered in multiple orientations, compliance for any orientation shall be permitted by documenting that the building meets the performance requirements in each of the four cardinal (north, east, south and west) orientations, or the "Worst" orientation. Compliance software tools may calculate the "Worst Case" orientation by rotating the building through the 4 or 8 cardinal orientations.

R405.4.2.2 Compliance report for certificate of occupancy. A compliance report submitted for obtaining the certificate of occupancy shall include the following:

1. Building street address, or other building site identification.
2. A statement indicating that the as-built building complies with Section R405.3.
3. A certificate indicating that the building passes the performance matrix for code compliance and listing the energy saving features of the buildings.
4. A site-specific energy analysis report that is in compliance with Section R405.3.
5. The name of the individual performing the analysis and generating the report.
6. The name and version of the compliance software tool.

R405.4.3 Additional documentation. The *code official* shall be permitted to require the following documents:

1. Verification that an EPL display card signed by the builder providing the building component characteristics of the *proposed design* will be provided to the purchaser of the home at time of title transfer.
2. Documentation of the component efficiencies used in the software calculations for the *proposed design*.

R405.5 Calculation procedure. Calculations of the performance design shall be in accordance with Sections R405.5.1 through R405.5.3.

R405.5.1 General. Except as specified by this section, the *standard reference design* and *proposed design* shall be configured and analyzed using identical methods and techniques.

R405.5.2 Residence specifications. The *standard reference design* and *proposed design* shall be configured and analyzed as specified by Table R405.5.2(1). Table R405.5.2(1) shall include, by reference, all notes contained in Table R402.1.2.

R405.5.3 Calculation requirements for glazing.

R405.5.3.1 Glass areas. All glazing areas of a residence, including windows, sliding glass doors, glass in doors, skylights, etc., shall include the manufacturer's frame area in the total window area. Window measurements shall be as specified on the plans and specifications for the residence.

Exception: When a window in existing exterior walls is enclosed by an addition, an amount equal to the area of this window may be subtracted from the glazing area for the addition for that overhang and orientation.

R405.5.3.2 Overhangs. Overhang effect is measured by Overhang Separation, which is the vertical measure of the distance from the top of a window to the bottom of the overhang. The overhang for adjustable exterior shading devices shall be determined at its most extended position. Nonpermanent shading devices such as canvas awnings shall not be considered overhangs. Permanently attached wood and metal awnings may be considered overhangs.

R405.5.3.3 Doors with glazing. For doors that are opaque or where the glass is less than one-third of the area of the door, the total door area shall be included in the door calculation. For unlabeled sliding glass doors or when glass areas in doors are greater than or equal to one-third of the area of the door, the glazing portion shall be included in the glazing calculation and the opaque portion of the door shall be included in the door calculation. When glass areas in doors are greater than or equal to one-third of the area of the door, the door shall be included in the glazing calculation as a total fenestration using the tested *U*-factor and solar heat gain coefficient.

R405.5.3.4 Maximum fenestration SHGC. The Proposed Design must have either an area-weighted average maximum fenestration SHGC of 0.50 or a window area-weighted average overhang depth of 4.0 feet or greater (all conditioned space windows must be included in the calculation). The area-weighted average maximum fenestration *U*-factor permitted using tradeoffs from Section R402.1.5 or R405 shall be 0.48 in Climate Zones 4 and 5 and 0.40 in Climate Zones 6 through 8 for vertical fenestration, and 0.75 in Climate Zones 4 through 8 for skylights. The area-weighted average maximum fenestration SHGC permitted using tradeoffs from Section R405 in Climate Zones 1 through 3 shall be 0.50.

TABLE R405.5.2(1)
SPECIFICATIONS FOR THE STANDARD REFERENCE AND PROPOSED DESIGNS

BUILDING COMPONENT	STANDARD REFERENCE DESIGN	PROPOSED DESIGN
Above-grade walls	Type: mass wall if proposed wall is mass; otherwise wood frame	As proposed
	Gross area: same as proposed	As proposed
	U-factor: as specified in Table R402.1.4	As proposed
	Solar absorptance = 0.75	As proposed
	Emittance = 0.90	As proposed
Basement and crawl space walls	Type: same as proposed	As proposed
	Gross area: same as proposed	As proposed
	U-factor: from Table R402.1.4, with insulation layer on interior side of walls	As proposed
Above-grade floors	Type: wood frame	As proposed
	Gross area: same as proposed	As proposed
	U-factor: as specified in Table R402.1.4	As proposed
Ceilings	Type: wood frame	As proposed
	Gross area: same as proposed	As proposed
	U-factor: as specified in Table R402.1.4	As proposed
Roofs	Type: composition shingle on wood sheathing	As proposed
	Gross area: same as proposed	As proposed
	Solar absorptance = 0.75	As proposed
	Emittance = 0.90	As proposed
Attics	Type: vented with aperture = 1 ft^2 per 300 ft^2 ceiling area	As proposed
Foundations	Type: same as proposed	As proposed
	Foundation wall area above and below grade and soil characteristics: same as proposed	As proposed
Opaque doors	Area: 40 ft^2	As proposed
	Orientation: North	As proposed
	U-factor: same as fenestration from Table R402.1.4	As proposed
Vertical fenestration other than opaque doors	Vertical fenestration area[h] = (a) The proposed vertical fenestration area, where the proposed fenestration area is less than 15 percent of the conditioned floor area, or (b) The adjusted vertical fenestration area, where the proposed fenestration area is 15 percent or more of the conditioned floor area. The adjusted vertical fenestration area shall be calculated as follows: $AVF_{adj} = AVF \cdot 0.15 \cdot CFA/AF$ where: AVF_{adj} = adjusted vertical fenestration AVF = proposed vertical fenestration area CFA = conditioned floor area AF = proposed total fenestration area	As proposed
	Orientation: equally distributed to four cardinal compass orientations (N, E, S & W)	As proposed
	U-factor: as specified in Table R402.1.4	As proposed
	SHGC: as specified in Table R402.1.2 except that for climates with no requirement (NR) SHGC = 0.40 shall be used	As proposed
	Interior shade fraction: 0.92 - (0.21 × SHGC for the standard reference design)	0.92 - (0.21 × SHGC as proposed)
	External shading: none	As proposed

(continued)

TABLE R405.5.2(1)—continued
SPECIFICATIONS FOR THE STANDARD REFERENCE AND PROPOSED DESIGNS

BUILDING COMPONENT	STANDARD REFERENCE DESIGN	PROPOSED DESIGN
Skylights	Skylight area = (a) The proposed skylight area, where the proposed fenestration area is less than 15 percent of the conditioned floor area, or (b) The adjusted skylight area, where the proposed fenestration area is 15 percent or greater of the conditioned floor area. The adjusted skylight area shall be calculated as follows: $ASKY_{-adj} = ASKY \cdot 0.15 \cdot CFA/AF$ where: $ASKY_{-adj}$ = adjusted skylight area $ASKY$ = proposed skylight area CFA = conditioned floor area AF = proposed total fenestration area	As proposed
	Orientation: as proposed	As proposed
	U-factor: as specified in Table R402.1.4	As proposed
	SHGC: as specified in Table R402.1.2 including footnote (b) of that table, except that for climates with no requirement (NR) SHGC = 0.40 shall be used	As proposed
	Interior shade fraction for the area of proposed skylights with SHGC ratings that include a pre-installed interior shade: 0.92 - (0.21 • SHGC for the standard reference design)	As proposed, with shades assumed closed 50% of the time
	External shading: none	As proposed
Thermally isolated sunrooms	None	As proposed
Air exchange rate	Air leakage rate of 7.00 air changes per hour in Climate Zones 1 and 2, and 3 air changes per hour in Climate Zones 3 through 8 at a pressure of 0.2 inches w.g. (50 Pa). The mechanical ventilation rate shall be in addition to the air leakage rate and the same as in the proposed design, but no greater than $0.01 \times CFA + 7.5 \times (N_{br} + 1)$ where: CFA = conditioned floor area N_{br} = number of bedrooms Energy recovery shall not be assumed for mechanical ventilation.	The measured air exchange rate[a]. The mechanical ventilation rate[b] shall be in addition to the air leakage rate and shall be as proposed.
Mechanical ventilation	None, except where mechanical ventilation is specified by the proposed design, in which case: Annual vent fan energy use: $kWh/yr = 0.03942 \times CFA + 29.565 \times (N_{br} + 1)$ where: CFA = conditioned floor area N_{br} = number of bedrooms	As proposed
Internal gains	$IGain = 17{,}900 + 23.8 \times CFA + 4104 \times N_{br}$ (Btu/day per dwelling unit)	Same as standard reference design.
Internal mass	An internal mass for furniture and contents of 8 pounds per square foot of floor area	Same as standard reference design, plus any additional mass specifically designed as a thermal storage element[c] but not integral to the building envelope or structure.
Structural mass	For masonry floor slabs, 80 percent of floor area covered by R-2 carpet and pad, and 20 percent of floor directly exposed to room air	As proposed
	For masonry basement walls, as proposed, but with insulation required by Table R402.1.4 located on the interior side of the walls	As proposed
	For other walls, for ceilings, floors, and interior walls, wood frame construction	As proposed
Heating systems[d, e]	Efficiency: in accordance with prevailing federal minimum standards Capacity: sized in accordance with Section R403.7 Fuel type: same as proposed	As proposed As proposed As proposed

(continued)

TABLE R405.5.2(1)—continued
SPECIFICATIONS FOR THE STANDARD REFERENCE AND PROPOSED DESIGNS

BUILDING COMPONENT	STANDARD REFERENCE DESIGN	PROPOSED DESIGN
Cooling systems[d, f]	Fuel type: electric Capacity: sized in accordance with Section R403.7. Efficiency: in accordance with prevailing federal minimum standards	As proposed As proposed As proposed
Service water heating[d, e, f, g]	Fuel type: as proposed Use: same as proposed design Efficiency: in accordance with prevailing federal minimum standards	As proposed gal/day = 30 + (10 × N_{br}) As proposed
Thermal distribution systems	Distribution system efficiency: 0.88	Thermal distribution system efficiency shall be as tested in accordance with ANSI/RESNET/ICC 380 or if not tested, shall be modeled as a Qn to outside of 0.080 for ducted systems. Hydronic and ductless systems shall be as specified in Table R405.5.2(2) if not tested.
	Duct location: entirely within the building thermal envelope Air handler location: entirely within the building thermal envelope Duct insulation: R-6	As proposed As proposed As proposed
Thermostat	Type: Manual, cooling temperature setpoint = 75°F; Heating temperature setpoint = 72°F	Same as standard reference

For SI: 1 square foot = 0.93 m², 1 British thermal unit = 1055 J, 1 pound per square foot = 4.88 kg/m², 1 gallon (US) = 3.785 L, °C = (°F-32)/1.8, 1 degree = 0.79 rad.

a. Where required by the *code official*, testing shall be conducted by an *approved* party. Hourly calculations as specified in the ASHRAE *Handbook of Fundamentals*, or the equivalent shall be used to determine the energy loads resulting from infiltration.

b. The combined air exchange rate for infiltration and mechanical ventilation shall be determined in accordance with Equation 43 of 2001 ASHRAE *Handbook of Fundamentals*, page 26.24 and the "Whole-house Ventilation" provisions of 2001 ASHRAE *Handbook of Fundamentals*, page 26.19 for intermittent mechanical ventilation.

c. Thermal storage element shall mean a component not part of the floors, walls or ceilings that is part of a passive solar system, and that provides thermal storage such as enclosed water columns, rock beds, or phase-change containers. A thermal storage element must be in the same room as fenestration that faces within 15 degrees (0.26 rad) of true south, or must be connected to such a room with pipes or ducts that allow the element to be actively charged.

d. For a proposed design with multiple heating, cooling or water heating systems using different fuel types, the applicable standard reference design system capacities and fuel types shall be weighted in accordance with their respective loads as calculated by accepted engineering practice for each equipment and fuel type present.

e. For a proposed design without a proposed heating system, a heating system with the prevailing federal minimum efficiency shall be assumed for both the standard reference design and proposed design.

f. For a proposed design home without a proposed cooling system, an electric air conditioner with the prevailing federal minimum efficiency shall be assumed for both the standard reference design and the proposed design.

g. For a proposed design with a nonstorage-type water heater, a 40-gallon storage-type water heater with the prevailing federal minimum energy factor for the same fuel as the predominant heating fuel type shall be assumed. For the case of a proposed design without a proposed water heater, a 40-gallon storage-type water heater with the prevailing federal minimum efficiency for the same fuel as the predominant heating fuel type shall be assumed for both the proposed design and standard reference design.

h. For residences with conditioned basements, R-2 and R-4 residences and townhouses, the following formula shall be used to determine fenestration area:

$AF = A_s \cdot FA \cdot F$

where:

AF = Total fenestration area.

A_s = Standard reference design total fenestration area.

FA = (Above-grade thermal boundary gross wall area)/(above-grade boundary wall area + 0.5 × below-grade boundary wall area).

F = (Above-grade thermal boundary wall area)/(above-grade thermal boundary wall area + common wall area) or 0.80, whichever is greater,

and where:

Thermal boundary wall is any wall that separates conditioned space from unconditioned space or ambient conditions.

Above-grade thermal boundary wall is any thermal boundary wall component not in contact with soil.

Below-grade boundary wall is any thermal boundary wall in soil contact.

Common wall area is the area of walls shared with an adjoining dwelling unit.

L and *CFA* are in the same units.

TABLE R405.5.2(2)
DEFAULT DISTRIBUTION SYSTEM EFFICIENCIES FOR PROPOSED DESIGNS[a]

DISTRIBUTION SYSTEM CONFIGURATION AND CONDITION	FORCED AIR SYSTEMS	HYDRONIC SYSTEMS[b]
Distribution system components located in unconditioned space	—	0.95
Untested distribution systems entirely located in conditioned space[c]	—	1
"Ductless" systems[d]	1	—

For SI: 1 cubic foot per minute = 0.47 L/s, 1 square foot = 0.093 m^2, 1 pound per square inch = 6895 Pa, 1 inch water gauge = 1250 Pa.

a. Default values given by this table are for untested distribution systems, which must still meet minimum requirements for duct system insulation.

b. Hydronic systems shall mean those systems that distribute heating and cooling energy directly to individual spaces using liquids pumped through closed-loop piping and that do not depend on ducted, forced airflow to maintain space temperatures.

c. Entire system in conditioned space shall mean that no component of the distribution system, including the air-handler unit, is located outside of the conditioned space.

d. Ductless systems shall be allowed to have forced airflow across a coil but shall not have any ducted airflow external to the manufacturer's air-handler enclosure.

R405.6 Calculation software tools. Calculation software, where used, shall be in accordance with Sections R405.6.1 through R405.6.3.

R405.6.1 Minimum capabilities. Calculation procedures used to comply with this section shall be software tools capable of calculating the annual energy consumption of all building elements that differ between the *standard reference design* and the *proposed design* and shall include the following capabilities:

1. Computer generation of the *standard reference design* using only the input for the *proposed design.* The calculation procedure shall not allow the user to directly modify the building component characteristics of the *standard reference design.*
2. Calculation of whole-building (as a single *zone*) sizing for the heating and cooling equipment in the *standard reference design* residence in accordance with Section R403.6.
3. Calculations that account for the effects of indoor and outdoor temperatures and part-load ratios on the performance of heating, ventilating and air-conditioning equipment based on climate and equipment sizing.
4. Printed *code official* inspection checklist listing each of the *proposed design* component characteristics from Table R405.5.2(1) determined by the analysis to provide compliance, along with their respective performance ratings (*R*-value, *U*-factor, SHGC, HSPF, AFUE, SEER, EF are some examples).

R405.6.2 Specific approval. Performance analysis tools meeting the applicable provisions of Section R405 shall be permitted to be *approved.* Tools are permitted to be *approved* based on meeting a specified threshold for a jurisdiction. The *code official* shall be permitted to approve tools for a specified application or limited scope.

R405.6.3 Input values. When calculations require input values not specified by Sections R402, R403, R404 and R405, those input values shall be taken from an *approved* source.

R405.6.3.1 Water-heating EF adjustment factors. The Energy Factor (EF) of an instantaneous water heater [those with capacity of two gallons (7.57 L) or less] in the Proposed home shall be reduced to 92 percent of the value in the manufacturer's documentation or AHRI *Directory of Certified Product Performance*.

R405.7 Requirements specific to credit options. Credit may be claimed in the software compliance calculation for technologies that meet prescriptive criteria specified as follows for various options.

R405.7.1 Installation criteria for homes claiming the radiant barrier option. The sheet radiant barrier or IRCC options may be claimed where the radiant barrier system is to be installed in one of the configurations depicted in Figure R405.7.1 and the following conditions are met:

1. It shall be fabricated over a ceiling insulated to a minimum of R-19 with conventional insulation and shall not be used as a means to achieve partial or whole compliance with a minimum attic insulation level of R-19. Either a sheet type or spray applied interior radiation control coating (IRCC) may be used.
2. If the radiant barrier material has only one surface with high reflectivity or low emissivity, it shall be facing downward toward the ceiling insulation.
3. The attic airspace shall be vented in accordance with Section R806 of the *Florida Building Code, Residential.*
4. The radiant barrier system shall conform to ASTM C1313, *Standard Specification for Sheet Radiant Barriers for Building Construction Applications*, or ASTM C1321, *Standard Practice for Installation and Use of Interior Radiation Control Coating Systems (IRCCS) in Building Construction* as appropriate for the type of radiant barrier to be installed. The operative surface shall have an emissivity not greater than 0.06 for sheet radiant barriers or 0.25 for interior radiation control coatings as demonstrated by independent laboratory testing according to ASTM C1371.

5. The radiant barrier system (RBS) shall conform with ASTM C1158, *Use and Installation of Radiant Barrier Systems (RBS) in Building Constructions for Sheet Radiant Barriers*, or ASTM C1321, *Standard Practice for Installation and Use of Interior Radiation Control Coating Systems (IRCCS) in Building Construction* for IRCC systems.
6. The radiant barrier shall be installed so as to cover gable ends without closing off any soffit, gable or roof ventilation.

R405.7.2 Installation criteria for homes claiming the cool roof option. The cool roof option may be claimed where the roof to be installed has a tested solar reflectance of greater than 4 percent when evaluated in accordance with ASTM methods E-903, C-1549, E-1918 or CRRC Method #1. Emittance values provided by the roofing manufacturer in accordance with ASTM C1371 shall be used when available. In cases where the appropriate data are not known, emittance shall be the same as the Standard Reference Design. Testing of a qualifying sample of the roofing material shall be performed by an approved independent laboratory with these results provided by the manufacturer.

R405.7.3 Installation criteria for homes using the unvented attic assembly option. The unvented attic assembly option may be used if the criteria in Section R806.5 of the *Florida Building Code, Residential,* have been met.

R405.7.4 Installation criteria for homes using the cross ventilation option. The cross ventilation option may be used if the following criteria have been met:

1. Operable aperture areas totaling a minimum of 12 percent of the floor area of the room shall be provided for all primary living areas and main bedrooms.

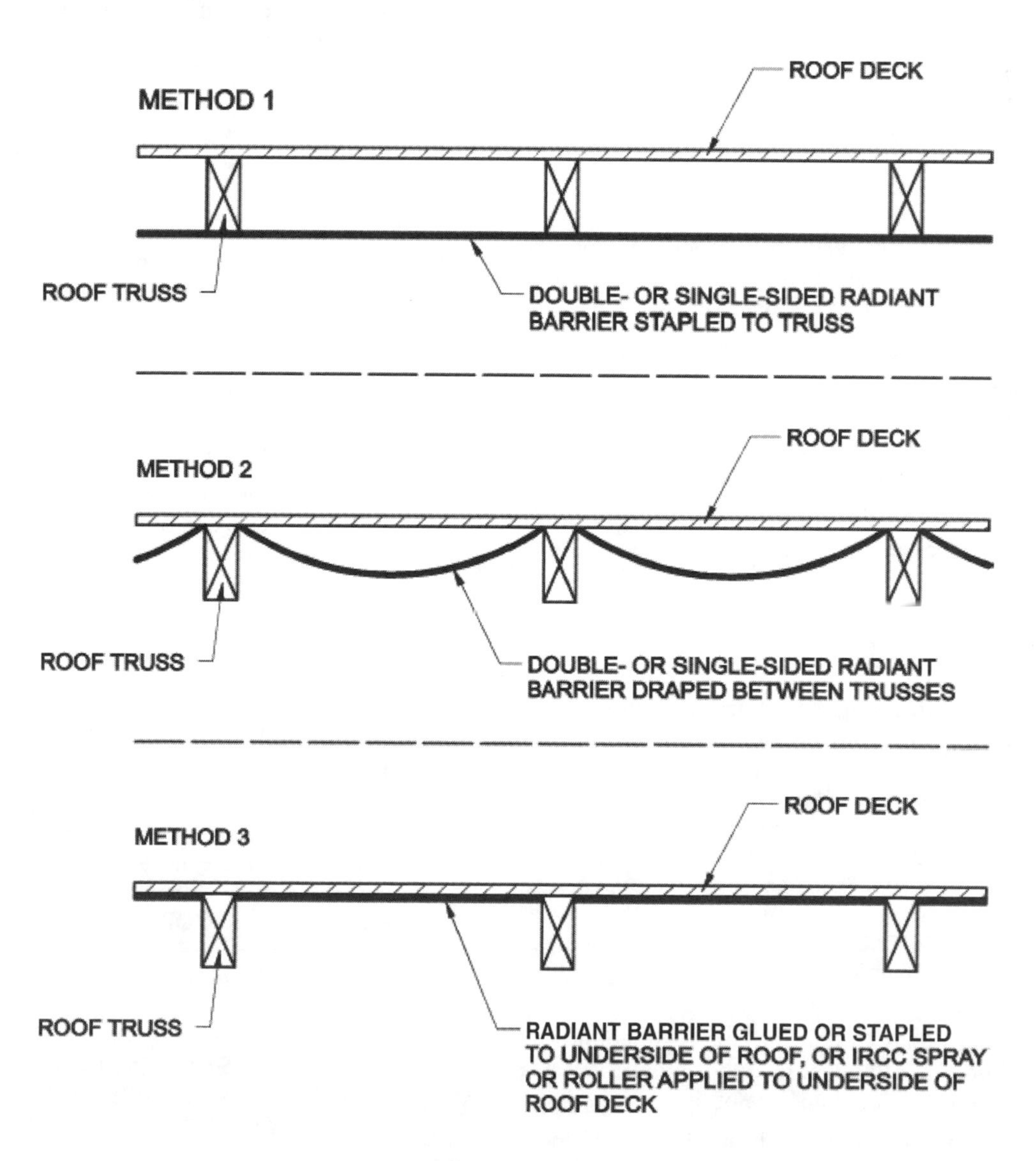

FIGURE R405.7.1
ACCEPTABLE ATTIC RADIANT BARRIER CONFIGURATIONS

2. Insect screens shall be provided for all operable windows, skylights and doors to be considered operable aperture area. All screened entry doors and interior doors in the ventilated areas shall be provided with either (1) mechanically attached door stops (or similar devices) to hold the door in an open position or (2) operable louvers.

3. The total aperture area shall be provided by a minimum of two distinct windows or one window and one skylight. Each operable unit shall provide not more than 70 percent of the total aperture area. The windows (or sliding glass doors) shall be placed in walls adjacent or opposite to each other. The windows may be placed on a single outside wall if a skylight or wing walls are used.

4. Where wing walls are included in the building design for ventilation purposes, they shall be placed between windows to create a high-pressure and a low-pressure zone on each window. Wing walls shall extend from the ground to eave height, be located on the windward side of the building and extend outward from the building a distance at least equal to one-half the width of the window. NOTE: This technique is effective only for areas that experience significant and continuous winds during the cooling months.

R405.7.5 Installation criteria for homes using the whole house fan option. The whole house fan option may be used if the following criteria have been met:

1. The whole house fan has been sized to provide a minimum of 20 air changes per hour for the entire house.

2. The fan installed shall have a free air cfm rating of at least three times the square footage of the conditioned area of the house.

3. To ensure adequate air exhaust, the house attic shall have gable, ridge or wind turbine vents whose total opening area is equal to four times the ceiling cutout area for the whole house fan. Soffit vents shall not be included in the exhaust vent area.

R405.7.6 Installation criteria for homes using the ceiling fan option. The ceiling fan option shall apply a 2 percent reduction in cooling energy use for the proposed design if one or more ceiling fans are installed in each of the bedrooms and a minimum of one ceiling fan is installed in all primary living areas (living rooms, family rooms or great rooms). This shall not include spaces designed to be dining rooms or dining areas. Areas separated by permanently fixed archways, walls or dividers shall be considered separate rooms. The following criteria shall be met:

1. Ceiling fans shall be installed with minimum fan blade diameters of no less than those listed in Table R405.7.6 for the size and shape of the room.

2. Where a primary living area is an "L-shaped" room and the smaller portion of this area is 8 feet by 10 feet (2438 mm by 3048 mm) or larger, a fan shall be installed in both the larger and smaller portions of the primary living area.

3. Ceiling fans shall be ENERGY STAR certified.

Exception: Credit shall not be taken for both ceiling fans and cross ventilation.

TABLE R405.7.6
FAN SIZING TABLE

LONGEST WALL LENGTH (feet)	MINIMUM FAN SIZE (inches)
= 12	36
> 12–16	48
> 16–17.5	52
> 17.5–25	56
> 25	2 fans (minimum of 48 inches each)

For SI: 1 inch = 25.4 mm, 1 foot = 304.8 mm.

R405.7.7 Installation criteria for homes claiming the heat recovery unit (HRU) option. The heat recovery unit option may be used for installation of a waste heat recovery unit (HRU) on either an air conditioner or a heat pump where the heat recovery unit has a minimum net useful heat exchange effect of 50 percent and meets the following criteria:

1. The net useful heat exchange effect shall be demonstrated by either a Form 400D-2017 prominently displayed on the unit with test results clearly visible for inspection or by an ARDM-certified refrigerant desuperheater seal affixed to the unit.

2. The net useful heat exchange effect shall have been determined by an independent laboratory testing to AHRI Standard 470.

3. If more than one air-conditioning system is installed in a residence and only one HRU is installed, energy load shall be based on the gallon capacity of the water heater to which it is coupled and the total capacity of the water heaters in the residence. In such case, the HRU shall be attached to the system serving the daytime primary living areas (family room, living room, kitchen, dining room and adjacent bedrooms and bathrooms).

R405.7.8 Installation criteria for homes claiming the dedicated heat pump option. The dedicated heat pump option may be used for a dedicated heat pump (also known as a heat pump water heater) installed either with a tank (an integral unit) or without tank (add-on to another water heater) based on the COP or energy factor (EF) of the system on which it is installed. No minimum rating is required for this equipment.

SECTION R406 ENERGY RATING INDEX COMPLIANCE ALTERNATIVE

R406.1 Scope. This section establishes criteria for compliance using an Energy Rating Index (ERI) analysis.

R406.2 Mandatory requirements. Compliance with this section requires that the provisions identified in Sections R401 through R404 labeled as "mandatory" and Section R403.5.3 of the 2015 *International Energy Conservation Code* be met. For buildings that do not utilize on-site renewable power production for compliance with this section, the building thermal envelope shall be greater than or equal to levels of efficiency and Solar Heat Gain Coefficient in Table 402.1.1 or 402.1.3 of the 2009 *International Energy Conservation Code.* For buildings that utilize on-site renewable power production for compliance with this section, the building thermal envelope shall be greater than or equal to levels of efficiency and Solar Heat Gain Coefficient in Table R402.1.2 or Table R402.1.4 of the 2015 *International Energy Conservation Code.*

Exception: Supply and return ducts not completely inside the building thermal envelope shall be insulated to a minimum of R-6.

R406.3 Energy Rating Index. The Energy Rating Index (ERI) shall be a numerical integer value that is based on a linear scale constructed such that the *ERI reference design* has an Index value of 100 and a *residential building* that uses no net purchased energy has an Index value of 0. Each integer value on the scale shall represent a 1-percent change in the annual total normalized modified loads of the *rated design* relative to the annual total loads of the *ERI reference design.* The ERI shall consider all energy used in the *residential building*.

R406.3.1 ERI reference design. The *ERI reference design* shall be configured such that it meets the minimum requirements of the 2006 *International Energy Conservation Code* prescriptive requirements.

R406.4 ERI-based compliance. The ERI for the *rated design* shall be determined in accordance with ANSI/RESNET/ICC 301, including Addendum A-2015, and be shown to have an ERI less than or equal to the appropriate value listed in Table R406.4.

TABLE R406.4
MAXIMUM ENERGY RATING INDEX

CLIMATE ZONE	ENERGY RATING INDEX
1	58
2	58
3	51
4	54
5	55
6	54
7	53
8	53

R406.5 Verification by approved agency. Verification of compliance with Section R406 shall be completed by an *approved* third party, in accordance with *Florida Statutes* 553.990 (Building Energy Efficiency Rating System).

R406.6 Documentation. Documentation of the software used to determine the ERI and the parameters for the residential building shall be in accordance with Sections R406.6.1 through R406.6.3.

R406.6.1 Compliance software tools. Computer software utilized for demonstration of code compliance shall have been approved by the Florida Building Commission in accordance with requirements of this code.

R406.6.2 Compliance report. Compliance software tools shall generate a report that documents that the ERI of the *rated design* complies with Sections R406.3 and R406.4. The compliance documentation shall include the following information:

1. Address or other identification of the residential building.
2. An inspection checklist documenting the building component characteristics of the *rated design.* The inspection checklist shall show results for both the *ERI reference design* and the *rated design*, and shall document all inputs entered by the user necessary to reproduce the results.
3. Name of individual completing the compliance report.
4. Name and version of the compliance software tool.

Exception: Multiple orientations. Where an otherwise identical building model is offered in multiple orientations, compliance for any orientation shall be permitted by documenting that the building meets the performance requirements in each of the four (north, east, south and west) cardinal orientations.

R406.6.3 Additional documentation. The *code official* shall be permitted to require the following documents:

1. Documentation of the building component characteristics of the *ERI reference design.*
2. A certification signed by the builder providing the building component characteristics of the *rated design.*
3. Documentation of the actual values used in the software calculations for the *rated design.*

R406.7 Calculation software tools. Calculation software, where used, shall be in accordance with Sections R406.7.1 through R406.7.3.

R406.7.1 Minimum capabilities. Calculation procedures used to comply with this section shall be software tools capable of calculating the ERI as described in Section R406.3, and shall include the following capabilities:

1. Computer generation of the *ERI reference design* using only the input for the *rated design.*

   The calculation procedure shall not allow the user to directly modify the building component characteristics of the *ERI reference design.*
2. Calculation of whole building, as a single *zone*, sizing for the heating and cooling equipment in the *ERI reference design* residence in accordance with Section R403.7.

3. Calculations that account for the effects of indoor and outdoor temperatures and part-load ratios on the performance of heating, ventilating and air-conditioning equipment based on climate and equipment sizing.
4. Printed *code official* inspection checklist listing each of the *rated design* component characteristics determined by the analysis to provide compliance, along with their respective performance ratings.

R406.7.2 Specific approval. Performance analysis tools meeting the applicable sections of Section R406 shall be *approved*. Tools are permitted to be *approved* based on meeting a specified threshold for a jurisdiction. The *code official* shall approve tools for a specified application or limited scope.

R406.7.3 Input values. When calculations require input values not specified by Sections R402, R403, R404 and R405, those input values shall be taken from an approved source.

**

CHAPTER 5 [RE]

EXISTING BUILDINGS

SECTION R501 GENERAL

R501.1 Scope. The provisions of this chapter shall control the *alteration*, repair, addition and change of occupancy of existing buildings and structures.

R501.1.1 Additions, alterations, or repairs: General. Additions, alterations, or repairs to an existing building, building system or portion thereof shall comply with Section R502, R503 or R504. Unaltered portions of the existing building or building supply system shall not be required to comply with this code.

R501.2 Existing buildings. Except as specified in this chapter, this code shall not be used to require the removal, *alteration* or abandonment of, nor prevent the continued use and maintenance of, an existing building or building system lawfully in existence at the time of adoption of this code.

R501.3 Maintenance. Buildings and structures, and parts thereof, shall be maintained in a safe and sanitary condition. Devices and systems that are required by this code shall be maintained in conformance to the code edition under which installed. The owner or the owner's authorized agent shall be responsible for the maintenance of buildings and structures. The requirements of this chapter shall not provide the basis for removal or abrogation of energy conservation, fire protection and safety systems and devices in existing structures.

R501.4 Compliance. *Alterations*, *repairs*, *additions* and changes of occupancy to, or relocation of, existing buildings and structures shall comply with the provisions for *alterations*, *repairs*, *additions* and changes of occupancy or relocation, respectively, in the *Florida Building Code, Residential*; *Florida Building Code, Building*; *Florida Fire Prevention Code*; *Florida Building Code, Fuel Gas*; *Florida Building Code, Mechanical*; *Florida Building Code, Plumbing*, and NFPA 70.

R501.5 New and replacement materials. Except as otherwise required or permitted by this code, materials permitted by the applicable code for new construction shall be used. Like materials shall be permitted for repairs, provided hazards to life, health or property are not created. Hazardous materials shall not be used where the code for new construction would not permit their use in buildings of similar occupancy, purpose and location.

** **R501.6 Historic buildings.** No provision of this code relating to the construction, *repair, alteration,* restoration and movement of structures, and *change of occupancy* shall be mandatory for *historic buildings* provided a report has been submitted to the code official and signed by the owner, a registered *design professional*, or a representative of the State Historic Preservation Office or the historic preservation authority having jurisdiction, demonstrating that compliance with that provision would threaten, degrade or destroy the historic form, fabric or function of the *building*.

R501.7 Building systems and components. Thermal efficiency standards are set for the following building systems and components where new products are installed or replaced in existing buildings, and for which a permit must be obtained. New products shall meet the minimum efficiencies allowed by this code for the following systems and components:

Heating, ventilating or air-conditioning systems;
Service water or pool heating systems;
Lighting systems; and
Replacement fenestration.

Exceptions:

1. Where part of a functional unit is repaired or replaced. For example, replacement of an entire HVAC system is not required because a new compressor or other part does not meet code when installed with an older system.
2. If the unit being replaced is itself a functional unit, such as a condenser, it does not constitute a repair. Outdoor and indoor units that are not designed to be operated together must meet the U.S. Department of Energy certification requirements contained in Section R303.1.2. Matched systems are required; this match may be verified by any one of the following means:
   a. AHRI data
   b. Accredited laboratory
   c. Manufacturer's letter
   d. Letter from registered P.E. State of Florida
3. Where existing components are utilized with a replacement system, such as air distribution system ducts or electrical wiring for lights, such components or controls need not meet code if meeting code would require that component's replacement.
4. Replacement equipment that would require extensive revisions to other systems, equipment or elements of a building where such replacement is a like-for-like replacement, such as through-the-wall condensing units and PTACs, chillers and cooling towers in confined spaces.

R501.7.1 Existing equipment efficiencies. Existing cooling and heating equipment in residential applications need not meet the minimum equipment efficiencies, including system sizing and duct sealing.

SECTION R502 ADDITIONS

R502.1 General. Additions to an existing building, building system or portion thereof shall conform to the provisions of this code as those provisions relate to new construction without requiring the unaltered portion of the existing building or building system to comply with this code. Additions shall not create an unsafe or hazardous condition or overload existing building systems. An addition shall be deemed to comply with this code where the addition alone complies, where the existing building and addition comply with this code as a single building, or where the building with the addition uses no more energy than the existing building. Additions shall be in accordance with Section R502.1.1, R502.1.2 or R502.1.3.

R502.1.1 Prescriptive compliance. Additions shall comply with Sections R502.1.1.1 through R502.1.1.4.

R502.1.1.1 Building envelope. New building envelope assemblies that are part of the addition shall comply with Sections R402.1, R402.2, R402.3.1 through R402.3.5, and R402.4.

Exception: Where nonconditioned space is changed to conditioned space, the building envelope of the addition shall comply where the UA, as determined in Section 402.1.5, of the existing building and the addition, and any alterations that are part of the project, is less than or equal to UA generated for the existing building.

R502.1.1.2 Heating and cooling systems. New heating, cooling and duct systems that are part of the addition shall comply with Sections R403.1, R403.2, R403.3, R403.5 and R403.6.

Exception: Where ducts from an existing heating and cooling system are extended to an addition, duct systems with less than 40 linear feet (12.19 m) in unconditioned spaces shall not be required to be tested in accordance with Section R403.3.3.

R502.1.1.3 Service hot water systems. New service hot water systems that are part of the addition shall comply with Section R403.4.

R502.1.1.4 Lighting. New lighting systems that are part of the addition shall comply with Section R404.1.

R502.1.2 Simulated performance alternative. The addition or existing building and addition together shall comply with Section R405 in its entirety.

R502.1.3 Energy Rating Index compliance alternative. The addition or existing building and addition together shall comply with Section R406 in its entirety.

**

SECTION R503 ALTERATIONS

R503.1 General. *Alterations* to any building or structure shall comply with the requirements of the code for new construction. *Alterations* shall be such that the existing building or structure is no less conforming to the provisions of this code than the existing building or structure was prior to the *alteration*.

Alterations to an existing building, building system or portion thereof shall conform to the provisions of this code as they relate to new construction without requiring the unaltered portions of the existing building or building system to comply with this code. Alterations shall not create an unsafe or hazardous condition or overload existing building systems. *Alterations* shall be such that the existing building or structure uses no more energy than the existing building or structure prior to the *alteration*. Alterations to existing buildings shall comply with Sections R503.1.1 through R503.2.

R503.1.1 Building envelope. Building envelope assemblies that are part of the alteration shall comply with Section R402.1.2 or R402.1.4, Sections R402.2.1 through R402.2.13, R402.3.1, R402.3.2, R402.4.3 and R402.4.5.

Exception: The following alterations need not comply with the requirements for new construction provided the energy use of the building is not increased:

1. Storm windows installed over existing fenestration.
2. Existing ceiling, wall or floor cavities exposed during construction provided that these cavities are filled with insulation.
3. Construction where the existing roof, wall or floor cavity is not exposed.
4. Roof recover.
5. Roofs without insulation in the cavity and where the sheathing or insulation is exposed during reroofing shall be insulated either above or below the sheathing.
6. Surface-applied window film installed on existing single pane fenestration assemblies to reduce solar heat gain provided the code does not require the glazing or fenestration assembly to be replaced.
7. Swimming pool filtration pumps and motors.

R503.1.1.1 Replacement fenestration. Where some or all of an existing fenestration unit is replaced with a new fenestration product, including sash and glazing, the replacement fenestration unit shall meet the applicable requirements for *U*-factor and SHGC as provided in Table R402.1.2.

R503.1.2 Heating and cooling systems. New heating, cooling and duct systems that are part of the alteration shall comply with Sections R403.1, R403.2, R403.3 and R403.6.

Exception: Where ducts from an existing heating and cooling system are extended, duct systems with less than 40 linear feet (12.19 m) in unconditioned spaces shall not be required to be tested in accordance with Section R403.3.3.

R503.1.3 Service hot water systems. New service hot water systems that are part of the alteration shall comply with Section R403.4.

R503.1.4 Lighting. New lighting systems that are part of the alteration shall comply with Section 404.1.

Exception: Alterations that replace less than 50 percent of the luminaires in a space, provided that such alterations do not increase the installed interior lighting power.

R503.2 Change in space conditioning. Any nonconditioned or low-energy space that is altered to become *conditioned space* shall be required to be brought into full compliance with this code.

> **Exception:** Where the simulated performance option in Section R405 is used to comply with this section, the annual energy cost of the proposed design is permitted to be 110 percent of the annual energy cost otherwise allowed by Section R405.3.

**

SECTION R504
REPAIRS

R504.1 General. Buildings, structures and parts thereof shall be repaired in compliance with Section R501.3 and this section. Work on nondamaged components necessary for the required *repair* of damaged components shall be considered part of the *repair* and shall not be subject to the requirements for *alterations* in this chapter. Routine maintenance required by Section R501.3, ordinary repairs exempt from *permit*, and abatement of wear due to normal service conditions shall not be subject to the requirements for *repairs* in this section.

R504.2 Application. For the purposes of this code, the following shall be considered repairs:

1. Glass-only replacements in an existing sash and frame.
2. Roof repairs.
3. Repairs where only the bulb and/or ballast within the existing luminaires in a space are replaced provided that the replacement does not increase the installed interior lighting power.

SECTION R505
CHANGE OF OCCUPANCY OR USE

R505.1 General. Spaces undergoing a change in occupancy that would result in an increase in demand for either fossil fuel or electrical energy shall comply with this code.

R505.2 General. Any space that is converted to a dwelling unit or portion thereof from another use or occupancy shall comply with this code.

> **Exception:** Where the simulated performance option in Section R405 is used to comply with this section, the annual energy cost of the proposed design is permitted to be 110 percent of the annual energy cost otherwise allowed by Section R405.3.

CHAPTER 6 [RE]

REFERENCED STANDARDS

This chapter lists the standards that are referenced in various sections of this document. The standards are listed herein by the promulgating agency of the standard, the standard identification, the effective date and title, and the section or sections of this document that reference the standard. The application of the referenced standards shall be as specified in Section 106.

AAMA

American Architectural Manufacturers Association
1827 Walden Office Square
Suite 550
Schaumburg, IL 60173-4268

Standard reference number	Title	Referenced in code section number
AAMA/WDMA/CSA 101/I.S.2/A C440—11	North American Fenestration Standard/ Specifications for Windows, Doors and Unit Skylights	R402.4.3

ACCA

Air Conditioning Contractors of America
2800 Shirlington Road, Suite 300
Arlington, VA 22206

Standard reference number	Title	Referenced in code section number
Manual D—09	Residential Duct Systems	C403.2.9.5
Manual J—2011	Residential Load Calculation Eighth Edition	R403.7.1
Manual S—13	Residential Equipment Selection	R403.7.1

AHRI

Air Conditioning, Heating, & Refrigeration Institute
2111 Wilson Blvd, Suite 500
Arlington, VA 22201

Standard reference number	Title	Referenced in code section number
470—06	Performance Rating of Desuperheater/Water Heaters	R405.7.7, Appendix RD Form R400D
1160—08	Performance Rating of Heat Pump Pool Heaters Directory of Certified Product Performance	R403.10.1.2, R405.6.3.1

ANSI

American National Standards Institute
25 West 43rd Street, 4th Floor
New York, NY 10036

Standard reference number	Title	Referenced in code section number
ANSI/RESNET/ ICC 301—2014	Standard for the Calculation and Labeling of the Energy Performance of Low-Rise Residential Buildings Using an Energy Rating Index	R406.4
ANSI/RESNET/ ICC 301—2014, Addendum A-2015	Amendment on Domestic Hot Water Systems	R406.4
ANSI/RESNET/ ICC 380—2016	Standard for Testing Airtightness of Building Enclosures, Airtightness of Heating and Cooling Air Distribution Systems and Airflow of Mechanical Ventilation Systems	R402.4.1.2, R403.3.2, Table R405.5.2(1) and Appendix RD
Z21.56-2006	Gas-Fired Pool Heaters	R403.10.4

APSP

The Association of Pool & Spa Professionals
2111 Eisenhower Avenue, Suite 500
Alexandria, VA 22314

Standard reference number	Title	Referenced in code section number
ANSI/APSP/ICC 14—14	American National Standard for Portable Electric Spa Energy Efficiency	R403.11
ANSI/APSP/ICC 15—11	American National Standard for Residential Swimming Pool and Spa Energy Efficiency with Addenda A approved January 9, 2013	R403.12

ARDM

Association of Refrigerant Desuperheater Manufacturers, Inc.
c/o Doucette Industries
4151 112 Terrace N
Clearwater, FL 33762

Standard reference number	Title	Referenced in code section number
ARDM—88	Residential Heat Recovery Installation Guide, First Edition	R405.7.7

ASHRAE

ASHRAE
1791 Tullie Circle NE
Atlanta, GA 30329-2305

Standard reference number	Title	Referenced in code section number
ANSI/ASHRAE Std. 62.2-10	Ventilation for Acceptable Indoor Air Quality	R403.6.2, Table R405.5.2(1)
ASHRAE—2013	ASHRAE Handbook of Fundamentals	R402.1.5, Table R405.5.2(1)
ASHRAE 193—2010	Method of Test for Determining the Airtightness of HVAC Equipment	R403.3.2.1

ASTM

ASTM International
100 Barr Harbor Drive, P.O. Box C700
West Conshohocken, PA 19428-2959

Standard reference number	Title	Referenced in code section number
C36/C36M—03	Standard Specification for Gypsum Wallboard	R202
C272—01	Test Method for Water Absorption of Core Materials for Structural Sandwich Construction	R303.2.1.3
C516—08	Vermiculite Loose Fill Thermal Insulation	Table R303.2.1
C549—06	Perlite Loose Fill Insulation	Table R303.2.1
C578—08b	Rigid, Cellular Polystyrene Thermal Insulation	Table R303.2.1
C665—06	Mineral-Fiber Blanket Thermal Insulation for Light Frame Construction and Manufactured Housing	Table R303.2.1
C727—01	Standard Practice for Installation and Use of Reflective Insulation in Building Constructions	Table R303.2.1
C739—08	Cellulosic Fiber Loose-Fill Thermal Insulation	Table R303.2.1
C764—07	Mineral Fiber Loose-Fill Thermal Insulation	Table R303.2.1
C1015—06	Standard Practice for Installation of Cellulosic and Mineral Fiber Loose-Fill Thermal Insulation	Table R303.2.1
C1029—08	Specification for Spray-applied Rigid Cellular Polyurethane Thermal Insulation	Table R303.2.1
C1158—05	Standard Practice for Use and Installation of Radiant Barrier Systems (RBS) in Building Construction	Table R303.2.1, R405.7.1
C1224—03	Reflective Insulation for Building Applications	Table R303.2
C1289—08	Faced Rigid Cellular Polyisocyanurate Thermal Insulation Board	Table 303.2
C1313—05	Sheet Radiant Barriers for Building Construction Applications	Table R303.2.1, R405.7.1
C1320—05	Standard Practice for Installation of Mineral Fiber Batt and Blanket Thermal Insulation for Light-frame Construction	Table R303.2.1
C1321—04	Standard Practice for Installation and Use of Interior Radiation Control Coating Systems (IRCC) in Building Construction	Table R303.2.1, Table R303.2, R405.7.1
C1363—11	Standard Test Method for Thermal Performance of Building Materials and Envelope Assemblies by Means of a Hot Box Apparatus	R303.1.1.1.3

ASTM—continued

C1371—04a	Test Method for Determination of Emittance of Materials Near Room Temperature Using Portable Emissometers	R405.7.1, R405.7.2
C1549—04	Standard Test Method for Determination of Solar Reflectance Near Ambient Temperature Using a Portable Solar Reflector	R405.7.2
E283—04	Test Method for Determining the Rate of Air Leakage Through Exterior Windows, Curtain Walls and Doors Under Specified Pressure Differences Across the Specimen	R402.4.4, Appendix RD
E779—10	Standard Test Method for Determining Air Leakage Rate by Fan Pressurization	R402.4.1.2
E903—96	Test Method for Solar Absorptance, Reflectance, and Transmittance of Materials Using Integrating Spheres	R405.7.2
E1827—11	Standard Test Methods for Determining Airtightness of Building Using an Orifice Blower Door	R402.4.1.2
E1918—06	Standard Test Method for Measuring Solar Reflectance of Horizontal and Low-sloped Surfaces in the Field	R405.7.2

CRRC

Cool Roof Rating Council\
449 15th Street, Suite 400
Oakland, CA 94612

Standard reference number	Title	Referenced in code section number
CRRC-1—2006	CRRC-1 Product Rating Program	R405.7.2

CSA

CSA Group
8501 East Pleasant Valley Road
Cleveland, OH 44131-5516

Standard reference number	Title	Referenced in code section number
AAMA/WDMA/CSA 101/I.S.2/A440—11	North American Fenestration Standard/Specification for Windows, Doors and Unit Skylights	R402.4.3
CSA 55.1—2012	Test Method for measuring efficiency and pressure loss of drain water heat recovery units	R403.5.4
CSA 55.2—2012	Drain water heat recover units	R403.5.4

DASMA

Door & Access Systems Manufacturers Association International
1300 Sumner Avenue
Cleveland, OH 44115-2851

Standard reference number	Title	Referenced in code section number
105—92(R2004)—13	Test Method for Thermal Transmittance and Air Infiltration of Garage Doors	R303.1.3

Florida Codes

Building Codes and Standards Office
Florida Department of Business and Professional Regulation
1940 N Monroe Street, Suite 90A
Tallahassee, FL 32399-0772

Standard reference number	Title	Referenced in code section number
FBC-B—Sixth Edition (2017)	Florida Building Code, Building	R201.3, R303.2
FBC-M—Sixth Edition (2017)	Florida Building Code, Mechanical	R403.6
FBC-FG—Sixth Edition (2017)	Florida Building Code, Fuel Gas	C201.3, R201.3
FBC-P—Sixth Edition (2017)	Florida Building Code, Plumbing	C201.3, R201.3
FBC-R—Sixth Edition (2017)	Florida Building Code, Residential	R202, R303.2, R402.1.1, R403.5, R403.6, R405.7.1, R405.7.3
FFPC—Sixth Edition (2017)	Florida Fire Prevention Code	C201.3, R201.3

Florida Codes—continued

FS	Florida Statutes	R103.1.1.1.2, R103.1.1.2, R104.4, R401.3, R402.4.1.2, R403.3.2, R406.5

FSEC

Florida Solar Energy Center
1679 Clearlake Road
Cocoa, FL 32922-5703

Standard reference number	Title	Referenced in code section number
FSEC-RR-54-00	"The HERS Rating Method and the Derivation of the Normalized Modified Loads Method", October 11, 2000, Fairey, P., J. Tait, D. Goldstein, D. Tracey, M. Holtz, and R. Judkoff. Available online at: http://www2.fsec.ucf.edu/en/publications/html/FSEC-RR-54-00/index.html	Appendix RC, C-1

ICC

International Code Council, Inc.
500 New Jersey Avenue, NW
6th Floor
Washington, DC 20001

Standard reference number	Title	Referenced in code section number
ICC 400—12	Standard on the Design and Construction of Log Structures	Table R402.5.1.1
IECC—15	International Energy Conservation Code®	R406.2
IECC—09	2009 International Energy Conservation Code®	R406.2
ECC—06	2006 International Energy Conservation Code®	R202, R406.3.1

IEEE

The Institute of Electrical and Electronic Engineers, Inc.
3 Park Avenue, 17th Floor
New York, NY 10016-5997

Standard reference number	Title	Referenced in code section number
515.1—2012	IEEE Standard for the Testing, Design, Installation, and Maintenance of Electrical Resistance Trace Heating for Commercial Applications	R403.5.1.2

ISO

International Organization for Standardization
Chemin de Blandonnet 8
CP 401
1214 Vernier
Geneva, Switzerland

Standard reference number	Title	Referenced in code section number
9806 (1994, 1995)	TEST Methods for Solar Collectors Part 1: Thermal performance of glazed liquid heating collectors including pressure drop, December 1, 1994 Part 2: Qualification test procedures, August 15, 1995 Part 3: Thermal performance of unglazed liquid heating collectors (sensible heat transfer only) including pressure drop, December 15, 1995	R403.5.6.2.1

NFPA

National Fire Protection Association.
1 Batterymarch Park
Quincy, MA 02169-7471

Standard reference number	Title	Referenced in code section number
70—14	National Electrical Code	R501.4

NFRC

National Fenestration Rating Council, Inc.
6305 Ivy Lane, Suite 140
Greenbelt, MD 20770

Standard reference number	Title	Referenced in code section number
100—2009	Procedure for Determining Fenestration Products *U*-factors—Second Edition	R303.1.3
200—2009	Procedure for Determining Fenestration Product Solar Heat Gain Coefficients and Visible Transmittance at Normal Incidence—Second Edition	R303.1.3
400—2009	Procedure for Determining Fenestration Product Air Leakage—Second Edition	R402.4.3

SRCC

Solar Rating and Certification Corporation
c/o Florida Solar Energy Center
1679 Clearlake Road
Cocoa, FL 32922-5703

Standard reference number	Title	Referenced in code section number
FSEC	Directory of Certified Solar Systems	R403.5.6.2.1
SRCC TM-1	Solar Domestic Hot Water System and Component Test Protocol, December 6, 2002	R403.5.6.2.1

UL

UL LLC
333 Pfingsten Road
Northbrook, IL 60062

Standard reference number	Title	Referenced in code section number
127—11	Standard for Factory Built Fireplaces	R402.4.2
515—11	Electrical Resistance Heat Tracing for Commercial and Industrial Applications including revisions through November 30, 2011	R403.5.1.2

US-FTC

United States-Federal Trade Commission
600 Pennsylvania Avenue NW
Washington, DC 20580

Standard reference number	Title	Referenced in code section number
CFR Title 16, Part 460	R-value Rule	R303.1.1.1, R303.1.1.1.2

Window and Door Manufacturers Association
2025 M Street NW, Suite 800
Washington, DC 20036-3309

Standard reference number	Title	Referenced in code section number
AAMA/WDMA/CSA 101/I.S.2/A440—11	North American Fenestration Standard/Specification for Windows, Doors and Unit Skylights	R402.4.3

APPENDIX RA

RECOMMENDED PROCEDURE FOR WORST-CASE TESTING OF ATMOSPHERIC VENTING SYSTEMS UNDER R402.4 OR R405 CONDITIONS $\leq$ 5 ACH_{50}

(This appendix is informative and is not part of the code.)

SECTION RA101 SCOPE

RA101.1 General. This appendix is intended to provide guidelines for worst-case testing of atmospheric venting systems. Worst-case testing is recommended to identify problems that weaken draft and restrict combustion air.

SECTION RA201 GENERAL DEFINITIONS

COMBUSTION APPLIANCE ZONE (CAZ). A contiguous air volume within a building that contains a Category I or II atmospherically vented appliance or a Category III or IV direct-vent or integral vent appliance drawing combustion air from inside the building or dwelling unit. The CAZ includes, but is not limited to, a mechanical closet, a mechanical room, or the main body of a house or dwelling unit.

DRAFT. The pressure difference existing between the *appliance* or any component part and the atmosphere that causes a continuous flow of air and products of *combustion* through the gas passages of the *appliance* to the atmosphere.

Mechanical or induced draft. The pressure difference created by the action of a fan, blower or ejector that is located between the *appliance* and the *chimney* or vent termination.

Natural draft. The pressure difference created by a vent or *chimney* because of its height and the temperature difference between the *flue* gases and the atmosphere.

SPILLAGE. Combustion gases emerging from an appliance or venting system into the combustion appliance zone during burner operation.

SECTION RA301 TESTING PROCEDURE

RA301.1 Worst-case testing of atmospheric venting systems. Buildings or dwelling units containing a Category I or II atmospherically vented appliance; or a Category III or IV direct-vent or integral vent appliance drawing combustion air from inside of the building or dwelling unit, shall have the Combustion Appliance Zone (CAZ) tested for spillage, acceptable draft and carbon monoxide (CO) in accordance with this section. Where required by the *code official*, testing shall be conducted by an *approved* third party. A written report of the results of the test shall be signed by the party conducting the test and provided to the *code official*. Testing shall be performed at any time after creation of all penetrations of the *building thermal* envelope and prior to final inspection.

Exception: Buildings or dwelling units containing only Category III or IV direct-vent or integral vent appliances that do not draw combustion air from inside of the building or dwelling unit.

The enumerated test procedure as follows shall be complied with during testing:

1. Set combustion appliances to the pilot setting or turn off the service disconnects for combustion appliances. Close exterior doors and windows and the fireplace damper. With the building or dwelling unit in this configuration, measure and record the baseline ambient pressure inside the building or dwelling unit CAZ. Compare the baseline ambient pressure of the CAZ to that of the outside ambient pressure and record the difference (Pa).
2. Establish worst case by turning on the *clothes dryer* and all exhaust fans. Close all interior doors that make the CAZ pressure more negative. Turn on the air handler, where present, and leave on if, as a result, the pressure in the CAZ becomes more negative. Check interior door positions again, closing only the interior doors that make the CAZ pressure more negative. Measure net change in pressure from the CAZ to outdoor ambient pressure, correcting for the base ambient pressure inside the home. Record "worst case depressurization" pressure and compare to Table RA301.1(1).

   Where CAZ depressurization limits are exceeded under worst-case conditions in accordance with Table A301.1(1), additional combustion air shall be provided or other modifications to building air-leakage performance or exhaust appliances such that depressurization is brought within the limits prescribed in Table RA301.1(1).
3. Measure worst-case spillage, acceptable draft and carbon monoxide (CO) by firing the fuel-fired appliance with the smallest Btu capacity first.
   a. Test for spillage at the draft diverter with a mirror or smoke puffer. An appliance that continues to spill flue gases for more than 60 seconds fails the spillage test.
   b. Test for CO measuring undiluted flue gases in the throat or flue of the appliance using a digital gauge in parts per million (ppm) at the 10-minute mark. Record CO ppm readings to be compared with Table

RA301.1(3) upon completion of Step 4. Where the spillage test fails under worst case, go to Step 4.

c. Where spillage ends within 60 seconds, test for acceptable draft in the connector not less than 1 foot (305 mm), but not more than 2 feet (610 mm) downstream of the draft diverter. Record draft pressure and compare to Table RA301.1(2).

d. Fire all other connected appliances simultaneously and test again at the draft diverter of each appliance for spillage, CO and acceptable draft using procedures 3a through 3c.

4. Measure spillage, acceptable draft, and carbon monoxide (CO) under natural conditions—without *clothes dryer* and exhaust fans on—in accordance with the procedure outlined in Step 3, measuring the net change in pressure from worst case condition in Step 3 to natural in the CAZ to confirm the worst case depressurization taken in Step 2. Repeat the process for each appliance, allowing each vent system to cool between tests.

5. Monitor indoor ambient CO in the breathing zone continuously during testing, and abort the test where indoor ambient CO exceeds 35 ppm by turning off the appliance, ventilating the space, and evacuating the building. The CO problem shall be corrected prior to completing combustion safety diagnostics.

6. Make recommendations based on test results and the retrofit action prescribed in Table RA301.1(3).

TABLE RA301.1(1)
CAZ DEPRESSURIZATION LIMITS

<table>
<tr><th>VENTING CONDITION</th><th>LIMIT (Pa)</th></tr>
<tr><td>Category I, atmospherically vented water heater</td><td>–2.0</td></tr>
<tr><td>Category I or II atmospherically vented boiler or furnace common-vented with a Category I atmospherically vented water heater</td><td>–3.0</td></tr>
<tr><td>Category I or II atmospherically vented boiler or furnace, equipped with a flue damper, and common vented with a Category I atmospherically vented water heater</td><td rowspan="4">–5.0</td></tr>
<tr><td>Category I or II atmospherically vented boiler or furnace alone</td></tr>
<tr><td>Category I or II atmospherically vented, fan-assisted boiler or furnace common vented with a Category I atmospherically vented water heater</td></tr>
<tr><td>Decorative vented, gas appliance</td></tr>
<tr><td>Power-vented or induced-draft boiler or furnace alone, or fan-assisted water heater alone</td><td>–15.0</td></tr>
<tr><td>Category IV direct-vented appliances and sealed combustion appliances</td><td>–50.0</td></tr>
</table>

For SI: 6894.76 Pa = 1.0 psi.

TABLE RA301.1(2)
ACCEPTABLE DRAFT TEST CORRECTION

OUTSIDE TEMPERATURE (°F)	MINIMUM DRAFT PRESSURE REQUIRED (Pa)
< 10	–2.5
10 – 90	(Outside Temperature ÷ 40) – 2.75
> 90	–0.5

For SI: 6894.76 Pa = 1.0 psi.

TABLE RA301.1(3)
ACCEPTABLE DRAFT TEST CORRECTION

CARBON MONOXIDE LEVEL (ppm)	AND OR	SPILLAGE AND ACCEPTABLE DRAFT TEST RESULTS	RETROFIT ACTION
0 – 25	and	Passes	Proceed with work
25 < × ≤ 100	and	Passes	Recommend that CO problem be resolved
25 < × ≤ 100	and	Fails in worst case only	Recommend an appliance service call and repairs to resolve the problem
100 < × ≤ 400	or	Fails under natural conditions	**Stop!** Work shall not proceed until appliance is serviced and problem resolved
> 400	and	Passes	**Stop!** Work shall not proceed until appliance is serviced and problem resolved
> 400	and	Fails under any condition	**Emergency!** Shut off fuel to appliance and call for service immediately

APPENDIX RB

SOLAR-READY PROVISIONS—DETACHED ONE- AND TWO-FAMILY DWELLINGS, MULTIPLE SINGLE-FAMILY DWELLINGS (TOWNHOUSES)

(The provisions contained in this appendix are not mandatory unless specifically referenced in the adopting ordinance.)

SECTION RB101 SCOPE

RB101.1 General. These provisions shall be applicable for new construction where solar-ready provisions are required.

SECTION RB102 GENERAL DEFINITION

SOLAR-READY ZONE. A section or sections of the roof or building overhang designated and reserved for the future installation of a solar photovoltaic or solar thermal system.

SECTION RB103 SOLAR-READY ZONE

RB103.1 General. New detached one- and two-family dwellings, and multiple single-family dwellings (townhouses) with not less than 600 square feet (55.74 m^2) of roof area oriented between 110 degrees and 270 degrees of true north shall comply with Sections RB103.2 through RB103.8.

Exceptions:

1. New residential buildings with a permanently installed on-site renewable energy system.
2. A building with a solar-ready zone that is shaded for more than 70 percent of daylight hours annually.

RB103.2 Construction document requirements for solar-ready zone. Construction documents shall indicate the solar-ready zone.

RB103.3 Solar-ready zone area. The total solar-ready zone area shall be not less than 300 square feet (27.87 m^2) exclusive of mandatory access or set back areas as required by the *Florida Fire Prevention Code*. New multiple single-family dwellings (townhouses) three stories or less in height above grade plane and with a total floor area less than or equal to 2,000 square feet (185.8 m^2) per dwelling shall have a solar-ready zone area of not less than 150 square feet (13.94 m^2). The solar-ready zone shall be composed of areas not less than 5 feet (1524 mm) in width and not less than 80 square feet (7.44 m^2) exclusive of access or set back areas as required by the *Florida Fire Prevention Code*.

RB103.4 Obstructions. Solar-ready zones shall be free from obstructions, including but not limited to vents, chimneys, and roof-mounted equipment.

RB103.5 Roof load documentation. The structural design loads for roof dead load and roof live load shall be clearly indicated on the construction documents.

RB103.6 Interconnection pathway. Construction documents shall indicate pathways for routing of conduit or plumbing from the solar-ready zone to the electrical service panel or service hot water system.

RB103.7 Electrical service reserved space. The main electrical service panel shall have a reserved space to allow installation of a dual pole circuit breaker for future solar electric installation and shall be labeled "For Future Solar Electric." The reserved space shall be positioned at the opposite (load) end from the input feeder location or main circuit location.

RB103.8 Construction documentation certificate. A permanent certificate, indicating the solar-ready zone and other requirements of this section, shall be posted near the electrical distribution panel, water heater or other conspicuous location by the builder or registered design professional.

APPENDIX RC
CALCULATION OF END USE ENERGY LOADS

RC-1 Calculation of end use energy loads for code compliance determination. The energy loads for heating, cooling and hot water in the *Proposed Design* home shall be normalized to account for the differences in improvement potential that exist across equipment types using the following formula in accordance with the paper "The HERS Rating Method and the Derivation of the Normalized Modified Loads Method," Research Report No. FSEC-RR-54-00, Florida Solar Energy Center.

$$nMEUL = REUL*(nEC\_x / EC\_r)$$

where:

nMEUL = normalized Modified End Use Loads (for heating, cooling or hot water) as computed using Commission-approved compliance software.

REUL = *Standard Reference Design* home End Use Loads (for heating, cooling or hot water) as computed using Commission-approved compliance software.

EC_r = estimated Energy Consumption for the *Standard Reference Design* home's end uses (for heating, including auxiliary electric consumption, cooling or hot water) as computed using Commission-approved compliance software.

and where:

$$nEC\_x = (a * EEC\_x - b)*(EC\_x * EC\_r * DSE\_r) / (EEC\_x * REUL)$$

where:

nEC_x = normalized Energy Consumption for *Proposed Design's* end uses (for heating, including auxiliary electric consumption, cooling or hot water) as computed using Commission-approved compliance software.

EC_r = estimated Energy Consumption for *Standard Reference Design* home's end uses (for heating, including auxiliary electric consumption, cooling or hot water) as computed using Commission-approved compliance software.

EC_x = estimated Energy Consumption for the *Proposed Design* home's end uses (for heating, including auxiliary electric consumption, cooling or hot water) as computed using Commission-approved compliance software.

EEC_x = Equipment Efficiency Coefficient for the *Standard Reference Design* home's equipment, such that EEC_x = the energy consumption per unit load in like units as the load, and as derived from the Manufacturer's Equipment Performance Rating (MEPR) such that EEC_x = 1.0 / MEPR for AFUE, COP or EF ratings, or such that EEC_x equals 3.413/MEPR for HSPF, EER or SEER ratings.

$$DSE\_r = REUL/EC\_r * EEC\_r$$

For simplified system performance methods, DSE_r equals 0.80 for heating and cooling systems. However, for detailed modeling of heating and cooling systems, DSE_r may be less than 0.80 as a result of part load performance degradation, coil airflow degradation, improper system charge and auxiliary resistance heating for heat pumps. Except as otherwise provided by these Standards, where detailed systems modeling is employed, it must be applied equally to both the *Standard Reference Design* and the *Proposed Design* homes.

EEC_r = Equipment Efficiency Coefficient for the *Standard Reference Design* home's equipment, such that EEC_r equals the energy consumption per unit load in like units as the load, and as derived from the Manufacturer's Equipment Performance Rating (MEPR) such that EEC_r equals 1.0/MEPR for AFUE, COP or EF ratings, or such that EEC_r equals 3.413/ MEPR for HSPF, EER or SEER ratings.

REUL = *Standard Reference Design* home End Use Loads (for heating or cooling) as computed using Commission-approved compliance software.

and where the coefficients 'a' and 'b' are as defined by Table RC-1(1).

TABLE RC-1(1) COEFFICIENTS 'a' AND 'b'

FUEL TYPE AND END USE	a	b
Electric space heating	2.4026	0.0000
Fossil fuel* space heating	1.0370	0.2962
Biomass space heating	0.7297	0.1583
Electric air conditioning	4.1020	0.0000
Electric water heating	0.9500	0.0000
Fossil fuel* water heating	1.3774	1.2217
* Such as natural gas, LP, fuel oil		

RC-2 Following normalization of the heating, cooling and hot water energy consumptions for the *Proposed Design* as specified in Section RC-1 above, the *Standard Reference Design* home's total reference end use loads for heating, cooling and hot water (REULtot) shall be compared with the *Proposed Design* home's total normalized modified end use loads for heating, cooling and hot water (nMEULtot). If the total normalized modified loads of the Proposed Design home (nMEULtot) are equal to or less than the total reference loads of the *Standard Reference Design* home (REULtot), the *Proposed Design* complies with this code.

APPENDIX RD

FORMS

ENERGY PERFORMANCE LEVEL (EPL) DISPLAY CARD

ESTIMATED ENERGY PERFORMANCE INDEX* = ____

The lower the Energy Performance Index, the more efficient the home.

1. New home or, addition 1.________
2. Single-family or multiple-family 2.________
3. No. of units (if multiple-family) 3.________
4. Number of bedrooms 4.________
5. Is this a worst case? (yes/no) 5.________
6. Conditioned floor area (sq. ft.) 6.________
7. Windows, type and area
   a) *U*-factor: 7a.________
   b) Solar Heat Gain Coefficient (SHGC) 7b.________
   c) Area 7c.________
8. Skylights
   a) *U*-factor 8a.________
   b) Solar Heat Gain Coefficient (SHGC) 8b.________
9. Floor type, insulation level:
   a) Slab-on-grade (*R*-value) 9a.________
   b) Wood, raised (*R*-value) 9b.________
   c) Concrete, raised (*R*-value) 9c.________
10. Wall type and insulation:
    A. Exterior:
      1. Wood frame (Insulation *R*-value) 10A1.________
      2. Masonry (Insulation *R*-value) 10A2.________
    B. Adjacent:
      1. Wood frame (Insulation *R*-value) 10B1.________
      2. Masonry (Insulation *R*-value) 10B2.________
11. Ceiling type and insulation level
    a) Under attic 11a.________
    b) Single assembly 11b.________
    c) Knee walls/skylight walls 11c.________
    d) Radiant barrier installed 11d.________
12. Ducts, location & insulation level
    a) Supply ducts R=________
    b) Return ducts R=________
    c) AHU location
13. Cooling system: Capacity:________
    a) Split system SEER________
    b) Single package SEER________
    c) Ground/water source COP________
    d) Room unit/PTAC EER________
    e) Other________ ________
14. Heating system:
    a) Split system heat pump HSPF________
    b) Single package heat pump HSPF________
    c) Electric resistance COP________
    d) Gas furnace, natural gas AFUE________
    e) Gas furnace, LPG AFUE________
    f) Other________ ________
15. Water heating system
    a) Electric resistance EF________
    b) Gas fired, natural gas EF________
    c) Gas fired, LPG EF________
    d) Solar system with tank EF________
    e) Dedicated heat pump with tank EF________
    f) Heat recovery unit HeatRec%________
    g) Other________ ________
16. HVAC credits claimed (Performance Method) ________
    a) Ceiling fans ________
    b) Cross ventilation ________
    c) Whole house fan ________
    d) Multizone cooling credit ________
    e) Multizone heating credit ________
    f) Programmable thermostat ________

*Label required by Section R303.1.3 of the *Florida Building Code, Energy Conservation,* if not DEFAULT.
I certify that this home has complied with the *Florida Building Code, Energy Conservation*, through the above energy saving features which will be installed (or exceeded) in this home before final inspection. Otherwise, a new EPL display card will be completed based on installed code compliant features.

Builder Signature:________________________ Date:________________________

Address of New Home: ________________________ City/FL Zip: ________________________

FORM R400D-2017
DESUPERHEATER, HEAT RECOVERY UNIT (HRU) WATER HEATER EFFICIENCY CERTIFICATION TESTS CONDUCTED IN ACCORDANCE WITH AHRI STANDARD 470

Laboratory:________________________________ Date of Test: ______________________

Report Approved By: ________________________ Report No: ________________________

Manufacturer: _____________________________ Model No:_________________________

Construction Type: _________________________

Recommended for use with refrigeration system capacities of ____________________ tons.

Design Pressure: ___________________________ Water side: ___________________ psig

Refrigerant side: ________________ psig

Test results at Standard Conditions:

Test refrigerant designation: ________________________

Tested at system capacity: __________________________ tons

Total system hot gas superheat: _____________________ Btu/h

Total useful heat exchange effect: ___________________ Btu/h

Water pump input: _________________________________ watts

NET SUPERHEAT RECOVERY: ____________________ %

FLORIDA BUILDING CODE, ENERGY CONSERVATION

Residential Building Thermal Envelope Approach

FORM R402-2017 **Climate Zone ☐**

Scope: Compliance with Section R401.2(1) of the *Florida Building Code, Energy Conservation*, shall be demonstrated by the use of Form R402 for single- and multiple-family residences of three stories or less in height, additions to existing residential buildings, alterations, renovations and building systems in existing buildings, as applicable. To comply, a building must meet or exceed all of the energy efficiency requirements on Table R402A and all applicable mandatory requirements summarized in Table R402B of this form. If a building does not comply with this method, or by the UA Alternative method, it may still comply under Section R405 of the *Florida Building Code, Energy Conservation*.

PROJECT NAME AND ADDRESS:	**BUILDER:**
OWNER:	**PERMITTING OFFICE:**
	JURISDICTION NUMBER:
	PERMIT NUMBER:

General Instructions:

1. **Fill in all the applicable spaces of the "To Be Installed" column on Table R402A with the information requested. All "To Be Installed" values must be equal to or more efficient than the required levels.**
2. **Complete page 1 based on the "To Be Installed" column information.**
3. **Read the requirements of Table R402B and check each box to indicate your intent to comply with all applicable items.**
4. **Read, sign and date the "Prepared By" certification statement at the bottom of page 1. The owner or owner's agent must also sign and date the form.**

1. New construction, addition, or existing building	1. ______	______
2. Single-family detached or multiple-family attached	2. ______	______
3. If multiple-family, number of units covered by this submission	3. ______	______
4. Is this a worst case? (yes/no)	4. ______	______
5. Conditioned floor area (sq. ft.)	5. ______	______
6. Windows, type and area		
a) *U*-factor:	**6a.** ______	______
b) Solar Heat Gain Coefficient (SHGC)	**6b.** ______	______
c) Area	**6c.** ______	______
7. Skylights		
a) *U*-factor:	**7a.** ______	______
b) Solar Heat Gain Coefficient (SHGC)	**7b.** ______	______
8. Floor type, area or perimeter, and insulation:		
a) Slab-on-grade (*R*-value)	**8a.** ______	______
b) Wood, raised (*R*-value)	**8b.** ______	______
c) Wood, common (*R*-value)	**8c.** ______	______
d) Concrete, raised (*R*-value)	**8d.** ______	______
e) Concrete, common (*R*-value)	**8e.** ______	______
9. Wall type and insulation:		
a) Exterior: 1. Wood frame (Insulation *R*-value)	**9a1.** ______	______
2. Masonry (Insulation *R*-value)	**9a2.** ______	______
b) Adjacent: 1. Wood frame (Insulation *R*-value)	**9b1.** ______	______
2. Masonry (Insulation *R*-value)	**9b2.** ______	______
10. Ceiling type and insulation		
a) Attic (Insulation R-value)	**10a.** ______	______
b) Single assembly (Insulation *R*-value)	**10b.** ______	______
11. Air distribution system:		
a) Duct location, insulation	**11a.** ______	______
b) AHU location	**11b.** ______	______
c) Total duct leakage. Test report attached.	**11c.** ______**cfm/100 s.f.**	**Yes ☐ No ☐**
12. Cooling system: a) type	**12a.** ______	______
b) efficiency	**12b.** ______	______
13. Heating system: a) type	**13a.** ______	______
b) efficiency	**13b.** ______	______
14. HVAC sizing calculation: attached	**14.** ______	**Yes ☐ No ☐**
15. Water heating system: a) type	**15a.** ______	______
b) efficiency	**15b.** ______	______

I hereby certify that the plans and specifications covered by this form are in compliance with the *Florida Building Code, Energy Conservation*.

PREPARED BY:______ **Date**______

I hereby certify that this building is in compliance with the *Florida Building Code, Energy Conservation*.

OWNER/AGENT:______ **Date:**______

Review of plans and specifications covered by this form indicate compliance with the *Florida Building Code, Energy Conservation*. Before construction is complete, this building will be inspected for compliance in accordance with Section 553.908, F.S.

CODE OFFICIAL:______

Date: ______

TABLE R402A

BUILDING COMPONENT	PRESCRIPTIVE REQUIREMENTS[1]		INSTALLED VALUES
	Climate Zone 1	Climate Zone 2	
Windows Skylights	*U*-Factor = NR SHGC = 0.25 *U*-factor = 0.75 SHGC = 0.30	*U*-Factor = 0.40[2] SHGC = 0.25 *U*-factor = 0.65 SHGC = 0.30	*U*-Factor = SHGC = *U*-factor = SHGC =
Doors: Exterior door	*U*-factor = NR	*U*-factor = 0.40[3]	*U*-factor=
Floors: Slab-on-Grade Over unconditioned spaces[4]	 NR R-13	 NR R-13	 *R*-Value =
Walls[4]: Ext. and Adj. Frame Mass Insulation on wall interior Insulation on wall exterior	 R-13 R-4 R-3	 R-13 R-6 R-4	 *R*-Value = *R*-Value = *R*-Value =
Ceilings[5]	R=30	R=38	*R*-Value =
Air infiltration	Blower door test is required on the building envelope to verify leakage ≤ 1 ACH; test report provided to code official.		Total leakage = ACH Test report attached? Yes ☐ No ☐
Air distribution system[5]: Air handling unit Duct *R*-value Air leakage[5]: Duct test Ducts in conditioned space	 Not allowed in attic *R*-value ≥ R-8 (supply in attics) or ≥ R-6 (all other duct locations) Postconstruction test Total leakage ≤ 4 cfm/100 s.f. Rough-in test Total leakage ≤ 4 cfm/100 s.f. (air handler installed) Total leakage ≤ 3 cfm/100 s.f. (air handler not installed) Test not required if all ducts and AHU are in conditioned space		Location: *R*-Value = Total leakage = _______ cfm/100s.f. Test report Attached? Yes ☐ No ☐ Location:
Air conditioning system: Central system ≤ 65,000 Btu/h Room unit or PTAC Other:	Minimum federal standard required by NAECA[6]: SEER 14.0 EER [from Table C403.2.3(3)] See Tables C403.2.3(1)-(11)		SEER = EER =
Heating system: Heat pump ≤ 65,000 Btu/h Gas furnace, non-weatherized Oil furnace, non-weatherized Other:	Minimum federal standard required by NAECA[6]: HSPF 8.2 AFUE 80% AFUE 83%		HSPF = AFUE = AFUE =
Water heating system (storage type): Electric[7] Gas fired[8] Other (describe):	Minimum federal standard required by NAECA[6]: 40 gal: EF = 0.92 50 gal: EF = 0.90 40 gal: EF = 0.59 50 gal: EF = 0.58		Gallons = EF = Gallons = EF =

NR = No requirement.

(1) Each component present in the As Proposed home must meet or exceed each of the applicable performance criteria in order to comply with this code using this method.

(2) For impact rated fenestration complying with Section R301.2.1.2 of the *Florida Building Code, Residential* or Section 1609.1.2 of the *Florida Building Code, Building,* the maximum *U*-factor shall be 0.65 in Climate Zone 2. An area-weighted average of *U*-factor and SHGC shall be accepted to meet the requirements, or up to 15 square feet of glazed fenestration area are exempted from the *U*-factor and SHGC requirement based on Sections R402.3.1, R402.3.2 and R402.3.3.

(3) One side-hinged opaque door assembly up to 24 square feet is exempted from this *U*-factor requirement.

(4) *R*-values are for insulation material only as applied in accordance with manufacturer's installation instructions. For mass walls, the "interior of wall" requirement must be met except if at least 50 percent of the insulation required for the "exterior of wall" is installed exterior of, or integral to, the wall.

(5) Ducts & AHU installed "substantially leak free" per Section R403.3.2. Test required by either individuals as defined in Section 553.993(5) or (7), *Florida Statutes*, or individuals licensed as set forth in Section 489.105(3)(f), (g) or (i), *Florida Statutes*. The total leakage test is not required for ducts and air handlers located entirely within the building thermal envelope.

(6) Minimum efficiencies are those set by the *National Appliance Energy Conservation Act* of 1987 for typical residential equipment and are subject to NAECA rules and regulations. For other types of equipment, see Tables C403.2.3(1-11) of the Commercial Provisions of the *Florida Building Code, Energy Conservation.*

(7) For other electric storage volumes, minimum EF = 0.97 - (0.00132 * volume).

(8) For other natural gas storage volumes, minimum EF = 0.67 - (0.0019 * volume).

TABLE R402B MANDATORY REQUIREMENTS			
Component	**Section**	**Summary of Requirement(s)**	**Check**
Air leakage	R402.4	To be caulked, gasketed, weatherstripped or otherwise sealed per Table R402.4.1.1. Recessed lighting: IC-rated as having ≤ 2.0 cfm tested to ASTM E 283. Windows and doors: 0.3 cfm/sq. ft. (swinging doors: 0.5 cfm/sf) when tested to NFRC 400 or AAMA/WDMA/CSA 101/I.S. 2/A440. Fireplaces: Tight-fitting flue dampers & outdoor combustion air.	
Programmable thermostat	R403.1.2	A programmable thermostat is required for the primary heating or cooling system.	
Air distribution system	R403.3.2 R403.3.4	Ducts shall be tested as per Section R403.3.2 by either individuals as defined in Section 553.993(5) or (7), *Florida Statutes,* or individuals licensed as set forth in Section 489.105(3) (f), (g) or (i), *Florida Statutes.* Air handling units are not allowed in attics.	
Water heaters	R403.5	Comply with efficiencies in Table C404.2. Hot water pipes insulated to ≥ R-3 to kitchen outlets, other cases. Circulating systems to have an automatic or accessible manual OFF switch. Heat trap required for vertical pipe risers.	
Swimming pools & spas	R403.10	Spas and heated pools must have vapor-retardant covers or a liquid cover or other means proven to reduce heat loss except if 70% of heat from site-recovered energy. Off/timer switch required. Gas heaters minimum thermal efficiency is 82%. Heat pump pool heaters minimum COP is 4.0.	
Cooling/heating equipment	R403.7	Sizing calculation performed & attached. Special occasion cooling or heating capacity requires separate system or variable capacity system.	
Lighting equipment	R404.1	At least 75% of permanently installed lighting fixtures shall be high-efficacy lamps.	

INDEX

I

L

M

O

P

V

W

People Helping People Build a Safer World

Helpful Tools for Your Energy Code

Energy Code Essentials: Based on the 2015 International Energy Conservation Code®

Uses a focused, concise approach to explain those code provisions essential to understanding the application of the IECC®. The information is presented in a user-friendly manner with an emphasis on technical accuracy and clear non-code language.

Features:

- Full-color illustrations, examples and simplified tables
- References to corresponding code sections
- A glossary of code and construction terms

Soft Cover #4831S15
PDF Download #8950P651

CODE AND COMMENTARY IN ONE!

2015 IECC Code and Commentary

This insightful reference contains the complete text of the *International Energy Conservation Code* plus expert commentary printed after each code section. The Code and Commentary is an ideal go-to reference for effective design, construction and inspection.

Features:

- All text, tables and figures from the IECC
- Expert technical commentary printed after each code section
- Suggestions for effective application

Soft cover #3810S15
PDF Download #3810SP15

INCLUDES BONUS ONLINE QUIZ!

The 2015 International Energy Conservation Code Study Companion

This helpful exam prep resource addresses total building performance in both residential and commercial structures.

Features:

- 10 study sessions
- 200 total study questions with answer key

Soft Cover #4807S15
PDF Download #8950P615

Energy Inspector's Guide: Based on the 2015 IECC® and ANSI/ASHRAE/IES Standard 90.1-2013

Provides a comprehensive review of requirements organized to be consistent with the inspection sequence for easy use on site.

Features:

- Spiral binding and durable laminated covers
- Fits in your pocket

Soft Cover #7808S15
PDF Download #8886P15

2015 IECC Turbo Tabs

Flip right to the most commonly used sections of the code! Plastic self-adhesive tabs feature key sections of the code printed on them in an easy-to-read format. For use with the Code or Commentary.

#0801TS15

Order Your Books Today! 1-800-786-4452 | www.iccsafe.org/books

16-13056